The Chemistry of Acid Rain

ACS SYMPOSIUM SERIES 349

The Chemistry of Acid Rain

Sources and Atmospheric Processes

Russell W. Johnson, EDITOR
Allied Signal Engineered Materials Research Center

Glen E. Gordon, EDITOR
University of Maryland

William Calkins, ASSOCIATE EDITOR
Wilmington, DE

A. Z. Elzerman, ASSOCIATE EDITOR
Environmental Systems Engineering

Developed from a symposium sponsored by
the Divisions of Petroleum Chemistry, Inc.,
Nuclear Chemistry and Technology,
Environmental Chemistry, and Fuel Chemistry
at the 191st Meeting
of the American Chemical Society,
New York, New York,
April 13–18, 1986

American Chemical Society, Washington, DC 1987

CHEM
SEP/AE

Library of Congress Cataloging-in-Publication Data

American Chemical Society. Meeting (191st: 1986:
New York, N.Y.)

The chemistry of acid rain: sources and atmospheric
processes
Russell W. Johnson, Glen E. Gordon, editors.
    p.   cm.—(ACS symposium series; 349)

"Developed from a symposium sponsored by the
Division of Petroleum Chemistry...at the 191st
Meeting of the American Chemical Society, New York,
N.Y., April 13-18, 1986."

Includes bibliographies and indexes.

ISBN 0-8412-1414-X
1. Acid rain—Congresses. 2. Atmospheric
chemistry—Congresses. 3. Air—Pollution—
Congresses.

I. Johnson, Russell W., 1948-   . II. Gordon, Glen,
1935-   . III. American Chemical Society. Division
of Petroleum Chemistry. IV. Title. V. Series.

TD196.A25A42   1986   87-19404
628.5′32—dc19   CIP

SD 10/16/87 LM

ACS Symposium Series

M. Joan Comstock, *Series Editor*

1987 Advisory Board

Foreword

The ACS SYMPOSIUM SERIES was founded in 1974 to provide a medium for publishing symposia quickly in book form. The format of the Series parallels that of the continuing ADVANCES IN CHEMISTRY SERIES except that, in order to save time, the papers are not typeset but are reproduced as they are submitted by the authors in camera-ready form. Papers are reviewed under the supervision of the Editors with the assistance of the Series Advisory Board and are selected to maintain the integrity of the symposia; however, verbatim reproductions of previously published papers are not accepted. Both reviews and reports of research are acceptable, because symposia may embrace both types of presentation.

Contents

INDEXES

Preface

During the past decade, acid deposition, more commonly called "acid rain" has been the air pollution problem of highest concern in the United States. It has caused serious political friction between environmentalists and power companies, between states that burn coal for electric power production and those upon whom the acid rain falls, and even between the United States and Canada, where many citizens feel they are victims of acid exported from the United States. To those who are not experts in atmospheric chemistry, it seems simple enough: What goes up must come down. If you want less acid rain, reduce emissions of sulfur and nitrogen oxides that produce it. However, the atmosphere is a complex system and if we do not understand the formation and deposition of acids, there is a definite possibility that we will devise solutions costing tens of billions of dollars without significantly lessening the severity of problems that have been attributed to acid rain.

Although the mechanism for the production and deposition of acid are not yet fully understood, atmospheric chemists and meteorologists have been studying these problems in depth for the past several years and have made considerable progress. Methods and instruments for reliable measurements of key species in air and clouds have been developed and exploited in field studies. Rates of reactions important in the formation of acids, sulfates, and nitrates have been measured. Huge amounts of reliable field data have been accumulated. Models have been developed and are being tested against bodies of field data.

The objective of this volume is to describe recent advances in the understanding of the sources and chemistry of acidic species in the atmosphere.

We thank the authors for their contributions to this volume.

Russell W. Johnson
Allied Signal Engineered Materials Research Center
Des Plaines, IL 60017-5016

Glen E. Gordon
University of Maryland
College Park, MD 20742

July 20, 1987

GENERAL

Chapter 1

A Decade of Acid Rain Research

Glen E. Gordon

Department of Chemistry and Biochemistry, University of Maryland,
College Park, MD 20742

Much progress has been made in our understanding of the sources,
formation and deposition of acid and sulfate. Large field studies can be
conducted with good quality control of analyses and data. In the gas
phase, ·OH radicals are known to be capable of converting SO_2 to sulfate fast enough to be important. Rates for H_2O_2, O_3 and O_2 in cloud
droplets are fast under certain conditions. However, serious gaps in
our knowledge still exist, especially methods for measuring and predict-
ing dry deposition and estimates of the supply of reactants to active
cloud systems. A focal point for development of the U. S. control
strategy is the Regional Acid Deposition Model (RADM). Uncertainties
in some features of the model are likely to be so large that it may not
provide credible predictions in a time soon enough to be useful to legis-
lators or regulators. Hybrid receptor models may be able to provide
some answers for sulfur species more quickly, although RADM should
ultimately yield more detailed predictions for more species. Many problems attributed to acid rain, especially damage to trees at high altitudes,
may be largely due to some other species, e.g., H_2O_2 or O_3.

In the late 1940s and the 1950s, concerns about air pollution increased enormously
because of episodes such as the London Fog of 1952, the Donora, PA episode of
1948, and other similar incidents. The air was physically being cleaned up by use of
electrostatic precipitators to remove most visible emissions; however, large amounts
of SO_2 were being released in metropolitan areas, and it was felt that the SO_2 combined with particles and droplets in the air was responsible for the abnormally high
death and illness rates observed during the episodes. London attacked its problems by
a variety of clean-up methods, the most important being the banning of coal-burning
in individual living units, resulting in a considerable improvement in both air quality
and local climate!

The main U. S. response was restrictions on the use of high sulfur fuels within
metropolitan areas, which had the effect of forcing in-town sources to switch to low
sulfur oil and gas and for new plants to have tall stacks and be built outside of cities.
As documented by Altshuller (1), these measures reduced urban levels of SO_2 to
nearly rural levels.

Nearly simultaneously with the U. S. success in reducing urban SO_2 levels, the
Community Health and Environmental Surveillance System (CHESS) reported that
adverse health effects result not from SO_2 itself, but from the secondary sulfates and

0097–6156/87/0349–0002$06.00/0
© 1987 American Chemical Society

H_2SO_4 formed by atmospheric chemical reactions after release of primary SO_2 (2). Furthermore, the moves taken to reduce SO_2 concentrations in cities simply moved the sources to rural areas and increased the altitudes of release, but did not reduce the total amount released. Since SO_2 is converted slowly to sulfate over long distances, concentrations of particulate sulfates were nearly as great over large rural areas of the eastern U. S. as in cities (1). Not only were these ubiquitous sulfates of concern because of health effects, but it was soon recognized that particulate sulfates were largely responsible for the haze that blankets huge areas of the East during Summer (3), even the "smoke" of the Great Smoky Mountains, which had previously been attributed to particles formed from terpenes emitted by trees. This set of problems related to the release of SO_2, mainly by coal-fired power plants, was the impetus for large field studies, especially the Sulfur Regional Experiment (SURE), supported by the Electric Power Research Institute (EPRI) (see G. M. Hidy, This Volume).

At about this point in the mid-1970s, results of CHESS were discounted, largely because of the measurement methods used (2). This does not necessarily mean that sulfates are not harmful to humans, but that we have no proof that they are. This would have removed much of the impetus for studies of atmospheric SO_2 and sulfates; however, at about that time, Likens and others (4) published contour plots of the pH of rainfall in the Eastern U. S. for the mid-1950s and the mid-1970s which purported to show that the acidity of precipitation had increased greatly over this period. Earlier, Swedish scientists had observed increasing acidity of lakes in Scandinavia, causing many species of fish to disappear from affected lakes. The decrease of fish life in many lakes of New England and Upper New York State was thought by many to be the result of acid rain. Later, damage to trees, especially high on mountain slopes, both in Europe and in the northeast U. S., was attributed to acid deposition. Since about two-thirds of the acid of rainfall is H_2SO_4 and one-third, HNO_3, the focus of atmospheric research in the eastern U. S. continued to be on sulfur species and, secondarily, nitrogen species.

Just when acid deposition was becoming the atmospheric research priority in the East, people in the West were becoming increasingly concerned about visibility degradation, again a problem largely caused by sulfates. Ironically visibility degradation is of much greater concern in the West, where visibility is much better than it is in the East! The reason appears to be that mountains of the West can be seen for distances of 100 km or more when haze levels are low, whereas the topography of the East and buildings in areas where most people live prevent one from seeing more than about 20 km even in clear air.

Thus, atmospheric research in the eastern U. S. has been dominated by the need for a better understanding of sulfur species, first because of presumed human health effects of SO_2, then because of human health effects of sulfates, and now because of effects of sulfate and acid upon plant and animal life (and, to a lesser extent, on building materials, statues, etc.) in the East, and because of visibility degradation in the West.

The huge increase of population and automobile traffic in the Los Angeles Basin during World War II gave rise to a new air pollution phenomenon called "smog", which was found to result from atmospheric reactions of hydrocarbons, CO and nitrogen oxides (NO_x) during frequent strong inversions in the Basin under influence of abundant sunshine in southern California. Originally the "photochemical smog" phenomena of southern California was seen as quite a different problem from the SO_2-and-fog problem of London and the eastern U. S., in part because episodes of the latter tended to occur in Fall and Winter, whereas smog is usually associated with warm weather and sunshine. Indeed, in the earlier years, when concentrations of sulfur oxides and particles were much higher in cities, the phenomena may have been different. However, under today's conditions, the two sets of problems clearly are closely related. Huge veils of particulate haze that blanket entire regions of the East now occur mainly between May and October. Improved knowledge of gas-phase kinetics resulting from studies of photochemical smog and of stratospheric problems of supersonic transports and chlorofluorocarbon compounds during the early 1970s has revealed many connections between sulfur chemistry and photochemistry because of the involvement of highly reactive transient species such as hydroxyl radicals ($\cdot$OH), as well as of more stable oxidants produced by photochemistry, e.g., O_3, H_2O_2. In recent years, most air pollution alerts in eastern cities have occurred because of high levels of oxidants (mainly O_3) during Summer, when sulfate levels are also very high.

Present Knowledge about Acid Rain

As demonstrated by papers presented at this Symposium, the increase of our knowledge about acid deposition in recent years has been enormous. The SURE project (Hidy, This Volume) demonstrated that huge field projects can be conducted with good quality control of samples, analyses and data. Kok, Tanner (This Volume) and others have developed highly sophisticated systems for measuring concentrations of many species, including the very important H_2O_2, in clouds and clear air with aircraft. In the area of mechanisms, we know that oxidation by $\cdot$OH radicals is the dominant gas-phase reaction in the conversion of SO_2 to H_2SO_4 and sulfate (5). Furthermore, we know that oxidation in solution by H_2O_2 is rapid and that by O_3 and O_2 (the latter catalyzed by metal ions or carbon soot) can be important under some conditions (6; Schwartz, This Volume).

Despite these advances, large gaps in our knowledge still exist. As demonstrated by many papers in this symposium, methods for collection and analysis of wet deposition are well established, but understanding of dry deposition remains poor. The Environmental Protection Agency (EPA) does not plan to do routine direct measurements of dry deposition for the time being. At most network stations, airborne concentrations will be measured and dry deposition rates will be calculated from them (Hicks et al., This Volume). Some stations will be equipped to do fast response eddy-correlation and airborne concentration measurements for further research on the method and comparison with results from nearby stations that will measure only airborne concentrations over longer averaging times (7, 8). Although the importance of $\cdot$OH radicals is clear and millions of dollars have been spent, no reliable, portable instrument for real-time measurement of their concentrations at low altitudes has been developed. We know that the reaction of H_2O_2 with SO_2 in cloud droplets is fast, but little is known about the supply of H_2O_2 to cloud droplets, which may limit the amount of sulfate formed.

Some of our largest areas of ignorance involve in-cloud processes. Most clouds evaporate, releasing any sulfate formed as sulfate aerosol. However, there is not usually enough airborne sulfate present to account for the sulfate in rain simply by washout of sulfate aerosol beneath the clouds (9). Thus, it appears that much of the sulfate brought down by rain must be formed in the clouds that are causing the rain. There is a lot of "action" in large storm clouds, e.g., strong updrafts and mixing, which may provide a good environment for extensive chemical reactions. However, the clouds must be supplied with reactants if sulfate is to be formed, and it's not clear if this happens. Unfortunately, most in-cloud studies have been conducted in gentle clouds. We may never be able to study large storm clouds, but investigators of the PRECP project (PRocessing of Emissions by Clouds and Precipitation) have developed methods for studying air flowing into and out of such systems (10, 11). A recent study by Dickerson et al. (11) demonstrated that air pollutants are rapidly transported to the upper troposphere by thunderstorms. After being transported to such high altitudes, they have much longer residence times and can be transported much greater distances than can pollutants confined to low altitudes. Thus, one of the most serious deficiencies in our knowledge is the almost complete lack of vertical concentration profiles of important species, with the exception of data from airplane spirals conducted during intensive study periods of the SURE project. Fortunately, a decision has been made recently to include vertical profile measurements in the studies designed to provide data for model testing ($\underline{8}$).

Can We Provide Timely Information for Design of Control Strategies?

The National Acid Precipitation Assessment Program (NAPAP) is under pressure to provide information needed for development of strategies for control of acid precipitation by about 1989. An important focal point of NAPAP research is the Regional Acid Deposition Model (RADM), a huge Eulerian model requiring input of large amounts of meteorological and source-emissions data. The model includes modules for treatment of transport and mixing of pollutants, chemical reactions in the gas and liquid phases, in-cloud processes, and wet and dry deposition. The hope is that of making RADM sufficiently reliable, as shown by tests against appropriate field data, that effects of various control strategies can be assessed by varying the input source-emissions data and observing predicted changes in airborne concentrations and deposition of various species ($\underline{8}$). Some modules of RADM (including the gas-phase chemistry module discussed by Stockwell, This Symposium) have been constructed, but none has been well tested. There are so many uncertainties, including those discussed above, that there is considerable doubt if RADM can be demonstrated to be reliable in time to be useful for development of control strategies. The recent move of RADM development from the National Center for Atmospheric Research (NCAR) to the State University of New York (SUNY) at Albany will surely slow it down by several months.

The U.S. and Canadian agencies dealing with the acid precipitation problem have been meeting to design coordinated field studies that should provide appropriate data for testing RADM ($\underline{8}$). A major component of the cooperative effort will be the Operational Evaluation Network supported by the electric-power industry via EPRI, an extension of the work previously done via the Utilities Deposition Network. Requests for proposals for many of the EPA-sponsored portions of the work, including the vertical profile measurements, were released in Jan., 1987. The target date for providing reliable source-receptor relationships by RADM has unfortunately slipped to 1991.

At present, we cannot say with certainty that reductions in emissions of SO_2 and NO_x will cause a proportional decrease in deposition of sulfur and nitrogen species. In their thorough review of this problem in 1983, the "Calvert Committee" of the National Academy of Sciences/National Research Council (NAS/NRC) summarized their findings with the carefully worded statement ($\underline{6}$):

"If we assume that other factors, including meteorology, remain unchanged, the annual average concentration of sulfate in precipitation at a given site should be reduced in proportion to a reduction in SO_2 and sulfate transported to that site from a source or region of a sources. If ambient concentrations of NO_x, nonmethane hydrocarbons, and basic substances (such as ammonia and calcium carbonate) remain unchanged, a reduction in sulfate deposition will result in at least as great a reduction in the deposition of hydrogen ion."

However, even this statement was not accepted by some critics, especially those of the Department of Energy laboratories ($\underline{12}$), who requested and received major funding for the PRECP project designed to investigate "non-linear" dependence of deposition of species upon emissions. Even if one accepts the conclusion of the NAS/NRC Committee, there is still a question of the distance scale for transport and deposition of sulfur and nitrogen species. For example, if emissions are reduced in Ohio, will the effects be mostly local, or will they extend appreciably into upper New York State and New England?

While the research community has been trying to provide reliable answers, pressure has been building, both internally and from Canada, for Congress to legislate controls. Two major bills for gradual phase-in of controls were under serious consideration during 1986. If we do not soon provide a scientific basis for decisions, they will probably be made without our involvement. It will surely be a devastating blow to the atmospheric research community, who have worked long and hard in seeking a good understanding of the problem, if decisions are made without their final results. Unfortunately, this is the nature of environmental regulations, which must often be made on the basis of incomplete information. If this happens, the priority for determining final answers (and with it, some of the funding) will surely be reduced. Not all would be lost, however, as we might be able to learn a great deal by following changes resulting from implementation of controls on the release of SO_2 and NO_x.

Are There Alternative Research Strategies?

Could the research community and those who fund research devise a strategy for providing answers that, while not as intellectually satisfying as predictions based on a reliable RADM, are credible? In my view, we could provide data on sulfur species in ways that save both money and time. If I were today required to devise a control strategy based on our present knowledge, I would base it on an empirical "engineering" model published by Fay et al. (13). Their model is a transfer function between the emissions of SO_2 by state and the observed deposition contours. The model contains little meteorological data except for an annual average wind vector in the Ohio River Valley (towards the Northeast) and a parameter for uniform dispersion in all directions obtained from least-squares fitting of the data. The model apportions sulfate observed at various stations to SO_2 emissions from the various states, but it is obviously useful only for averaging times of one year or more.

The model of Fay et al. is crude, but one could do better by using "hybrid receptor models." Most conventional models used by EPA and other agencies, including the RADM, are source-based models in which source emissions are treated by dispersion models, which may also include chemical reactions and deposition, as in the case of RADM. Receptor models involve measurement of concentrations of many species and other parameters (e.g., wind speeds and directions, mixing heights, etc.) to identify sources of the airborne materials (14). Receptor models have mostly been used in urban areas to identify sources of airborne particles based on their elemental concentrations (e.g., V are Ni from oil-fired power plants, Pb from motor vehicles). Recently, receptor models have begun to be applied to regional and global scale problems. A "hybrid" receptor model is one that combines the receptor model with some aspects of conventional source-based models.

Rahn and Lowenthal (15, 16) proposed a set of ratios of concentrations of six elements (V, Mn, Sb, Zn, As and In) to that of Se on airborne particles as indicators of the origins of air masses from various large regions of North America and other continents. They used the tracer patterns to apportion the areas of origin of particles collected during each of many sampling periods at Underhill, VT and Narragansett, RI, determined the ratio of sulfate concentrations to those of the tracers for various seasons, and used the ratios to assign observed sulfate to the source regions. In disagreement with most current thinking, they find that about half of the sulfate in New England is of fairly local origin. While there has been much criticism of the details of their method, the basic idea may provide a useful approach to apportionment of sulfate.

Lewis and Stevens (This Volume and 17) have provided a useful framework for hybrid receptor modeling in which one calculates concentrations of various sulfur species relative to those of some tracer that is fairly unique to the sulfur source, e.g., Se as a tracer from coal-fired power plants. Equations are written for SO_2 conversion to sulfate and for deposition of gaseous SO_2 and particulate sulfate and Se vs. time (or distance, assuming a wind velocity). Kitto and Anderson (This Volume) note that gas-phase B may be an excellent gas-phase tracer for coal-fired power plants, simulating the deposition features of SO_2, but not being converted to some other species, as SO_2 is. Gordon and Olmez ([18]) performed calculations of ratios of B/SO_2, SO_4/Se, SO_4/SO_2, etc. in a crude model of air masses moving up the Ohio River Valley and into the Northeast. Their results were in surprisingly good agreement with measurements by Kitto and Anderson and by Fogg and Rahn ([19]). However, when Tuncel et al. (This Volume) attempted more detailed fits to absolute concentrations of the sulfur species and Se vs. distance up the Ohio River Valley, they obtained poor agreement with any reasonable choices of parameters. It was impossible to account for the observed amounts of sulfate at a rural station in Kentucky without greatly overpredicting its concentrations at stations farther up the Valley. Lewis and Stevens (This Volume) gave a preliminary account of the application of the hybrid receptor model to data collected in the 1983 Deep Creek Lake experiment. Samples were collected from several coal-fired power plants upwind of an ambient site near Deep Creek Lake, MD that is strongly influenced by emissions from those plants. Data on concentrations of gas- and particulate-phase sulfur and particulate Se were used to calculate an SO_2 conversion rate of about 6%/hr, which is quite reasonable for August conditions. More data will be available soon from the Deep Creek Lake experiment, which will allow investigators to perform more thorough tests and development of hybrid receptor models.

The most sophisticated of the hybrid models is that of Samson et al. (presented by Keeler, This Symposium). They calculate back trajectories for each sampling period of a large data set and assume that sources of observed species are normally distributed about the trajectory, with a dispersion parameter that increases with distance from the receptor. By weighting the backward trajectories by observed concentrations during the sampling periods, they build up contours of potential strengths of the observed species in source areas around the receptor. Their model also has provision for treating dry deposition between the source areas and the receptor and, most important, they have constructed a gridded precipitation data set, which allows them to determine the extent of rain or snow that falls through specific air masses associated with each sampling period. One can, thus, include assumptions about the fraction of airborne material removed as a function of precipitation intensity and duration. This will allow them to include the effects of precipitation much more directly than in any other model of which I am aware. They might discover, for example, that the transport of acid and sulfate precursors from the Ohio River Valley to the Northeast is governed strongly by whether or not any rain falls on the air mass during its transit.

One of the most important projects in progress in the field of hybrid receptor modeling is the Allegheny Mountain study by Pierson et al. of Ford Motor Co.(This Volume). Concentrations of many ions, major, minor and trace elements in airborne particles, rain, dew and fog and other parameters were measured at Allegheny Mt., PA and Laurel Hill, 35 km to the northwest, from 5 to 28 Aug 1983, approximately simultaneously with the Deep Creek Lake studies discussed above. These two huge data sets are now nearly complete and ready for detailed interpretations by the participants and other researchers in the field. In particular, Keeler is working with the Ford group to apply the Samson method to the data.

In my view, hybrid receptor models are the most likely approach for provide reasonable answers to the sulfate deposition problem within a time that they might be of use in influencing controls that may be imposed on SO_2 and NO_x sources. This does not mean that there is no need for further field studies. The Allegheny Mt. and Deep Creek Lake data sets were taken so close together that one would feel much safer if similar data were available at several other sites, e.g., the three sites of the Ohio River Valley study ([20]) and one or two sites to the northeast of Allegheny Mt., say Whiteface Mt., NY and Underhill, VT, which have been well studied in the past. Furthermore, as noted above, there is still a strong need for vertical concentration profiles. The recent work of Dickerson et al. (11) shows that we cannot develop a reliable model without inclusion of vertical movements of pollutants.

An irony of the acid-deposition problem is that the sulfur problem could be understood quickly and at an affordable cost if one could release radioactive $^{35}SO_2$ from some coal-fired plants along with normal SO_2. Feasibility calculations indicate that this could be done with radiation exposures to the general public well within guidelines, as ^{35}S decays by weak β emission with an 87-day half life (21). Nuclear detection methods are so sensitive that very little activity needs to be observed to obtain valid measurements. Radioactive sulfur is the perfect tracer of the dispersion, transport, tranformation and deposition of normal sulfur. Samples of sulfur enriched in certain stable isotopes could, in principle, be used as tracers, but in the MATEX (Massive Aerometric Tracer Experiment) Feasibility Study, Hidy et al. (22) found that the cost of stable isotopes would be prohibitive. No one has very seriously proposed the use of radioactive sulfur because of public fears of exposure. Perhaps with the much greater exposures many people now find they are receiving from natural radioactivity in their houses, they will be less concerned about a small exposure from an experiment. Hidy et al. investigated many schemes for tracing the behavior of sulfur in the atmosphere, mainly by releases of non-reactive tracers from SO_2 sources. However, the non-reactive tracers provide information only about dispersion and transport, but not reaction and deposition. The overall uncertainties in determining the behavior of sulfur using only non-reactive tracers are predicted to be so large that Hidy et al. did not recommend that such experiments be initiated at this time. Ondov and Kelly (23) are developing a promising tracer for particles of certain sizes based on the use of enriched isotopes of certain rare earth elements.

What Is the Larger Picture?

Those of us involved in acid deposition research become so deeply involved in the subject that we may lose sight of the overall problem. Several important points in this regard were made by Dr. J. Laurence Kulp, Director of NAPAP, in informal comments during the Symposium. He noted the recent emphasis on damage to trees, especially in the forests of Germany. In general, the damage is worst for species growing near the tops of mountains. As they are frequently bathed in fog, some may feel that their problems are caused by direct deposition of fog droplets. However, Kulp noted that stresses of many kinds increase with altitude until one reaches the timberline, above which no species can survive. Thus, trees at higher elevations are quite vulnerable to many effects, the most frequent of which is drought. Other things such as parasites can affect trees. In regard to air pollution effects, he noted that ozone, at levels frequently encountered today, is known to have deleterious effects on field crops such as soybeans and tobacco. He pointed out that recent evidence suggests that H_2O_2 itself may produce damage to trees. Thus, we must keep in mind that the acid and sulfate we are studying are just one of many possible causes of the damages that have been ascribed to acid precipitation. As in the case of many environmental problems, there may be a synergism between a combination of pollutants such as acid or sulfate and oxidants such as O_3 and H_2O_2.

If it turns out that the damage to trees results largely from oxidants, the detailed studies of atmospheric chemistry related to acid formation as being done under NAPAP will be needed for development of optimal control strategies in addition to the shorter term hybrid approaches to the understanding of sulfur species discussed above. Even if these more complex studies related to RADM are not available until the early 1990s, they will be of ultimate value. As noted by Woodman and Cowling in a recent review of damage to forests (24), it is unlikely that factors responsible for tree damage will be identified sooner than that.

Literature Cited

1. Altshuller, A. P. Environ. Sci. Technol. 1980,14, 1337.
2. Report prepared for the Committee on Science and Technology, U. S. House of Representatives, "The Environmental Protection Agency's Research Program with Primary Emphasis on the Community Health and Environmental Surveillance System." U. S. Govt. Printing Office, Washington, D. C., 1976.
3. Weiss, R. E.; Waggoner, A. P.; Charlson, R. J.; Ahlquist, N. C. Science 1977, 195, 979.
4. Cogbill, C. V.; Likens, G. E. Water Resources Res. 1974, 10, 1133.
5. Calvert, J. G.; Stockwell, W. R. Environ. Sci. Technol. 1983, 17, 428A.
6. Committee on Atmospheric Transport and Chemical Transformation in Acid Precipitation, "Acid Deposition: Atmospheric Processes in Eastern North America"; National Academy Press: Washington, D. C., 1983.
7. Hicks, B. B. Water, Air Soil Pollut. 1986, 30, 75.
8. Durham, J.; Dennis, R.; Laulainen, N.; Renne, D.; Pennell, B.; Barchett, R.; Hales, J. "Regional Eulerian Model Field Study and Evaluations: Proposed Management and Technical Approaches," EPA Office of Research and Development, Aug., 1986.
9. Newman, L. E. Presented at the American Chemical Society Nat'l. Meeting, Honolulu, Hawaii, Mar. 1979.
10.Michael, P., ed. "PRECP - The Department of Energy's Program on Non-Linearity of Acid Precipitation Processes, Summary of FY1984-1985 Operational Plan," Brookhaven Nat'l. Laboratory Informal Report No. BNL-34842, May, 1984.
11. Dickerson, R. R.; Huffman, G. J.; Luke, W. T.; Nunnermacker, L. J.; Pickering, K. E.; Leslie, A. C. D.; Lindsey, C. G.; Slinn, W. G. N.; Kelly, T. J.; Daum, P. H.; Delany, A. C.; Greenberg, J. P.; Zimmerman, P. R.; Boatman, J. F.; Ray, J. D.; Stedman, D. H. Science 1987, 235, 460.
12. Committee on Science and Technology, U. S. House of Representatives, Hearings on "Acid Rain: Implications for Fossil R&D," U. S. Govt. Printing Office, Washington, D. C., 1983.
13. Fay, J. A.; Golomb, D.; Kumar, S. Atmos. Environ. 1980, 14, 355.
14. Hopke, P. K. "Receptor Modeling in Environmental Chemistry"; Wiley-Interscience: New York, 1985.
15. Rahn, K. A.; Lowenthal, D. H. Science 1984, 223, 132.
16. Rahn, K. A.; Lowenthal, D. H. Science 1985, 228, 275.
17. Lewis, C. W.; Stevens, R. K. Atmos. Environ. 1985, 19, 917.
18. Gordon, G. E.; Olmez, I. In "Receptor Methods for Source Apportionment"; Pace, T. G., Ed.; APCA: Pittsburgh, PA, 1986; pp. 229-238.
19. Fogg, T. R.; Rahn, K. A. Geophys. Res. Lett. 1984, 11, 854.
20. Shaw, R. W.; Paur, R. J. Atmos. Environ. 1983, 17, 1431; 2031.
21. Michael, P. Presented at NAPAP Review, Boston, MA, Aug. 1983.
22. Hidy, G. M.; Hansen, D. A.; Bass, A. "Feasibility and Design of the Massive Aerometric Tracer Experiment (MATEX)," Electric Power Research Institute Report No. EA-4305, 1985.
23. Ondov, J. M.; Kelly, R. Unpublished data, University of Maryland and National Bureau of Standards, 1986.
24. Woodman, J. N.; Cowling, E. B. Environ. Sci. Technol. 1987, 21, 120.

RECEIVED March 2, 1987

Chapter 2

Subcontinental Air Pollution Phenomena

G. M. Hidy

Desert Research Institute, P.O. Box 60220, Reno, NV 89506

This paper discusses aspects of the accumulating body
of observations characterizing deposition of airborne
acid forming substances. Of particular interest are
sulfur and nitrogen oxides species. The focus of the
observations and interpretation is on subcontinental
(or regional) scale phenomena extending over areas of
10^6 km^2. Spatial and temporal distributions of ambient
sulfur oxide (or sulfate) and nitrogen oxide (or
nitrate) concentrations and precipitation chemistry
are summarized as they reflect dry and wet deposition.
Comparisons are given between conditions in the
eastern and western United States. The importance of
variability in deposition exposure, within year and
from year-to-year, is outlined. Evidence of linkage
between source emissions and receptor measurements is
included to complete the discussion.

Since the mid-1970's, increasing interest has emerged in the environmental consequences of the large scale deposition of atmospheric
contaminants. The deposition of acid-forming constituents, sulfate
and nitrate, is of particular concern for potentially adverse
ecological effects. These species derive from the oxidation of
sulfur dioxide (SO_2) and nitrogen oxides (NO and NO_2). Over most if
not all of the North American Continent, emissions of these gases
are believed to be dominated by man's activities, especially from
fossil fuel combustion, and the production or refining of metals.
The "scale" of exposure for deposition covers exposure from
pollutants in large, subcontinental areas, the order of 10^6 km^2.
although regional ambient air concentrations are well below levels

mandated by the U.S. Clean Air Act, deposition conditions may still
be sufficiently large in some areas to cause long term effects,
particularly in remote, susceptible areas. There are no known
direct public health effects of deposition, and other regional
effects are hypothetical, except possibly for surface water quality.
Thus, there is great concern for realizing "significant benefits"
from large increases in incremental costs of pollution control to
address deposition exposure.

Specifications of "benefit" from reduction of deposition has
required a major investment in studies of airborne acid-forming
substances and their consequences to aquatic and terrestrial ecosystems. A major part of these studies has resulted in considerably
improved knowledge of the sulfate and nitrate deposition conditions
in North America, as well as knowledge of the atmospheric processes
affecting these distributions. In this paper, aspects of the current state of knowledge in deposition patterns are summarized, with
notes about unresolved issues.

Distribution of Deposition Exposure

Deposition of atmospheric contaminants takes place in two principal
forms -- dry, by absorption of gases or by particle collection at a
surface, and -- wet, by scavenging and deposit via precipitation. A
third form ("occult" deposition) is sometimes cited -- the collection of material on surfaces via fog or mist. Of the three, the
bulk of our knowledge centers on wet deposition. Although some
ambient concentration data have been acquired, the data are very
limited in temporal and spatial coverage. Data are virtually non-
existent in remote western areas, particularly in alpine areas where
ecosystems are believed to be susceptible. A few exploratory
measurements of fog deposition have been obtained at mountain sites,
but no systematic monitoring has been attempted. The fog component
is not discussed further here; available observations suggest that
clouds and fog have higher concentrations of acid formers than precipitation (but apparently carry a relatively small part of the
total burden in most situations).

Eastern United States (EUS). The regionally representative distribution of ambient sulfur oxides and nitrogen oxides over the northeastern United States was first characterized in the late 1970's
from data taken in the Sulfate Regional Experiment (SURE). The
results have been reported in several publications [1]. Concentrations of SO_2 in the East range from 6-26 $\mu g/m^3$, and particulate
sulfate concentrations are 4-8 $\mu g/m^3$. The SURE NO_x and NO_3^- data
are uncertain in quality compared with the SO_x (SO_2 + SO_4^{2-}) data
because of measurement ambiguities. Estimated average ambient
nitrate concentrations range from 0.3-0.5 $\mu g/m^3$, much of which is
believed to be nitric acid vapor. NO_x concentration distributions

were less well characterized, but are reported in the 7-20 $\mu g/m^3$ range, mainly as NO_2.

Evidence shows that the ambient concentrations of SO_x and NO_x in the EUS are linked with broad areas of high emission density associated with metropolitan areas and heavy industrialization. Comparison between regionally representative concentrations in world remote areas, and those observed in the EUS show elevations of a factor of ten in mean concentrations, with short term average concentrations even higher than baseline conditions.

Elevated concentrations of sulfate and nitrate associated with zones of high emission density are also found in precipitation. The geographical concentration distributions in precipitation are similar to those found for airborne sulfate (SO_x and NO_x emission distributions are similar in the EUS).

Although direct measurements are extremely limited, the dry component of deposition can be estimated qualitatively from data noting that the deposition rate is the product of a deposition velocity and ambient concentration observations at ground level. For example, taking suitable values of deposition velocity, listed for example in Table II, and data from the SURE (2), estimates of the annual average dry deposition rate for sulfur are the order of 6-60 kgS/ha-yr in the East. This is compared with values of 4-16 kgS/ha-yr in wet deposition. Although dry deposition levels of NO_x have not been reported, they would be lower than sulfur, since the ambient concentrations are similar but the deposition velocity is smaller. Wet deposition of nitrate based on available data in 1980 is 2-7 kgN/ha-yr.

Comparison between deposition components for conditions in EUS indicates that the dry component will substantially exceed the wet component near sources. This results from ambient concentrations for SO_2 average about 10-20 ppb, and NO_2 concentration exceed 10 ppb near sources (<50 km distance). At distances far from sources, the two components are said to be similar in magnitude, for circumstances measured in remote areas of eastern Canada, the wet component exceeds dry deposition.

Western United States (WUS). Less is known about deposition conditions in the West. However, data are becoming available from which a picture of exposure can be deduced. Of particular interest is a comparison between eastern and western deposition because of differences in their chemical climatological conditions. Examples of such differences are listed in Table I.

To illustrate western precipitation chemistry as compared with remote conditions and EUS, H^+, SO_4^{2-} and HNO_3^- concentrations are shown in Figure 1. The remote areas shown include marine and continental stations located at very remote sites over the world. Shown in the Figure are San Carlos, Venezuela (SC), Poker Flats,

TABLE 1

SUMMARY AND COMPARISON BETWEEN WESTERN AND EASTERN U.S. CLIMATOLOGICAL CONDITIONS
(From Hidy & Young, Environ. Res. & Tech., Unpubl. Report)

CATEGORY	WEST	EAST
1. Emissions Distributions	Large urban areas are low SO_2 emitters and high NO_x emitters. Large industrial sources are geographically isolated and separated by distances in excess of 50-500 km. SO_2 emissions historically have been dominated by non-ferrous smelting activity. High emission areas are generally oriented normal to prevailing westerly air flow, with separation by large areas isolated by mountain ranges.	Large urban areas and industrial sources blend together over much of the East. Emissions are much larger in the East, accounting for more than 70% of the U.S. national SO_x and NO_x emissions. Emission distributions are oriented to accumulate in prevailing air flow downwind across the U.S. from the Missouri River eastward.
2. Wind Patterns	Westerly winds prevail, but are strongly modified by near surface flow with terrain. Flow patterns for storm conditions are influenced by outbreaks of arctic air disturbances which draw air northward in circulations from the Gulf of Mexico and the Gulf of California -- giving a strong north-south flow condition.	Transport patterns are contained within a broad westerly transport. Storm and fair weather conditions vary, but flow is generally associated with large scale cyclone and anticyclone systems. Pollution accumulates regionally in stagnation conditions and is followed by removal in stormy weather, but generally flow occurs from the west across the eastern continent.
3. Mixing	Large oscillation in mixing height with diurnal change and season, but generally daytime conditions yield high mixing heights compared with the East. Tendency to form strong surface inversions suppressing mixing at night.	Mixing height is diurnally and seasonally variable, but tends to be shallower than in the West, except along coastal areas and mountain valley conditions.
4. Arid Conditions	Most of the West is dominated by an arid climate compared with the East. The notable exceptions are the Pacific Northwest and certain alpine areas which accrue heavy precipitation in winter. There are generally extremes in precipitation exposure in the West which are not prevalent in the East.	Most of the East is subjected to high precipitation both within year and from year to year, with contributions of snow and rain, even in alpine or lake areas. This is a strong contrast with the West.

Continued on next page.

TABLE 1 (Continued)

SUMMARY AND COMPARISON BETWEEN WESTERN AND EASTERN U.S. CLIMATOLOGICAL CONDITIONS
(From Hidy & Young, Environ. Res. & Tech., Unpubl. Report)

CATEGORY	WEST	EAST
5. Sunshine and Cloud Cover	With exception of coastal areas and Pacific Northwest, cloud cover is much less in the West than the East, with drier air inland over intermountain areas. At high altitude, solar radiation is much stronger than in eastern mountains.	Cloud cover often regionally extensive, tends to be prevalent and persistent, along with heavy haze much of the year. Mountains and alpine areas see more cloud cover and in-cloud conditions than in (intermountain) West.
6. Cloud Type Occurrence	Cloud occurrence is seasonally dependent in the inter-mountain area. Surface fog and clouds are prevalent all year around the Pacific Coast, but clouds and fog occur mainly in winter in other areas. Summers are dominated by thunderstorms. Because of high altitude, surface clouds are likely to contain more ice than in the East. The prevalence of riming is not well characterized.	Surface clouds and fog occur frequently at alpine levels in the East. The content of ice or super-cooled water is strongly seasonal, with high occurrence in winter. No comparisons are available but the frequency of occurrence of fog and riming is probably higher in the East than in the West.
7. Precipitation Occurrence	In deposition sensitive areas of the West, precipitation is dominated by winter snow, except for coastal ranges in California where winter rainfall is important. In southwestern desert states, precipitation frequency is quite high in the summer, from thunderstorm activity.	In the East, precipitation occurs more uniformly year around with combined snow and rain.

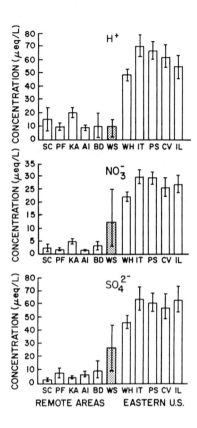

Figure 1. Comparison between precipitation concentrations in world remote areas (left), the eastern U.S. (right) and the western states (WS). The range shown for the first two categories is the standard deviation of annual mean values. For the western states, the range is the values for different sites observed between 1981 and 1984. (Data for the first two from Galloway et al, 3; for the western states, Hidy & Young, Environ. Res. & Tech., unpubl. report)(Data reproduced with permission from Ref. 3. Copyright 1984 AAAS).

Alaska (PF), Katherine, Australia (KA), Amsterdam Island, Indian
Ocean, (AI), and Bermuda, Atlantic Ocean (BD). The eastern U.S.
sites include Multistate Atmospheric Power Production Pollution
Study (MAP3S) sites at Whiteface Mountain, NY (WH) Ithaca, NY (IT),
Pennsylvania State University (PS), Charlottesville, VA (CV) and
Urbana, IL (IL). The western states are National Atmospheric
Deposition Program (NADP) sites with a continuous record between
1981-1984 (in Colorado, California, Washington, Oregon and Arizona).
The comparisons suggests that $[H^+]$ in the WUS precipitation is
equivalent to global remote conditions, but $[SO_4^{2-}]$ and $[NO_3^-]$ are
intermediate between remote and EUS "polluted" conditions.

     In both the East and the West, precipitation sulfate tends to
be larger than nitrate concentrations, except near large sources of
NO_x in the West.

     An interesting feature of WUS precipitation is that the annual
average sulfate concentrations are well correlated with calcium
(Figure 2). $[H^+]$ is much less well correlated with either $[SO_4^{2-}]$
or $[NO_3^-]$ -- correlation coefficient (r) = 0.577 and 0.546 respectively. This is quite different from EUS conditions where the anions
are well correlated with $[H^+]$. The reason for the strong association between $[Ca^{2+}]$ and $[SO_4^=]$ in western precipitation may be
associated with scavenging of gypsum rich soil dust, or may be
related to reactions of scavenged limestone dust and sulfuric acid.
Figure 2 suggests a range for the influence of soil dust, and a
value for a sulfate background. A line of slope unity can be drawn
through the data points at SO_4^{2-} concentrations less than 20 µeq/1.
This is stoichiometrically consistent with $CaSO_4$. The intercept at
zero Ca^{2+} concentration is 5 µeq/1 SO_4^{2-}. This value is consistent
with a global precipitation background expected from remote sites
shown in Figure 1. Above 20 µeq/1 SO_4^{2-}, there is deviation from
the 1:1 slope line suggesting the influence of a non-soil dust
influenced component (excess SO_4^{2-}). This component could be
identified with unneutralized acidic air pollution over the WUS.
From Figure 1, the average of the "excess" sulfate over the West
would be about 5 µeq/1, much smaller than levels found in the EUS.

     Measurements of ambient concentrations of species in remote
locations of the West are very limited. However, the few that exist
show the western rural levels much lower than in the East. Typical
examples are listed in Table II.

Table II. Estimates of Annual Dry Deposition For
Rural/Background Areas in the West
(After Hidy & Young, Environ., Res. & Tech.,
unpublished report)

Species	Typical Concentration*	Deposition Velocity (cm/sec)		Estimated Dry Deposition Rate** (kg/ha-yr)
SO_2	1 ppb	0.5		2
SO_4^{2-}	2 $\mu g/m^3$	0.2		0.3
			Total	2.3
NO_2	1 ppb	0.1		0.2
HNO_3	0.5 ppb	1.0		0.9
NO_3^-	0.5 $\mu g/m^3$	0.2		0.1
			Total	1.1

**As sulfur & nitrogen

These values are used with deposition velocities to give an estimate
of western dry deposition. Wet deposition of SO_4^{2-} and NO_3^- respectively are 0.8-4.6 kgS/ha-yr. and 0.7-2.3 kgN/ha-yr. These rates are
generally well below the levels in the EUS.

   In the West, dry deposition is a similar level as wet deposition for S and N in many areas, except near sources and in arid-
desert conditions where wet deposition is negligible. Since measurements of wet deposition are taken in valleys with low precipitation,
they underestimate the wet component somewhat for alpine (ecologi-
cally susceptible) conditions. The alpine and subalpine areas in
the West have much higher annual precipitation rates than lower
elevations.

Variability

Characterization of variability in deposition is important for
bounding uncertainties in exposure levels. Also this aspect of deposition is crucial to describing the "predictability" of source-
receptor relationships (SRRs)(4).

   With acquisition of observations over a period of years, the
variability in deposition rates has become better known. Like the
result of all atmospheric processes, deposition is highly variable
at a given site and between sites; and within year, or from year-to-
year.

   Variability in observations derives from the measurement
process itself, changes in input (emissions), and the "stochastic"
character of atmospheric processes influencing emitted material
before it is returned to the earth. The uncertainties in the
measurement process for precipitation have been defined

quantitatively. For wet deposition, sampling is identified as the major area of measurement uncertainty, especially for snow.

Typical total variability in concentration of species in bulk samples is shown for sulfate in Figure 3. These data contain variations that include a measurement component and the influence of atmospheric changes. The data are reported for monthly samples in the U.S. Geological Survey (USGS) network of New York State. The data represent one of the longest records available, from 1965 to 1984. The year-to-year changes at the site, show a small, systematic downward drift in annual median sulfate concentration on which is superimposed a monthly variable component. The normal range of monthly (within year) variation is shown by the standard deviation, and the range of values in a year are also shown. Two outlier points are included which cannot be rationalized by measure-ment uncertainty, but are out of the statistically expected range. This record illustrates well that several years of data are needed to establish a mean condition, and provide a basis for describing "natural" variability.

Variability in dry deposition is partly reflected in ambient concentrations, which vary over a much wider range than estimates of emissions. This range is ascribed to meteorological influence (1). A large and ill-defined variation in dry deposition stems from surface conditions. Key to change is the moisture on a surface as well as biological assimilation capability; both change diurnally and seasonally (2).

Intersite variability has been studied for both ambient concentration data (1), and for wet deposition (5). Intersite correlations for ambient SO_2 and SO_4^{2-} concentrations in the EUS show dramatic differences in spatial scale. SO_2 concentrations have highly localized patterns of correlation that exclude a regional character. In contrast, airborne sulfate correlations are highly regional in character. Spatial variability in sulfate is dominated by two to three components that can be identified with prevailing, persistent meteorological conditions (1).

The spatial scale of intersite correlation differs somewhat with location. However, the average pattern for wet sulfate and nitrate correlation is shown with spacing of stations in Figure 4. The graphs represent an agglomeration of correlation data between 1981 and 1984 for more than 20 EUS sites. The distance over which correlation occurs for sulfate extends almost to 2000 km, but corre-lation decreases rapidly below less than 0.5 within 100 km. A similar pattern is found for nitrate, except the station spacing reflecting no correlation is less than for sulfate (approximately 1200 km).

The intersite correlations illustrate well the regional character of sulfate and nitrate deposition in the EUS. Circumstan-tial evidence for a similar spatial scale of influence also has been reported for the West (6).

Variability in deposition patterns may be associated with certain dominant meteorological patterns (1). As noted above, ambient conditions can be classified meteorologically. Some evi-dence for such a classification also exists for wet deposition (5).

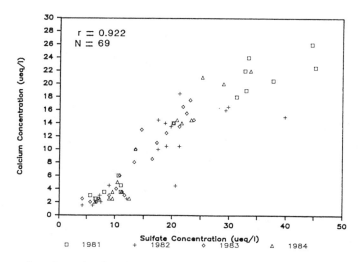

Figure 2.   Correlation between calcium and sulfate concentration
in western precipitation.   Data for 1981–1984 – annual averages
of NADP stations.   (From Hidy & Young, Environ. Res. & Tech.,
unpubl. report.)

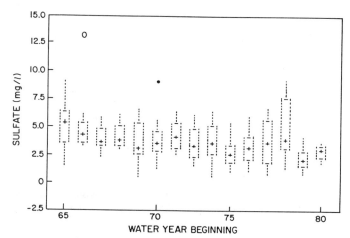

Figure 3.   Trend in annual median values of sulfate concentration
in bulk deposition samples at Hinckley, NY (crosses).   Variability is also indicated in the boxplot by the standard deviations
(–) and the range (vertical bars) and outliers (0, ●)(Reproduced
with permission from Ref. 4.   Copyright 1984 APCA).

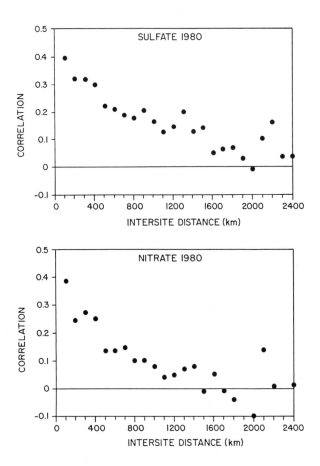

Figure 4.   Scale of regional phenomena in precipitation sulfate
and nitrate as indicated by intersite correlations.   Data are an
average of several sites in EUS.   (Reproduced with permission
from Ref. 5.   Copyright 1985 Electric Power Research Inst.).

Source-Receptor Relationships.

Ultimately the mitigation to the environmental effects of acid deposition requires decrease in exposure through emission reduction. There has been considerable debate about how much and where reductions can be achieved from practical planning for SO_2 and NO_x emission reduction. An important aspect of the predictability issue lies in the uncertainties in the non-linear character of atmospheric processes affecting deposition rates (2).

Perhaps the best evidence for establishing a directly proportional relationship between emission change is comparison between long term trends like those shown in Figure 3 with emission changes over the same time period. Such a direct relation is suggested in sulfate (and possibly NO_3^-) data in bulk deposition taken at Hubbard Brook, NH (e.g., Figure 5). An average decrease in sulfate of about 2%/yr between 1970 and 1982 (not shown in Figure 5) is essentially the same as that estimated from decrease in regionwide SO_2 emissions (4,7).

With the discussion of spatial correlation above, it is logical to expect that any relation between emissions and regionally representative deposition measurements should be consistent for several sites. To test this, the Hubbard Brook results were compared with limited data from the USGS bulk deposition network, primarily located in New York State (4). The stations selected are rural and are within 550 km of one another. Qualitative comparison of trend indicators in the data are summarized in Table III.

Table III.   Summary of Apparent Trends[a] in Annual Median Precipitation Chemistry Data from the USGS Sites and Hubbard Brook (1965-1980) Sites (Reproduced with permission from Ref. 4, Copyright 1984 APCA)

Parameter	Hubbard Brook	Hinckley NY	Canton NY	Mays Pt. NY	Salamanca NY	Athens PA
Precipitation	+	0	0	0	0	0
SO_4^{2-}	−	−	−	0	0	0+
NO_3^-	+0	+	0	+	0	+
NH_4^+	0	+	+	+	0	+
pH	+	−	0	0	−	0

[a] Trend indicators are: (+) upward, (−) downward, and (0) no trend.

These indicators are based on estimated significant change by statistical testing (4). The summary indicates that the trends are not consistent for sulfate, or for other constituents.

Spatial and temporal weighting also have been used on the USGS data to obtain yearly averaged sulfate deposition for New York

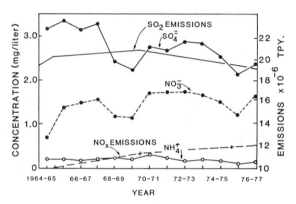

Figure 5. Comparison between EUS SO$_2$ and NO$_x$ emissions and annual weighted concentrations of SO$_4{}^{2-}$, NO$_3^-$, and NH$_4^+$ in bulk deposition at the Hubbard Brook Experimental Forest from 1964 to 1977. Line through emissions is drawn through estimates each five year period from 1965. (From Hidy, 8).

State. Bilonik's results (9) indicate a maximum in sulfate deposition in the 1971-1973 period as compared with an apparent EUS SO_2
emissions maximum between 1970 and 1975. Since deposition rate is a
dimensionally consistent parameter with emission rate, these results
qualitatively tend to support an SO_2 emission-deposition relationship for the EUS.

The lack of spatial consistency in relating SO_4^{2-} concentration
to SO_2 emissions may be the result of differences in the influence
of sources near a given site, to an inadequate quantitative data
base, or to meteorological differences in exposure. A test of the
first factor was attempted, calculating the effect of regionally
different emission changes on different receptors, accounting for
reduction in source effect with distance from the UMACID model (5).
The results of the calculation are given in Figure 6. The receptor
locations are western New York State (WNY); North Central
Pennsylvania (NCPA); Muskoka, Ont.; Whiteface Mountain, NY (WFM);
and northeastern New Hampshire (VT-NH). There are clearly geographical differences in expected changes with SO_2 emissions after
1965, and the sulfate deposition change should not necessarily be
linear since the apparent emissions were not changing linearly over
the period. Nevertheless, a down trend in sulfate should have been
observed consistently if meteorological variability was similar from
site-to-site. These results are ambiguous. The ambiguity derives
in part from subregional differences in emission change over the
EUS. The Hubbard Brook data are considered higher quality than the
USGS set (7). Thus, the Hubbard Brook data are relied upon for
supporting a linear source-receptor relationship.

A test for proportionality between SO_2 emissions and precipitation sulfate also has been attempted for the West (6). Smelter
emissions have dominated SO_2 emissions in the WUS. These emissions
changed by more than 50% over the 1980-1984 period. Analysis of
annual averaged $[SO_4^{2-}]$ data from NADP for several western sites
(mostly in Colorado) provided circumstantial evidence for a proportional SRR. These results were challenged by others (10, 11).
However, reanalysis of the same data for monthly variation appears
to give a stronger case for proportionality (Oppenheimer, M.,
Epstein, D., _Nature_, in press) over distances of influence beyond
1000 km. The new analysis also places in perspective within year
(seasonal), and year-to-year variability.

The reason for the strength of proportionality relationship in
the western data relative to the East is not apparent; however, it
may be related to the size of the emission change "signal" in the
meteorological "noise" compared with historic conditions in the
East.

In estimating the reliability of theoretical predictions, it is
important to take into account the year-to-year variability in SRRs
estimated from meteorological transport. The prediction-reliability
question is central to constructing a cost effective practical

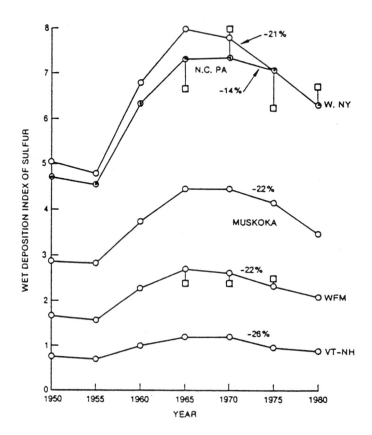

Figure 6.   Estimated contribution to wet deposition of sulfate from SO_2 emissions in the eastern U.S. and southeastern Canada based on 1978 meteorology. The wet deposition index is the deposition rate if meteorology were the same in each year. The percentage change shown on each line corresponds to the calcu- lated reduction in wet deposition from emission change, with meteorological conditions assumed to be uniform from year to year. The expected range of uncertainty in estimate of wet deposition using actual precipitation rather than 1978 levels are indicated by squares and vertical bars. (Reproduced with permission from Ref. 4. Copyright 1984 APCA).

design for selective emission control improving deposition in distant, susceptible areas. Actual observational data are very limited through which tests of model validity and performance can be made. Data to test the sensitivity of such calculations are even less available.

An exploratory analysis of the range of variability that may be expected was attempted by Samson et al (see Hidy et al, 5, p. II-2-98). Their calculations used actual meteorological data to estimate a geographical distribution of "natural potential" for emissions from a source area to reach a receptor area. If wind conditions exist such that wind blows all the time from the source over the receptor, for example, this potential would be unity. Calculations of "natural potential" were made using meteorological data for several years. The year-to-year variation in natural potential distribution is shown in Figure 7 for the EUS. The example concerns the Upper Ohio River Valley source complex. Near to the source area and downwind (eastward), there is a 20% variability in natural potential, while at greater distances and upwind (westward), the coefficient of variation in potential increases. These calculations give at least a qualitative picture of the reliability in air transport conditions influencing SRRs, picking a single test year. If the wind field and mixing conditions were the only source of variability, the predictions could be reasonably reliable in certain key areas. However, other variation such as air chemistry, cloud scavenging and precipitation are additional factors unaccounted for in such calculations.

A number of workers have become concerned about such questions so that research in uncertainties has expanded. Unfortunately, the observations describing chemical variability in both dry and wet deposition are very limited for direct study. There is need for a major investment in field programs to acquire such data.

Summary.

This paper has summarized certain features of observations characterizing dry and wet deposition of airborne acid forming species, in particular, sulfate and nitrate. The regional or subcontinental character of deposition distributions over the United States is noted. Example data are cited showing differences in characteristic deposition between the West and the East. The West experiences sulfate and nitrate deposition well below that found in the East, but larger than global remote sites are suggested. Relating acidity to sulfate and nitrate in the West is confounded by the strong association between calcium and sulfate in western precipitation. Dry and wet deposition have similar rates far from sources (both in the East and the West). Sulfate tends to dominate acid species in precipitation, except near large sources of NO_x.

Meteorological processes, emission changes and measurement uncertainty lead to variability in deposition rates. Deposition measurements are uncertain mainly from ambiguities in sampling techniques. Meteorological variability produces potentially large within year and year-to-year differences in exposure to deposition.

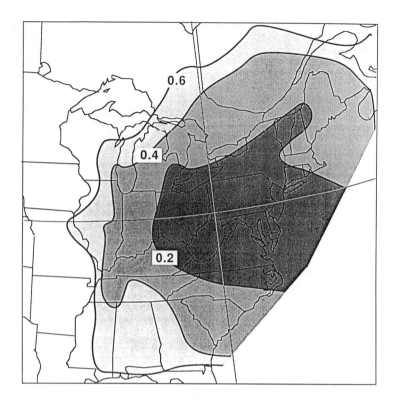

Figure 7. Variation in year-to-year trajectory calculations
beginning from the upper Ohio River Valley. The curves represent
the coefficient of variation in the distributions of annual
"natural potential" of material released in the upper Ohio River
Valley reaching locations downwind from this source area.
(Redrawn and reproduced with permission from Ref. 5. Copyright
1985 Electric Power Research Inst.).

The reliable estimation of source impact on receptor conditions is difficult from theory because of undetermined uncertainties. Inference from comparison between emissions and measurements offers an alternative to calculations. Measurements in the East have yielded ambiguous source-receptor relationships. However, evidence suggests that recent changes in sulfate deposition in the West are linked with relatively large changes in SO_2 emissions from non-ferrous metal smelters, especially in New Mexico and Arizona.

Meteorological variability needs to be considered in estimating the reliability of source-receptor calculations.

Acknowledgments

Part of this study was derived from research sponsored by the Electric Power Research Institute and West Associates, Inc.

Literature Cited

1. The Sulfate Regional Experiment: Report of Findings, EA-1901(3), Electric Power Research Institute: Palo Alto, CA, 1983.
2. Acid Deposition; Atmospheric Processes in Eastern North America, National Academy of Sciences, 1983.
3. Galloway, J. N.; Likens, G. E.; Hawley, M. E. Science: 1984, 226, 829-831.
4. Hidy, G. M.; Hansen, D. A.; Henry, R. C.; Ganesan, K.; Collins, J. J. Air Poll. Contr. Assn. 1984, 31, 333-354.
5. Feasibility and Design of the Massive Aerometric Tracer Experiment (MATEX), EA-4305 (2), Electric Power Research Institute: Palo Alto, CA, 1985.
6. Oppenheimer, M.; Epstein, C.; Yuhnke, R. Science 1985, 229, 854-858.
7. Acid Deposition. Long Term Trends, National Academy of Sciences, 1986.
8. Hidy, G. M. Proc. 2nd Nat'l. Symposium on Acid Rain, Pittsburgh Chamber of Commerce, Pittsburgh, PA, 1982.
9. Bilonik, R. A. Atmos. Environ. 1985, 19, 1829-1845.
10. Hidy, G. M. Science 1986, 233, 10.
11. Newman, L.; Benkovitz, C. Science 1986, 233, 11-12.

RECEIVED February 3, 1987

Chapter 3

Acid Deposition and Atmospheric Chemistry at Allegheny Mountain

W. R. Pierson[1], W. W. Brachaczek[1], R. A. Gorse, Jr.[1], S. M. Japar[1], J. M. Norbeck[1], and G. J. Keeler[2]

[1]Research Staff, Ford Motor Company, P.O. Box 2053, Dearborn, MI 48121
[2]Department of Atmospheric and Oceanic Sciences, University of Michigan, Ann Arbor, MI 48109

In August, 1983, members of the Research Staff of Ford Motor Company carried out a field experiment at two rural sites in southwestern Pennsylvania involving various aspects of the acid deposition phenomenon. This presentation will focus on the wet (rain) deposition during the experiment, as well as the relative importance of wet and dry deposition processes for nitrate and sulfate at the sites. Other aspects of the experiment have been discussed elsewhere: the chemistry of dew and its role in acid deposition (1), the dry deposition of HNO_3 and SO_2 to surrogate surfaces (2), and the role of elemental carbon in light absorption and of the latter in visibility degradation (3).

<u>EXPERIMENTAL</u>

The experiment was conducted August 5-28, 1983 on abandoned radio towers atop Allegheny Mountain (elevation 838 meters) and Laurel Hill (elevation 850 meters, 35 km NW of Allegheny Mountain) in southwestern Pennsylvania (Fig. 1). Both sites are heavily forested and experience little local vehicle traffic.

At the Allegheny Mountain site atmospheric aerosol and gas measurements, and light-scattering and condensation-nuclei-count measurements, were made atop the tower 14 to 17 meters above the ground. Wind speed and direction, and atmospheric temperature, pressure and humidity, were continuously recorded. Rain (and dew) was collected in a 500 m^2 mowed clearing 60 meters north of the tower. Rain was collected on an event basis 1.8 meters above the ground into tared polyethylene bottles, using a wet-only collector (Wong Laboratories Mark V), equipped with a retracting lid actuated by a rain sensor. The standard collector bucket was supplanted by a 30.5-cm diameter polyethylene funnel fitted into the tared collection bottle. The rainfall amount (in mm or in $1/m^2$) was determined from the sample weight and the collector geometry. The sampling setup was similar at Laurel Hill.

As soon as each rain stopped, the sample was removed, capped, and refrigerated at the site. It was then transported to the field laboratory in Somerset (midway between the sites) where it was weighed and kept refrigerated (never frozen). The analytical

procedures were similar to those previously described (1) for dew
samples. Quantities measured included pH, conductivity, total
titratable acid, and (by ion chromatography) $SO_4^=$, NO_3^-, NO_2^-, PO_4^{3-},
F^-, Cl^-, and Br^-.

The unused portions of the rain samples were transported to
Dearborn, still refrigerated. Some 7 months later they were re-
analyzed; to selected samples H_2O_2 was added before analysis (final
$[H_2O_2] = 1.5\%$) to make certain that all S(IV) had been oxidized to
sulfate. At this time NH_4^+, Na and K were determined by ion chromatography.

Atmospheric NO_2, SO_2, and O_3 were measured by various methods
(1, 4, 5). light scattering was measured by integrating nephelo-
meters. $HNO_3(g)$ and aerosol NO_3^- were measured by the denuder
difference method (6-8) using MgO-coated denuder tubes and nylon
membrane filters, with ion chromatographic nitrate determination on
alkaline filter extracts. Valid ammonia data were not obtained
during any of the rain periods.

Aerosol samples were collected on filters of various types
(including impactors and virtual impactors) and analyzed for H^+,
NH_4^+, $SO_4^=$, and other components. The filter, denuder, and impinger
samples were collected in 1/2- to 24-hour periods synchronized with
each other but not generally with the onset or stop of rain.
Accordingly it should be understood that, in the treatment that
follows, the atmospheric concentrations of aerosol components, HNO_3,
and impinger SO_2 that we will associate with the rain samples are the
average concentrations over the several-hour period during which the
given rain occurred, and not the concentrations just during the rain
itself. Inspection of the continuous SO_2, NO_x, O_3, CNC and b_{scat}
traces indicates that use of the longer period does not materially
influence the results.

RESULTS AND DISCUSSION

Rain Chemistry.   The characteristics of the 17 rain events at
the two sites are summarized and compared in Table 1 to the dew
samples and the one settled fogwater sample collected at Allegheny
Mountain (1). (The dew was sampled in a manner that excluded prior
dry deposition. The representativeness of the fogwater sample is
unknown - other fogs occurred but no samples were collected.)

A number of conclusions concerning rain are evident from Table
1:

- The rain was acidic, with the volume-averaged pH of 3.5 being
  perhaps somewhat lower than that of the average summer rain in
  the northeast (9-14).
- H^+ accounted for about 90% of the total rain acidity.
- The rain H^+ could be accounted for in terms of H_2SO_4 and HNO_3.
- The $SO_4^=/NO_3^-$ equivalents ratio of about 3.7 in the rain was
  comparable to that characteristic of summer rains in the
  northeast, i.e., about 2.3 to 4 (9-17).
- The Laurel Hill rains were about 10% more concentrated in all
  species than those collected at Allegheny Mountain (in agreement
  with atmospheric aerosol and trace gas concentrations at the
  sites).

When the composition of the rain is compared with that of the dew and the fog, a number of points emerge:
- While the ranges in ion concentrations, including H^+, are wider in dew samples, the ranges overlap so that the dew was qualitatively similar to dilute rain.
- The $SO_4^=/NO_3^-$ concentration ratio in the rain was about 3.7 equivalents per equivalent vs. a ratio of about 2.5 in the dew. This is not surprising since significant amounts of sulfate are introduced into rain by nucleation scavenging (18) while aerosol sulfate deposition to dew is minimal (1). (In fact, at Allegheny Mountain (1) SO_2 was responsible for about 80% of the dew $SO_4^=$.)
- There is little evidence of the presence of S(IV) in the rain and fogwater samples (that is, no significant increase in sulfate was seen between the prompt and delayed analyses). By contrast, there is evidence of considerable S(IV) (up to 40%) remaining unoxidized in the dew at the end of the night (1).
- The chemistry of the one settled fogwater sample is similar to that of the more concentrated rains.

Acid Deposition Fluxes in Rain.   Table 2 lists cumulative amounts of various species deposited per unit area in rain, dew and fog during the experiment. Table 2 also shows the fluxes obtained by dividing the accumulation by the sum of collection times. The

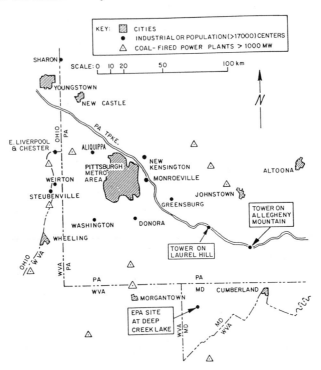

Figure 1. The site of the field experiment in southwestern Pennsylvania.

Table 1. Comparison of rain properties at Allegheny and Laurel, August 1983, with Allegheny dew and settled fogwater (volume-weighted averages) *

		Rain - Allegheny (n = 12)	Rain - Laurel (n = 5)	Dew (n = 15)	Fog (n = 1)[a]
pH		3.5 (3.1-3.75)	3.5 (3.3-3.6)	4.0 (3.5-5.3)	3.47
Titratable acid,	μeq/liter	324 (227-763)	349 (317-615)	108 (16-382)	350
H^+	"	290 (178-741)	311 (257-550)	91 (5.5-347)	340
NH_4^+	"	53 (15-116)	70 (61-119)	8 (0-55)	144
Na^+, K^+, Mg^{2+}, Ca^{2+}	"	39 (8-99)	70 (48-159)	41 (14-99)	155
NO_2^-	"	0.6-1.0	0.6-1.3	0.7 (0.1-2.0)	-
NO_3^-	"	68 (41-252)	86 (63-202)	32 (3-138)	230
SO_4^{2-} prompt	"	256 (125-700)	294 (249-575)	73 (10-254)	387
delayed	"	262 (138-700)	299 (251-575)	81 (14-251)	373
Cl^-	"	8 (3-25)	8.5 (6-21)	5 (0.3-16)	26
Ion balance $\Sigma+/\Sigma-$		1.15	1.16	1.27	0.99
Λ, μmho cm^{-1}		115 (67-271)	122 (109-220)	42 (10-137)	159
Λ accounted for		106%	111%	94%	107%

[a] Does not include all fog events.

* Volume-weighted averages are the amount of a given species deposited per unit area throughout the experiment divided by the amount of water deposited per unit area throughout the experiment. The prompt and delayed sulfate data are, respectively, the field-laboratory results and the re-analyses 7 months later.

greater frequency of rain at Allegheny Mountain produced about a 4-fold greater accumulation of all ionic species there than at Laurel Hill. This reflects the randomness of summer convective precipitation (approximately 70% of the rain at Allegheny Mountain was convective in nature).

Comparison of the deposition efficiencies of rain, dew and fog at Allegheny Mountain shows that during the 21-day experiment, rain was responsible for the deposition of 60 times more acidity (together with related species) than was deposited during dew periods or with settled fogwater.

Precipitation in the vicinity of Allegheny Mountain is about 107 cm per year (19), or close to the rate recorded in Table 2. If the ratio between deposition by rain and deposition to dew during the sampling period is also representative of the year, then it follows that the annual total acid deposited in rain is very roughly 60 times as great as that deposited to dew or in settled fogwater.

Scavenging Ratios for $SO_4^=$ and NO_3^- by Rain. If it is assumed that the concentration of a pollutant in precipitation is dependent on its concentration in the air in which the precipitation forms, then the scavenging ratio, W_i, can be defined as

$$W_i = C_i^r / C_i^a$$

Table 2. Deposition totals and deposition fluxes associated with rain at

Allegheny and Laurel, August 1983; Allegheny dew and settled fogwater

shown for comparison

	Rain-Allegheny (n = 12)	Rain-Laurel (n = 5)	Dew (n = 15)	Fog (n = 1)
August 7-27 Accumulations:				
Water g/m^2	51000	12940	2722	(~590)[a]
Titratable acid μeq/m^2	16500	4513	295	(~210)[a]
H$^+$ "	14800	4017	247	(~200)[a]
NH$_4^+$ "	2570	898	22	(~185)[a]
NO$_3^-$ "	3440	1113	88	(~140)[a]
SO$_4^{2-}$ prompt "	13100	3799	197	(~230)[a]
delayed "	13400	3860	220	(~230)[a]
Fluxes (accumulations/collection times)				
Water mg/m^2/sec	1700	700	5	3.3
Titratable acid neq/m^2/sec	550	244	0.53	1.2
H$^+$ "	490	217	0.44	1.1
NH$_4^+$ "	85	49	0.04	0.5
NO$_3-$ "	115	60	0.16	0.8
SO$_4^{2-}$ prompt "	440	206	0.35	1.28
delayed "	450	209	0.39	1.24

a   Order-of-magnitude estimate, based on the estimate that 5 times as much was deposited during the experiment as in the one 10-hour sample that was analyzed. The representativeness of the sample composition is not known.

where $C_i{}^a$ and $C_i{}^r$ are the volume concentrations of species i in air (equivalents per cubic meter of air) and in the rainwater (equivalents per cubic meter of liquid water, i.e., milli-equivalents per liter). The calculation of scavenging ratios using ground-level atmospheric data further assumes that the ground-level pollutant data are representative of the air scavenged by a precipitating cloud. This assumption appears at least partially justified at locations remote enough from sources for vertical mixing to have occurred (18).

Washout ratios for aerosol $SO_4{}^=$ and for total $NO_3{}^-$ (HNO_3 + aerosol $NO_3{}^-$) are presented in Table 3. These washout ratios presuppose, in accordance with Barrie's treatment (18), that SO_2 does not contribute to the rain $SO_4{}^=$ and that both HNO_3 and aerosol $NO_3{}^-$ contribute to the rain $NO_3{}^-$. Accordingly, the sulfate ratios are upper limits on W_{SO_4}; and the $NO_3{}^-$ ratios reported are close to, and only slightly less than, W_{NO_3} for HNO_3 alone since HNO_3 is highly soluble and dominates the total $NO_3{}^-$. Thus from Table 3,

$$W_{aerosol\ SO_4} = < 9 \times 10^5$$

$$W_{HNO_3} = > 19 \times 10^5$$

These results are similar to daily-averaged values reported by Barrie (18) for sites in eastern Canada (1978-1981). His mass scavenging ratios, multiplied by 890 (the ratio between the density of water and that of air at the 838-m altitude of Allegheny Mountain in order to match units), give the following averages for 4 remote locations: $W_{SO_4} = 9 \times 10^5$ to 14×10^5 for aerosol $SO_4{}^=$; $W_{t-NO_3} = 19 \times 10^5$ to 26×10^5 for total $NO_3{}^-$ (HNO_3 + aerosol $NO_3{}^-$). For one suburban/rural site Barrie obtains $W_{SO_4} = 10 \times 10^5$, $W_{t-NO_3} = 11 \times 10^5$.

<u>Estimation of Wet and Dry Acid, $NO_3{}^-$, and $SO_4{}^=$ Deposition Budgets at Allegheny Mountain</u>. To gauge the relative importance of wet and dry deposition, the wet-deposition measurements need to be accompanied by dry-deposition estimates. Nighttime dry deposition to dew was measured in the present experiment (1), but we lack good estimates of dry deposition at night when dew was absent and, more important, we lack a good estimate of dry deposition during the day when deposition velocities are expected to be largest. To deal with this deficiency two alternative approaches are adopted as follows.

First, nylon and Teflon 142-mm-diameter membrane filters were set out as surrogate collection surfaces above the canopy at Allegheny during daylight on five days during the 1983 experiment, to gauge the relative importance of aerosol $NO_3{}^-$ and $SO_4{}^=$ deposition (on Teflon) and the deposition of HNO_3 and SO_2 (nylon-Teflon difference)-(2). The applicability of surrogate surfaces to real ones, however, is questionable on several grounds. For HNO_3 the sticking efficiency to nylon is probably (20) 100%; for SO_2 the sticking efficiency is less than 100% but greater than zero (21); and sticking efficiencies are by no means the only issue.

The second approach is to use the measured ambient concentrations in combination with deposition velocities reported in the literature (21-23).

The two approaches give effectively the same results. For example, the average HNO_3 deposition velocity measured by micro-meteorological methods above a forest in east Tennessee or on summer

Table 3   Rain Scavenging Ratios for $SO_4^=$ and NO_3^-

Rain #	Rain* $SO_4^=$ (μeq/l)	Aerosol (neq/m³)	SO_2 (neq/m³)	$W_{SO_4^=}$	Rain NO_3^- (μeq/l)	HNO_3 (neq/m³)	total NO_3^- (neq/m³)	$W_{t-NO_3^-}$
Allegheny Mountain								
1	260	440	653	5.9×10^5	58	46.9	55.8	10.4×10^5
2	207	440	653	4.7×10^5	70	46.9	55.8	12.5×10^5
3	276	213	681	12.9×10^5	63	19.5	21.3	29.6×10^5
4	138	213	681	6.5×10^5	63	19.5	21.3	29.6×10^5
5	230	176	704	13.1×10^5	150	27.9	43.4	34.6×10^5
6	163	811	1181	2.0×10^5	41	73.7	87.5	4.7×10^5
10	700	388	980	18.0×10^5	139	153	154	9.0×10^5
12	284	755	849	3.8×10^5	79	70.0	74.6	10.6×10^5
13	650	755	849	8.6×10^5	212	70.0	74.6	28.4×10^5
14	537	755	849	7.1×10^5	252	70.0	74.6	33.8×10^5
15	542	773	754	7.0×10^5	161	75.9	81.7	19.7×10^5
Laurel Hill								
1	392	226	1066	17.3×10^5	135	36.6	41.6	32.5×10^5
2	252	830	660	3.0×10^5	63	-	78.5	8.0×10^5
3	273	158	864	17.3×10^5	72	77.8	83.8	8.6×10^5
4	573	377	1044	15.2×10^5	194	103	117	16.6×10^5
average				$(9.5 \pm 5.6) \times 10^5$				$(19 \pm 11) \times 10^5$

*Results from the delayed analyses where available

Table 4.   Sources of NO_3^- and $SO_4^=$ deposition at Allegheny Mountain, August 5-28, 1983[a]

	NO_3^- (μeq/m^2)	$SO_4^=$ (μeq/m^2)
Rain (12 events)	3440	13400
Fog (1 event)	140	230
Dew (15 events)	88	220
Dry - without dew	2400[b]	5000[c]

[a]   For NO_3^- 1 μequivalent = 1 μmole; for $SO_4^=$ 2 μequivalents = 1 μmole.

[b]   Based on deposition to nylon surrogate surfaces; does not include substances not depositing to nylon (e.g., NO_2).

[c]   Based on the measurement of dry deposition to nylon surrogate surfaces we estimate that SO_2 contributed about 5000 μeq/m^2 of dry deposition to the $SO_4^=$ total. Aerosol $SO_4^=$ adds another 300 μeq/m^2 or less.

days over an Illinois pasture (22) is about the same as the 2.5 ± 1.5 cm/sec measured by the surrogate collectors (together with atmospheric concentrations) in the present experiment. The 0.5 cm/sec SO_2 deposition velocity to the surrogate collectors is in the range reported to vegetation (23) (average ~ 0.7 cm/sec). The 0.05 cm/sec deposition velocity of aerosol $SO_4^=$ to the surrogate collectors is in the range given in the literature (23).

The results employing daytime dry deposition estimates from the surrogate collectors are given in Table 4; these estimates presuppose that the five days are representative. While rain accounted for some 60% of the NO_3^- deposition, dry deposition of HNO_3 in the absence of dew appears also to be important. This similar to the estimate made by Huebert (22) in the Illinois experiment that HNO_3 dry deposition accounted for 48% of the NO_3^- wet/dry deposition. For $SO_4^=$ deposition, rain is again the dominant medium; however, the dry deposition of SO_2 may also be important. The contributions of dry-deposited aerosol nitrate and sulfate, not listed in Table 4, were small (about 5%) at the site.

If we now suppose that SO_2 is tantamount to H_2SO_4 in acidifying potential, on grounds that SO_2 readily oxidizes to H_2SO_4, and if we recall that the NO_3^- and $SO_4^=$ in the rain/dew/fog samples can be regarded as mostly HNO_3 and H_2SO_4, then the total strong acid deposited in the experiment can be apportioned from Table IV roughly as follows:

> 47% = H_2SO_4 in rain (34% SO_2 scavenging, 13% aerosol $SO_4^=$
>   scavenging)
> 23% = SO_2 dry deposition without dew
> 16% = HNO_3 in rain
> 11% = HNO_3 dry deposition without dew
> 3% = HNO_3 and H_2SO_4 in fog and dew

At the rates implied by Table IV, total wet and dry H^+ deposition would be about 300 moles H^+/hectare/month - in August.

ACKNOWLEDGMENTS

We are pleased to acknowledge the assistance of the Pennsylvania Turnpike Commission in providing access and electric power to the two sites and helping us set up the experiment; we are especially indebted to Warren E. Kipp, Robert E. Davis, Nevin A. Miller, Carl Baker and the crew at the Allegheny Mountain Tunnel, and the Chief Engineer and Deputy Executive Director of the Pennsylvania Turnpike Commission, Robert H. Klucher. At Ford, we are indebted to Richard Floyd, Lee C. Westwood, Y. T. Liu, and G. E. Fisher for their participation in the chemical analysis. Ford participants in the field experiment itself included Karen M. Adams, James W. Butler, Ann C. Cleary, James C. Dziadosz, Larry P. Haack, Thomas J. Korniski, William K. Okamoto, and Michael J. Rokosz. Jeffrey M. Masters, formerly of the University of Michigan, participated in the field and handled the on-site meteorology. Prof. Perry J. Samson of the University of Michigan assisted in the trajectory analysis and meteorology. We thank William J. Courtney of Northrop Services and Thomas G. Dzubay, Charles W. Lewis, and Robert K. Stevens of EPA/ESRL for their collaboration including field intercalibration and the use of their instruments. We are grateful to E. Eugene Weaver, who returned from Ford retirement to help, with Adele Weaver, on the field experiment. We thank Prof. James A. Lynch of the Pennsylvania State University for sharing detailed rain data with us from his Laurel Hill site. Our work was supported in part by the National Science Foundation under Industry/University Cooperative Research Grant NO. ATM-8507282 to the University of Michigan.

LITERATURE CITED

(1) Pierson, W.R., Brachaczek, W.W., Gorse, R.A., Jr., Japar, S.M. and Norbeck, J.M., Paper No. 85-7.4, Air Pollution Control Association 78th Annual Meeting, Detroit, June (1985); J. Geophys. Res. 91, 4083 (1986).

(2) Japar, S.M., Brachaczek, W.W., Gorse, R.A., Jr., Norbeck, J.M. and Pierson, W.R., presented at Muskoka '85: International Symposium on Acidic Precipitation, Minett, Ontario, September (1985).

(3) Japar, S.M., Brachaczek, W.W., Gorse, R.A., Jr., Norbeck, J.M., and Pierson, W.R., Atmos. Environ. 20, 1281 (1986).

(4) Holdren, M.W. and Spicer, C.W., Environ, Sci. Tech., 18, 113 (1984).

(5) Pierson, W.R., Brachaczek, W.W., Truex, T.J., Butler, J.W., and Korniski, T.J., Annals N.Y. Acad. Sci. 338, 145 (1980).

(6) Appel, B.R., Tokiwa, Y., and Haik, M., Atmos. Environ. 15, 283 (1981).

(7) Shaw, R.W., Jr., Stevens, R.K., Bowermaster, J., Tesch, J.W., and Tew, E., Atmos. Environ. 16, 845 (1982).

(8) Spicer, D.W., Howes, J.E., Jr., Bishop, T.A., Arnold, L.H., and Stevens, R.K., Atmos. Environ. 16, 1487 (1982).

(9) Bowersox, V.C. and de Pena, R.G., J. Geophys. Res. 85, 5614 (1980).

(10) Bowersox, V.C. and Stensland, R.G., Paper No. 81-6.1, Air Pollution Control Association 74th Annual Meeting, Philadelphia, June (1981).

(11) Altwicker, E.R. and Johannes, A.H., Paper No. 81-6.2, Air Pollution Control Association 74th Annual Meeting, Philadelphia, June (1981)

(12) Pack, D.H., Atmos. Environ. 16, 1145 (1982).

(13) Hales, J.M., et al, Atmos. Environ. 16, 1603 (1982).

(14) Pratt, G.C. and Krupa, S.V., Atmos. Environ. 17, 1845 (1983).

(15) Galloway, J.N. and Likens, G.E., Atmos. Environ. 15, 1081 (1981).

(16) Henderson, R.G. and Weingartner, K., Atmos. Environ. 16, 1657 (1982)

(17) Wilson, W.E. and Husar, R.B., Society of Automotive Engineers Technical Paper Series, Paper No. 830647 (1983).

(18) Barrie, L.A., J. Geophys. Res. 90, 5789 (1985).

(19) National Oceanographic and Atmospheric Administration, Climates of the States, Vol. 2 (Gale Research Co., Detroit (1978)), P. 852.

(20) Durham, J.L. and Stockburger, L., Atmos. Environ. 20, 559 (1986).

(21) Fowler, D., Atmos. Environ. 12, 369 (1978).

(22) Huebert, B.J. and Robert, C.H., J. Geophys. Res. 90, 2085
     (1985).
(23) Schmel, G.A., Atmos. Environ. 14, 983 (1980).

RECEIVED May 15, 1987

Chapter 4

The Western Atlantic Ocean Experiment

James N. Galloway[1], Thomas M. Church[2], Anthony H. Knap[3], Douglas M. Whelpdale[4], and John M. Miller[5]

[1]Department of Environmental Sciences, University of Virginia, Charlottesville, VA 22903
[2]College of Marine Studies, University of Delaware, Newark, DE 19711
[3]Bermuda Biological Station, St. Georges West 1-15, Bermuda
[4]Atmospheric Environment Service, 4905 Dufferin Street, Downsview, Ontario M3H 5T4, Canada
[5]National Oceanic and Atmospheric Administration, 8060 13th Street, Silver Spring, MD 20910

The Western Atlantic Ocean Experiment (WATOX) investi-
gates the flux and fate of sulfur, nitrogen, and trace-
metal and trace-organic compounds eastward from North
America. Using a variety of sampling platforms (ships,
aircraft, islands), samples of gases, aerosols, and
precipitation have been used to determine the impact of
North America on atmospheric chemical cycles of the
western Atlantic Ocean. This paper provides an overview
of the results obtained since WATOX began in 1980.

The Western Atlantic Ocean Experiment (WATOX) is designed to determine the amount and the fate of selected sulfur, nitrogen, metal
and organic compounds advected eastward from North America. The
specific atmospheric fluxes being investigated are depicted in
Figure 1 and explained in Table I; the participating universities
and agencies are listed in Table II. This paper presents a brief
overview of the approach we are using to achieve the above-stated
objectives and summarizes our accomplishments.

The measurement program has two components, long-term and
intensive. For the long-term component, data collection to determine the composition of wet deposition at Lewes, Delaware, and on
Bermuda began in 1980. In 1984, another site was added at Adrigole,
Ireland. From 1981 to 1985 during May-October, precipitation samples were also collected on two ships cruising weekly between New
York City, Bermuda, and Nassau. Precipitation-chemistry data from
the three land-based sites and from the ships were used to calculate

Table I.   WATOX Fluxes and Methods (see Fig. 1)

Fluxes from Fig. 1	Determination Methods
A. Emission to North American atmosphere	Literature search
B. Advection eastward	Calculations; land-based and aircraft sampling
C. Wet deposition	Field measurements on ships, on Bermuda, and at Lewes, DE
Dry deposition	Concentration measurements on ships, on Bermuda, and at Lewes, DE
D. Atmospheric transformations	Calculations; atmospheric measurements
E. Emission from sea surface	Calculations; estimates from literature
F. Advection eastward	Calculations; land-based, ship-based, and aircraft sampling

Table II.   Members of the WATOX Consortium

Investigator and Agency	
J. N. Galloway University of Virginia Charlottesville, VA	WATOX director Atmospheric deposition of S and N compounds and organic acids
T. M. Church University of Delaware Newark, DE	Atmospheric deposition of trace-metal elements
A. H. Knap Bermuda Biological Station St. Georges, Bermuda	Atmospheric deposition of trace-organic compounds
J. M. Miller NOAA Silver Spring, MD	Transport and air-mass trajectories
D. M. Whelpdale Atmospheric Environment Service Toronto, Canada	Transport and air-mass trajectories
J. Boatman NOAA Boulder, CO	Aircraft coordination

rates of wet deposition and to track air masses eastward from North America.

The intensive component of the WATOX measurement program (Intensives) involves periodic sampling to ascertain the processes controlling the transport, transformation, and deposition of

materials to the western Atlantic Ocean. During the seven Intensives that have already taken place (Table III), each of which
lasted from one to four weeks, instruments specifically designed to
determine atmospheric concentrations of gas and aerosol species were
placed at land-based sites and on ships and aircraft. For each
Intensive, scientists from institutions that were not part of the
WATOX consortium were invited to participate in such a way as to
complement the skills and research abilities of the permanent WATOX
personnel.

The first two Intensives (WATOX-82 and WATOX-83, see Table III)
investigated changes in the composition of air parcels that travel
from North America to Bermuda. During WATOX-82 and WATOX-83, scientists from General Motors and the University of Miami measured
concentrations of trace gases and aerosols at Lewes, Delaware, and
High Point, Bermuda.

WATOX-84, the third Intensive, used data from samples collected
onboard the RV Knorr as it traveled between North America and Africa.
These data were used to support the gas and aerosol data from WATOX-
82 and WATOX-83 and to test new shipboard precipitation-collection
instruments.

WATOX-82, -83, and -84 sampled air in the marine boundary
layer. These sea-level measurements gave no information about upper-
air transport. To overcome this deficiency, the fourth through the
seventh Intensives incorporated data collected onboard two NOAA
research aircraft, the NOAA WP-3D and the NOAA KingAir. (See
Table III for the specific species measured.) Both aircraft carried
sampling and analytical equipment designed to determine the vertical
and horizontal chemical structure of the atmosphere.

For WATOX-85 the KingAir flew missions east of Newport News,
Virginia, and adjacent to Bermuda during passages of winter cold
fronts between North America and Bermuda. During these flights
atmospheric gases and aerosols were sampled and the data were
recorded as a function of altitude and latitude.

We used both aircraft for WATOX-86A. The WP-3D (based at
McGuire Air Force Base, New Jersey) flew parallel to the coast
between Newfoundland and Florida and the KingAir (based at Hanscom
Field near Boston, Massachusetts) flew a course off Cape Cod. WATOX
86-B used only the King Air during three weeks in February of 1986.
Data from both 86-A and -B were used to analyze further the vertical
and the horizontal chemical structure of the atmosphere. WATOX-86C
used the KingAir out of Bermuda to determine the advection fluxes of
sulfur and nitrogen species when airflow was controlled by the
Bermuda High and thus unimpacted by emissions from North America.

Summary of Findings

Eastward Advection of S and N from North America. To make an initial estimate of transport and advection eastward from North
America, Miller and Harris (1) have calculated back trajectories
from Bermuda and have developed a flow climatology covering seven
years--from January 1975 to December 1981. Using the GAMBIT-1 model
from the NOAA Air Resources Laboratory, this group has produced 10-
day back trajectories for the 850-mb level, on a daily basis, covering this seven-year period. Miller and Harris (1) have adopted a

Table III.   WATOX Intensives

Name/Date	Location	Platform	Species Measured
WATOX–82 August	Lewes Bermuda	Ground (G, A, P) Ground (G, A, P)	Gas: NO, NO_x, SO_2, O_3, CO Aerosol: NO_3, SO_4, trace metals Precipitation: Major ions, trace metals, organic acids, trace organics
WATOX–83 February	Lewes Bermuda	Ground (G, A, P) Ground (G, A, P)	Gas: NO, NO_x, SO_2, O_3, CO Aerosol: NO_3, SO_4, trace metals Precipitation: Major ions, trace metals, organic acids, trace organics
WATOX–84 May	Atlantic (Dakar to Boston)	R. V. Knorr (G, A, P)	Gas: HNO_3, SO_2, DMS Aerosol: NO_3, SO_4, trace metals, organic acids Precipitation: Major ions, trace metals, organic acids, trace organics
WATOX–85 Mar/Apr	Lewes Bermuda	Ground (G, A, P) Ground (G, A, P)	Gas: NO, NO_x, total S, CO, CO_3, trace organics Aerosol: trace metals, NO_3, SO_4 Precipitation: Major ions, trace metals, organic acids, trace organics
WATOX–86A January	Lewes Bermuda McGuire AFB Hanscom Field	Ground (P) Ground (P) WP–3D (G, A) KingAir (G, A)	Gas: HNO_3, PAN, NO, NO_2, NO_x SO_2, DMS, CO, O_3, trace organics, organic acids Aerosol: NO_3^-, $SO_4^=$, trace metals, organic acids, trace organics Precipitation: Major ions, organic acids, trace organics
WATOX–86B February	Lewes Bermuda Hanscom Field	Ground (P) Ground (P) KingAir (G, A)	Gas: HNO_3, PAN, NO, NO_2, NO_x SO_2, DMS, CO, O_3, trace organics, organic acids Aerosol: Trace metals, NO_3, SO_4 Precipitation: Major ions, organic acids, trace organics
WATOX–86C June	Lewes Bermuda Bermuda	Ground (P) Ground (P) KingAir (G, A)	Gas: HNO_3, PAN, NO, NO_2, NO_x SO_2, DMS, CO, O_3, trace organics, organic acids Aerosol: Trace metals, NO_3, SO_4 Precipitation: Major ions, organic acids, trace organics

NOTE: (G) means that gas was collected, (A), aerosol, (P), precipitation.

classification scheme that stratifies airflow as a function of
compass sector. This classification shows that, for almost 60% of
the seven years, there was a direct flow of air off the North
American continent.

To determine the advection rate of S and N eastward from North
America, Whelpdale and his colleagues (2) calculated air-mass advection as a function of latitude and altitude (Figure 2). Then, using
representative ground-level and above-ground concentrations of trace
sulfur and nitrogen species, Galloway and his colleagues (3) calculated advection fluxes of S and N by combining the longitudinal and
altitudinal variations of air-mass flux with the longitudinal and
altitudinal variations of the atmospheric concentrations of S and N
compounds (Figures 3 and 4). They report a broad maximum in S and N
transport between 38° N and 52° N. Of the S and N emitted to the
atmosphere of eastern North America, about 34% and 22-69%, respectively, are advected eastward. Transport at all altitudes up to at
least 5.5 km is important.

Impact of North American Emissions on Wet Deposition to the Western
Atlantic Ocean. Wet deposition has been collected by event during
WATOX at two sites on Bermuda, one site near Lewes, Delaware, and on
board ships. These wet-deposition samples have been analyzed for
acidic species, metals, and organic compounds. This section discusses our interpretation of the marine precipitation-chemistry data
and the results of our analyses as well as the influence of North
American emissions on precipitation composition.

In interpreting marine precipitation-chemistry data, the differentiation of sea-salt and non-sea-salt (or excess sea-salt) components is essential. Uncertainties in such calculations arise from
the uncertainties regarding (1) the composition of seawater, (2) the
analyses, (3) the amount of dry-deposited sea salt in the samples,
(4) the validity of assuming a purely marine source for the sea-salt
reference species, and (5) the validity of assuming no fractionation
during or after the production of sea-salt aerosols. Keene and his
colleagues at the University of Virginia (4) assessed these uncertainties and evaluated the assumptions by analyzing the composition
of precipitation collected on Bermuda. They report significant
concentrations of locally derived alkali and alkaline earth metals
as well as evidence of the influence of continental and non-sea-salt
marine sources of excess SO_4^{2-} concentrations. These observations
suggest that the past assumptions involved in sea-salt corrections
are not always valid. Therefore, to select the appropriate reference species, individual data sets should be evaluated using objective criteria.

The concentration of excess components in precipitation is the
difference between the total concentration and the sea-salt component of the total concentration. There are often large uncertainties associated with excess concentrations resulting from small
differences between large numbers. Hawley, Galloway, and Keene
(University of Virginia, Charlottesville, unpublished data) have
derived a nomogram technique to determine the uncertainty involved
knowing only the total concentration of the element in question
(e.g., $SO_4^=$), the total Na^+ concentration, and the respective analy-

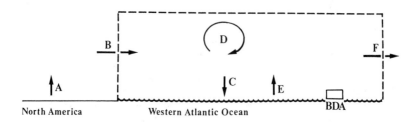

Figure 1. A conceptual overview of the fluxes being investigated
in WATOX and their method of measurement (see also Table I).

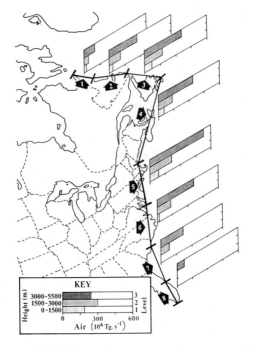

Figure 2. Net air flux as a function of latitude and altitude.
(Reprinted with permission from ref. 2. 1984 Pergamon Journals.)

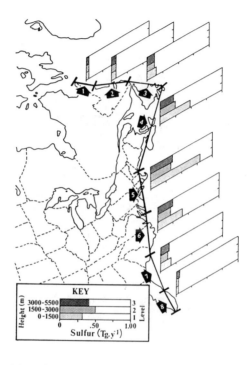

Figure 3.   Net sulfur flux as a function of latitude and altitude.
(Reprinted with permission from ref. 3.   1984 Pergamon Journals.)

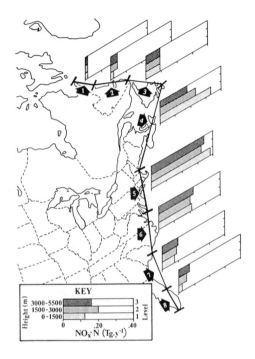

Figure 4.   Net nitrogen flux as a function of latitude and
altitude.   (Reprinted with permission from ref. 3.   1984 Pergamon
Journals.)

excess concentrations as a function of excess and total concentrations. At point $\underline{A}$, where the total and excess $SO_4^=$ concentrations are 60 µeq/l and 18 µeq/l, respectively, the relative standard error of the calculated excess concentration is 20%. However, at point $\underline{B}$, the error is 40% due to the greater contribution of sea-salt $SO_4^=$. This illustrates that the errors of the calculated excess concentration are not only a function of the analytical uncertainties but also of the relative abundance of the excess and sea-salt components (see also $\underline{4}$).

The use of the site on Bermuda to collect precipitation that is chemically representative of the marine environment assumes that Bermuda itself does not influence the amount or composition of the precipitation. Because the island is low and narrow, its configuration did not influence the amount ($\underline{5}$) although it could affect the composition. In analyses of precipitation from two sites on Bermuda, the sea-salt and excess Ca^{2+} components of precipitation were found to increase as a result of turbulence at the sea/land and air/land interfaces, respectively (Galloway, J. N.; Tokos, J. J.; Whelpdale, D. M; Knap, A. H., University of Virginia, Charlottesville, unpublished data). Also for samples taken from precipitation-collection sites downwind of the island, concentrations of excess $SO_4^=$ and H^+ were slightly increased by local sources. However, the impact of the island on the total excess $SO_4^=$ and H^+ concentrations was small relative to the off-island sources.

WATOX also used ships as platforms to collect precipitation for chemical analyses. To test the impact on the precipitation composition of the fossil fuels used by the ships for propulsion, Galloway, Knap, and Church ($\underline{6}$) had precipitation samples collected on the windward and leeward bridge wings of two ships sailing between New York and Bermuda. They report that the samples from the windward bridge wings are unaffected by the ship and are thus representative of marine precipitation and appropriate for use in analyses of the major chemical constituents sought.

As part of the WATOX research on the major inorganic species in wet deposition in the western Atlantic Ocean, Jickells and his colleagues ($\underline{7}$) sampled rain collected on Bermuda between May 1980 and May 1981. They state that there is a strong correlation between the presence of sulfuric and nitric acids and the meteorological back trajectories of Bermuda storm systems to the North American continent. This suggests the long-range transport of acid-rain precursors to Bermuda from the North American continent. The results of the work by Jickells and his colleagues is supported by the analyses reported by Galloway, Knap, and Church ($\underline{6}$) of precipitation data collected on board ships in the western Atlantic Ocean.

In addition, the analyses of four years of wet-deposition data collected on Bermuda by event also supported these conclusions (Galloway, J. N.; Artz, R. S.; Keene, W. C.; Church, T. M.; Knap, A. H., University of Virginia, Charlottesville, unpublished data). Using the NOAA ARL air-mass trajectory model, the WATOX researchers stratified volume-weighted averages of precipitation composition by compass sector. The results of these stratifications for excess $SO_4^=$ (Figure 6) showed that Bermuda was an ideal sampling platform for air that, at times, was directly impacted by anthropogenic tical uncertainties. Figure 5 shows the relative standard error of

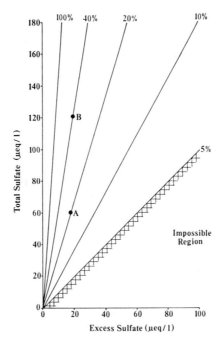

Figure 5. Relative standard error of excess sulfate as a function of total and excess sulfate concentrations (Hawley, M. E.; Galloway, J. N.; Keene, W. C., University of Virginia, Charlottesville, unpublished data).

Volume Weighted Composition
of Precipitation

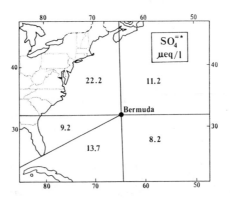

Figure 6. Volume-weighted excess $SO_4^=$ concentration in Bermuda precipitation as a function of air-mass trajectory.

sources in North America and, at other times, was impacted by air
the composition of which was more controlled by marine processes.

Church et al. (8), in presenting additional information derived
from WATOX research, report on the ocean's influence on precipitation from storms that leave the North American continent and transit
over the western Atlantic. They pay particular attention to this
oceanic influence on the sulfur and nitrogen precursors of acid
rains. They further report that, although sea salt contributes over
half (by weight) of the salt in precipitation at the coast and over
three quarters of the salt in precipitation at Bermuda, most sulfate
(90% at the coast and 50% at Bermuda) is in excess of sea salt.
Since Galloway, Likens and Hawley (9) have found that precipitation
on Bermuda has significantly more excess $SO_4^=$, NO_3^-, and H^+ than
more remote marine areas, Church and his colleagues (8) have attributed these components to the long-range transport of sulfur and
nitrogen precursors in the marine troposphere with the sulfuric-acid
component dominating.

Besides using ships to collect precipitation to be analyzed for
major ions as reported by Galloway, Knap, and Church (6), WATOX-84
also used ships to sample precipitation, gases, and aerosols to
determine the metal, organic, and major S and NO_x species. Church
and his colleagues (10) have reported on a cruise across the North
Atlantic from Dakar, Senegal, to Woods Hole, Massachusetts, that
transited the area of 18°–48° N, 18°–70° W during the spring. Different air masses that influence the North Atlantic are analyzed
from shipboard samples of air collected during this cruise. These
samples have been analyzed for aerosols (N, S, sea salt), gases
(SO_2, DMS, MSA, HNO_3, synthetic organics), and precipitation (major
inorganic ions, organic acids, and trace elements). The results of
these analyses showed that the composition of the lower atmosphere
over the North Atlantic is strongly influenced by continental air
masses. When air masses have origins that have passed over areas of
high emission in North Africa (easterlies) or North America (wester-
lies) within 1–2 days, the concentrations of acid precursors and
synthetic hydrocarbons in the air and of strong acids, trace metals,
and, to a lesser extent, organic acids in precipitation approach
those found in eastern North America. Even off the northwest coast
of Africa, trajectory analyses link the Mediterranean region with
aerosol and precipitation chemistry suggestive of biomass or petroleum burning. The burden of atmospheric deposition to the greater
North Atlantic may influence the oceanic surface chemistry of this
region.

Using techniques developed for the sampling and analyses of
trace metals in marine precipitation by Tramantano, Scudlark, and
Church (Environ. Sci. Technol., in press), Church et al. (11) and
Jickells et al. (12) have also reported on concentration measurements of the trace metals Cd, Cu, Fe, Mn, Ni, Pb, V, and Zn in wet
deposition at Lewes, Delaware, and on Bermuda. The purpose of this
facet of the WATOX research was to assess the sources of, the transport to, and the wet deposition of trace metals to the western
Atlantic Ocean during nonsummer months. At this time of the year,
trace metals are likely to be transported by a westerly air-mass
flow from North America to the open Atlantic. Church and his colleagues report that the concentrations and wet deposition of trace

metals are greater in samples from the Delaware coast than from
those on Bermuda, the order at both sites is similar (Fe > Zn > Pb >
Cu, Mn, Ni > V > Cd). The trace-metal enrichment factors for all
metals but Mn (based on crustal Fe) are significantly greater than
unity; again the order is the same in samples from the Delaware
coast as from those from Bermuda (Cd > Pb > Zn > Cu > Ni > V). This
evidence suggests common North American sources for the trace metals
found in western Atlantic precipitation as well as the important
atmospheric transport of trace metals to the Atlantic Ocean. The
calculations using enrichment factors from Na-based sea-salt aerosol
indicate that the recycling of trace metals from the sea surface,
although generally not considered to be important, could be a potentially significant process contributing to the Mn and V enrichments
found in precipitation samples from the open western Atlantic.

Cutter and Church (13) have determined selenium species in
western Atlantic precipitation so that the emission sources using
this sulfur analogue, which is enriched in fossil fuels (primarily
coal), can be more exactly identified. The results show a correlation of both total Se and the Se IV:Se VI ratio with increasing
protons and excess sulfur in precipitation from Lewes, Delaware, and
on Bermuda. Their hypothesis is that, although some reduced forms
(1 nM/kg) may come from background oceanic emissions, most oxidized
Se is a reflection of fossil-fuel emissions from North America.

As part of the WATOX program to investigate the long-range
transport of components from North America to the western Atlantic,
Knap (14) has reported on trace-organic contaminants in 51 samples
of precipitation collected on Bermuda from 1 October 1982 to 1 April
1983. He presents data on alpha and gamma isomers of hexachloro-
cyclohexane (HCH), chlordane, and dieldrin and notes the presence of
PCBs and phthalate esters in some samples although they are not
quantified. The rainwater concentrations of the compounds that he
does quantify vary and the size of events are not apparently related
to the concentrations, indicating possible gas-phase scavenging.
All the compounds on which Knap reports indicate a seasonality with
generally higher concentrations in the winter months. The HCH and
dieldrin concentrations show a correlation with air-mass trajec-
tory--storms originating in the southeastern North Atlantic have
concentrations a factor of four lower than storms originating west
of Bermuda. Knap concludes that precipitation is depositing some
pesticides and synthetic organic chemicals to the North Atlantic
Ocean.

Although HCOOH and CH_3COOH are important chemical constituents
of cloud water and precipitation, we do not yet know the sources for
these compounds in the atmosphere. In a paper discussing their
research on organic acids in wet deposition, Keene and Galloway (15)
report on 465 precipitation samples from 14 continental and marine
sites around the world that were analyzed in an attempt to identify
the source of HCOOH and CH_3COOH. Of these samples, 133 were collected as part of the WATOX program. They also report that continental precipitation during growing seasons contains higher absolute
concentrations of organic acids and higher ratios of $HCOO_T$ ($HCOOH_{aq}$
+ $HCOO^-$) to CH_3COO_T (CH_3COOH_{aq} + CH_3COO^-) than do marine precipitation and continental precipitation during nongrowing seasons. The
concentrations of $HCOO_T$ and CH_3COO_T in precipitation at most

locations are also highly correlated. These results support the hypothesis that organic acidity in precipitation may originate from two major sources: volatile vegetative constituents over continents and an unknown, weaker source in both continental and marine regions.

Relative to similar ratios of $HCOO_T$ to CH_3COO_T in the aqueous phase, differences in precipitation pH result in large regional differences in calculated equilibrium vapor-phase concentrations. The mechanism by which proportionate concentrations of $HCOO_T$ and CH_3COO_T are maintained in the aqueous phase has not yet been determined.

Comparisons between precipitation from impacted and that from remote regions indicate that anthropogenic emissions, although possibly important near large population and industrial centers, are probably not major sources of organic acids in precipitation over broad geographic regions (9). Galloway and his colleagues (University of Virginia, Charlottesville, unpublished data) also found that the region where a storm originated did not have a significant influence on the amount of organic acids deposited on Bermuda by precipitation. This evidence supported the hypothesis that organic acids found in the remote marine troposphere might have a local, possibly biogenic, source.

The Impact of North American Emissions on the Composition of the Atmosphere over the Western Atlantic Ocean. As part of WATOX-82 (August 1982) and WATOX-83 (January and February 1983), General Motors Research Laboratories operated air-monitoring sites on the Atlantic coast near Lewes, Delaware, and on the southwest coast of Bermuda, 1250 km to the southeast of the Delaware site. Their overall purpose was to study the transformations of the principal acid-precipitation precursors, NO_x and SO_x species, as they were transported under conditions not complicated by emissions from local sources. Three papers have resulted from this study (16, 17, 18).

In the first paper, Wolff and his colleagues (16) describe the measurements of gas and particulate species found in the Lewes samples and the composition and sources of sulfate aerosol. On the average, the total-suspended-particulate (TSP) concentration at Lewes is 27.9 $\mu g/m^3$ while the PM10 (mass of particles with diameters $\leq$ 10 μm) concentration is 22.0 $\mu g/m^3$, or 79% of the TSP. The PM10 consists of 6.1 $\mu g/m^3$ of coarse particles (CPM, diameters = 2.5 μm to 10 μm) and 15.9 $\mu g/m^3$ of fine particles (FOM, diameters < 2.5 μm). On a mass basis, the most important constituents of the fine-particulate fraction are sulfate compounds at 50% and organic compounds at 30%. The mean light-extinction coefficient corresponds to a visual range of from 18 km to 20 km. Most of the extinction can be attributed to sulfate (60%) and organic carbon (13%). Particle-size measurements show that the mass median aerodynamic diameter for both species is 0.43 μm. This is a larger particle size for carbons than has previously been reported and results in a more efficient light-scattering aerosol. Wolff and his colleagues (16) conclude that their principal-component analyses indicate that coal-combustion emissions from the midwestern United States are the most significant source of the sulfate found in Lewes during the summer and winter.

The second paper by Wolff and his colleagues (17) reports on the transformations of aerosol and gaseous species over the western Atlantic Ocean during transport from North America. They write that the concentrations and composition of fine-aerosol and trace-gas species on Bermuda are governed by the type of air mass influencing the island. During incursions of air from the northeastern United States, which are most frequent during the winter, they have found higher concentrations of anthropogenically derived species, such as $SO_4^=$, HNO_3, SO_2, O_3, Pb, Se, and elemental carbon. Higher $SO_4^=$ concentrations are associated with higher concentrations of the coal-burning tracer Se and of HNO_3 and O_3. The latter two relationships suggest a photochemical role and an association of HNO_3 with coal burning. SO_2 is strongly associated with the oil-burning tracer, V. Wolff and his colleagues report intrusions of air from the northeastern United States during the February 1983 Intensive (WATOX-83). However, there were also some intrusions during the August 1982 Intensive (WATOX-82) although the summer was dominated by a southeasterly flow containing high concentrations of fine crustal material, probably from the Sahara Desert.

Although Wolff et al. (17) find that there are more intrusions from North America during the summer, they also find that there are some during the winter. Their research shows that days with a southeasterly airflow are associated with high levels of Si, Ti, K, Fe, Ca, and Mn as well as the lowest enrichment factors for all anthropogenic species. The enrichment factors for the crustal species are generally independent of wind direction for K. They go on to suggest that woodburning in the northeastern United States may be the source of the higher K enrichment factors found during the winter. They used their Bermuda NO_x and SO_x data to make a rough estimate of the fluxes of these species in the last 1500 km from North America to a north/south line 1250 km east of the United States, which passes through Bermuda. Significant amounts of both NO_x and SO_x advected off the East Coast reached Bermuda and the fluxes appear to be consistent with the fluxes calculated by Galloway et al. (3).

In the third paper that resulted from the WATOX research in which the General Motors Research Laboratories took part, Gibson, Korsog, and Wolff (18) compare the atmospheric concentrations of trace-organic species from samples at Lewes, Delaware, to those from Bermuda. Their purpose was to ascertain the transformation reactions of nitroaromatic, polycyclic organic matter (POM), and benso-(a)pyrene (BaP) during transport from North America. They report that the ratios of 1-nitropyrene and hydroxynitropyrenes to inert marker species (fine-particule lead, selenium, and elemental carbon) are considerably higher at a remote site on Bermuda than in Delaware. Gibson and his colleagues suggest that these nitroaromatic POM are formed in atmospheric reactions. The ratio of BaP to the marker species is similar at the two sites, which does not reflect the expected loss of BaP in atmospheric photochemical reactions.

The Influence of North American Emissions on the Surface Ocean. The increased deposition of fixed nitrogen to an ocean has the potential to affect the primary productivity in the surface of that ocean. Knap and his colleagues (19), in their WATOX-related research on the influence of inorganic fixed nitrogen (nitrate and ammonium) on the surface ocean, analyzed two years of precipitation data for nitrate and ammonium concentrations. They conclude that, on the average, precipitation plays only a minor part in providing inorganic fixed nitrogen for primary productivity in oligotrophic ocean areas. They believe this to be true in spite of the considerable increase of nitrate from anthropogenic sources found in rainwater over the past 100 years. However, precipitation is an episodic process and the deposition rate of fixed nitrogen is not the same for all events. Of the total inorganic fixed nitrogen, 40% is wet deposited by only 11% of the 126 events evaluated by Knap and his colleagues. Based on this, they speculated that occasional "hot" events may be important on short time (about one day) and space (a few hundred kilometers) scales.

The WATOX data on atmospheric inputs of trace metals into and out of the Sargasso Sea in the North Atlantic have been used, in association with sediment recycling rates, to generate approximately self-consistent budgets for a range of trace elements in the Sargasso Sea. Only for Al, Fe, Mn, and V are additional lateral oceanic inputs necessary to close such budgets for the western Atlantic. Thus for Cu, Ni, Zn, Pb, and Cd--all of which are enriched on atmospheric particulates--atmospheric deposition represents the largest input to the western Atlantic. Much of the Cd, N, and Zn is recycled along with nutrients and these are then largely exported from the western Atlantic. Sedimentary recycling of the Cu may account for much of the total Cu flux to the sediments as measured with sediment traps. Jickells and his colleagues ([20]) conclude that, if the atmospheric concentrations of Cd, Cu, Ni, Pb, and Zn are currently enriched in western Atlantic precipitation by anthropogenic processes, then the atmospheric input to the Sargasso Sea must have increased by as much as two orders of magnitude since prehistoric times.

Knap, Binkley, and Dueser ([21]) used the WATOX data on atmospheric inputs of trace organics to the surface of the Sargasso Sea in conjunction with data from sediment traps to investigate the flux of contaminant substances to the deep Sargasso Sea. They had a sediment trap moored 3200 m below the ocean surface for two years to study the concentrations of polychlorinated byphenyls (PCBs), chlordanes, and dieldrin. These researchers report a deep-sea flux of PCBs of 1.6 $\mu g/m^2$ yr, which is surprisingly similar to the atmospheric flux of these compounds of 1.6-3.1 $\mu g/m^2$ yr calculated from the measured concentrations of the WATOX-82. They conclude that, because their data correlate well with the data on organic carbon, the deposition mechanism to the sediment is probably associated with biogenic particles.

Beyond the Western Atlantic Ocean. Whelpdale and his colleagues (Whelpdale, D.M.; Eliassen, A.; Galloway, J. N.; Dovland, H.; Miller, J. M. *Tellus*, in press) have examined the transport of North American sulfur emissions across the north Atlantic Ocean to Europe. In a review of available precipitation-sulfate data from the north Atlantic and adjacent coastal regions, they report a concentration field consistent with known source distributions and meteorological factors. The excess sulfate concentration of marine background

precipitation is 6-8 µeq/l and excess $[SO_4^=]$ decreases from
>50 µeq/l with offshore flows at the North American east coast and
to 8-15 µeq/l with onshore flows at the European west coast. This
decay is consistent with a distance constant of 2400 km and a residence time of approximately 80 hours and, in turn, corresponds to a
trans-Atlantic flux of anthropogenic sulfur of 0.3-0.4 Tg/yr.
Whelpdale et al. report further on a second independent estimate
based on the application of a climatological dispersion model that
accounts for long-term average diffusion, wet and dry deposition,
and SO_2 to $SO_4^=$ transformation. Using this model, they calculate a
flux of North American anthropogenic sulfur at the European west
coast of 0.2 Tg/yr, which agrees with the first estimate.

At the distance of the European west coast, North American
anthropogenic emissions account for approximately 4 µeq/l in precipitation. This is less than the marine background of 6-8 µeq/l and
much less than the annual average excess $[SO_4]$ value of approximately 30 µeq S/l appropriate for much of the coastal region. Whelpdale et al. conclude, therefore, that, on the average, the amount of
North American anthropogenic sulfur reaching Europe is small compared to that from other sources.

Summary

Over the past few years, participants in the WATOX program have been
able to estimate the eastward advection of sulfur, nitrogen, and
trace-metal and trace-organic species from North America as well as
their impact on the precipitation and surface waters of the western
Atlantic Ocean. The data base compiled by the WATOX consortium,
although extensive, is small relative to the size of the region and
the degree of spatial and temporal variability of the measured
components. Thus, research on the impact of North American emissions on the atmosphere and on the surface waters of the western
Atlantic Ocean continues. We are still using aircraft, islands, and
ships to investigate the changes in the North American plume as it
transits the Atlantic Ocean, the atmospheric transport of materials
across the Atlantic, and the impact of atmospheric deposition in the
surface ocean.

Acknowledgments

This paper is a contribution from the Western Atlantic Ocean
Experiment (WATOX) and the Bermuda Biological Station. We gratefully acknowledge the support of the National Oceanic and Atmospheric Administration of the United States, the Canadian Atmospheric
Environment Service, and the Bermuda government. We also thank
William Keene and Alex Pszenny for their constructive comments. We
acknowledge and appreciate the typing services of Brenda Morris and
the editorial talents of Mary-Scott Marston.

Literature Cited

1. Miller, J. M.; Harris, J. M. Atmos. Environ. 1985, 19, 409-414.
2. Whelpdale, D. M.; Low, T. B.; Kolomeychuk, R. J. Atmos. Environ.
   1984, 18, 1311-1327.

3. Galloway, J. N.; Whelpdale, D. M.; Wolff, G. T. Atmos. Environ. 1984, 18, 2595–2608.

4. Keene, W. C.; Pszenny, A. A. P.; Galloway, J. N.; Hawley, M. E. J. Geophys. Res. 1986, 91, 6647–6658.

5. Nemkosky, M. J., Jr. Local Area Forecaster's Handbook, Naval Oceanographic Command Detachments: Bermuda, 1980.

6. Galloway, J. N.; Knap, A. H.; Church, T. M. J. Geophys. Res. 1983, 88, 10,859–10,864.

7. Jickells, T.; Knap, A.; Church, T.; Galloway, J.; Miller, J. Nature 1982, 297, 55–57.

8. Church, T. M.; Galloway, J. N.; Jickells, T. D.; Knap, A. H. J. Geophys. Res. 1982, 87, 11,013–11,018.

9. Galloway, J. N.; Likens, G. E.; Hawley, M. E. Science 1984, 226, 829.

10. Church, T. M.; Whelpdale, D. M.; Andreae, A. O.; Galloway, J. N.; Keene, W. C.; Knap, A. H.; Tokos, J. J. EOS 1986, 67, 896.

11. Church, T. M.; Tramantano, J. M.; Scudlark, J. R.; Jickells, T. D.; Tokos, J. J.; Knap, A. H.; Galloway, J. N. Atmos. Environ. 1984, 18, 2657–2664.

12. Jickells, T. D.; Knap, A. H.; Church, T. M. J. Geophys. Res. 1984, 89, 1423–1428.

13. Cutter, G.; Church, T. Nature 1986, 322, 720–722.

14. Knap, A. H. EOS 1985, 66, 833.

15. Keene, W. C.; Galloway, J. N. J. Geophys. Res. 1986, 91, 14,466.

16. Wolff, T. G.; Kelly, N. A.; Ferman, M. A.; Ruthkosky, M. S.; Stroup, D. P.; Korsog, P. E. J. Air Pollut. Control Assoc. 1986, 36, 585–591.

17. Wolff, G. T.; Ruthkosky, M. S.; Stroup, D. P.; Korsog, P. E.; Ferman, M. A.; Stedman, D. H.; Wendel, G. J. Atmos. Environ. 1986, 20, 1229–1239.

18. Gibson, T. L.; Korsog, P. E.; Wolff, G. T. Atmos. Environ. 1986, 20, 1575–1578.

19. Knap, A.; Jickells, T.; Pszenny, A.; Galloway, J. Nature 1986, 320, 158–160.

20. Jickells, T. D.; Church, T. M.; Dueser, W. G.; Knap, A. H.; Tramantano, J. M. Int. Conf. Heavy Metals in Environment, Vol. 2, 1986, pp. 347–349.

21. Knap, A. H.; Binkley, K. S.; Dueser, W. G. Nature 1986, 319, 572–574.

RECEIVED March 14, 1987

RECEPTOR MODELS

Chapter 5

Hybrid Receptor Models

C. W. Lewis and R. K. Stevens

Atmospheric Sciences Research Laboratory, U.S. Environmental Protection Agency, Research Triangle Park, NC 27711

A hybrid receptor model is defined as a specified mathematical procedure which uses not only the ambient species concentration measurements that form the input data for a pure receptor model, but in addition source emission rates or atmospheric dispersion or transformation information characteristic of dispersion models. By utilizing more information hybrid receptor modeling promises improved source apportionment estimates or, more fundamentally, consideration of problems that are inaccessible in terms of classical receptor modeling. Several examples of hybrid receptor modeling are reviewed, emphasizing the great variety in possible approaches, and in the choice of input versus output quantities. A simple illustration is given of a hybrid receptor model applied to the comprehensive ambient-source-meteorological data base collected at Deep Creek Lake, Maryland during summer 1983.

A hybrid receptor model is any procedure for estimating the sources of ambient air pollutants at a receptor site, which makes use of both receptor and dispersion (source) modeling approaches. Thus, not only are the ambient species measurements which form the input data for a pure receptor model used, but also source emission rates or atmospheric dispersion or transformation information characteristic of dispersion models. By exploiting simultaneously the strengths of the two complementary approaches we expect to minimize their individual weaknesses. The natural domain of hybrid receptor models is in the treatment of reactive air pollutants, such as particular organics, SO_2/sulfate and NO_x/nitrate. In the (non-exhaustive) review of existing hybrid receptor models which follows we hope to illustrate the variety of possible approaches, and the flexibility in the choice of input data versus calculated outputs, depending on what information is available. Finally, a comprehensive ambient-source meteorological data base collected at Deep Creek Lake, Maryland, during summer 1983 is described and used in a simple application of one hybrid receptor model.

Hybrid Receptor Model Examples

Reactive Organic Chemical Mass Balance (Friedlander).   In the original formulation of the CMB receptor model (1) it was recognized that the fractional amounts of various chemical species emitted by a source are not necessarily conserved during the transport of the species to the receptor site. This could occur through both physical (differential dispersion or deposition) or chemical (removal due to atmospheric reactions) processes. This possibility was acknowledged by writing the CMB equations in the form

$$C_i = \sum_j \alpha_{ij} \, a_{ij} \, S_j \tag{1}$$

where C_i is the concentration of species i measured at the receptor site, a_{ij} (<1) is the mass fraction of species i in the emissions from source j, α_{ij} (<1) is the fractional decrease in a_{ij} during transport, and S_j is the (unknown) impact of source j at the receptor. Practically every application of CMB, however, has set each decay factor α_{ij} to unity.   An exception is the attempt by Friedlander (2) to derive an expression for decay factors to be used in the source apportionment of chemically reactive polycyclic aromatic hydrocarbons (PAH) in Los Angeles.   Friedlander's result is

$$\alpha_{ij} = (1 + K_i \theta)^{-1} \tag{2}$$

where K_i is the first order reaction rate constant for PAH species i, and θ is its average residence time in the atmosphere. This result illustrates that a CMB receptor model that includes decay factors is actually a hybrid model, because the calculation of decay factor values requires information (reaction rates and dispersion considerations) that a strictly receptor approach cannot provide.

Tracer Hybrid Receptor Model (Lewis).   Lewis and Stevens (3) have derived a hybrid receptor model for describing the secondary sulfate from an SO_2 point source. The resulting expression for secondary sulfate concentration M_{SO_4} at the receptor has the form

$$M_{SO_4} = M_p A T \tag{3}$$

with M_p being the mass concentration at the receptor of primary fine particles from the source (calculated from a classical receptor model), A representing the ratio of source mass emission rates for SO_2 and fine particles, and T describing both the transformation of SO_2 to sulfate in the atmosphere and its loss due to deposition. The function T has a simple analytical form depending on average values of the transformation and deposition rates, and the time of transit between source and receptor. Thus, the calculation of secondary sulfate from Equation 3 can be thought of as the result of "grafting" additional emission ratio and wind speed information onto a conventional receptor modeling solution for the primary impact of the source. The principal advantage of Equation 3 is that all of the secondary sulfate dispersion -- and some of the deposition -- complexity is implicitly contained in M_p, which acts as the "tracer" for the source.

An especially simple use of Equation 3 is possible if a particular chemical is known to be emitted only by the source of interest. Such an application is given in the last section of this article.

Gordon and Olmez (4) have used Equation 3 to model sulfate resulting from a multiple source distribution of coal-burning emissions, such as in the Ohio River Valley. Their results are quantitatively consistent with measured aerosol S/Se ratios of about 1700 and 3000, within and downwind of this region.

Source Finding Hybrid Receptor Model (Yamartino). The starting point of this model (5) is a set of equations of the form

$$C_{kt} = \sum_j R_{jkt}\, Q_j \tag{4}$$

where C_{kt} is the concentration of a pollutant at receptor site k during time interval t, Q_j is the emission rate of the pollutant from source j (an identifiable source or a source region), and R_{jkt} is the transfer coefficient between source j and receptor k for the meteorological conditions existent during time interval t. The C_{kt}'s are measured quantities, the R_{jkt}'s are to be calculated from a dispersion model (e.g., Gaussian plume), and the Q_j's are unknowns. The Q_j's are found by a least squares criterion, i.e., the correct set of Q_j's is assumed to be the one that minimizes

$$\chi^2 = \sum_{t,k} \left(C_{kt} - \sum_{j=1}^{J} R_{jkt}\, Q_j\right)^2 / (\Delta C_{kt})^2 \tag{5}$$

where J is the number of sources or source regions considered, and ΔC_{kt} is the uncertainty in C_{kt}. While Equation 4 bears a superficial resemblance to that of a conventional CMB receptor model approach, it is actually very different: the former is concerned with one pollutant observed at multiple receptors and times, while the latter involves multiple pollutants observed at one receptor and time; the source strengths in the former are those as observed at the source, while in the latter they describe the impact at the receptor; the former requires meteorological information (to calculate the R_{jkt}'s), while the latter has no such requirement.

Yamartino (6) has summarized the applications of this approach, which include determining the sources of CO at an airbase, the sources of SO_2 in West Berlin, and the wet deposition of sulfur in Eastern Northern America. The last application required estimates of rate constants as well as meteorological data to be inputted to calculate the transfer coefficients.

Diffusion Hybrid Receptor Model (Fay). This approach, beginning with the work of Fay and Rosenzweig (7), is perhaps the most interesting of all the hybrid models that have been proposed to date. Not only is it able to address the usual source apportionment problem of estimating source impacts (of SO_2 and secondary sulfate) at a receptor site but it simultaneously generates estimates for the conversion and deposition rate constants and meteorological parameters that are influencing the pollutant transfer between source and receptor. Consequently, we choose to review this model in more detail than the others considered here.

The starting point of the model are Eulerian diffusion equations whose solutions are the ambient concentrations of primary (SO_2) sulfur, x_p, and secondary (sulfate) sulfur, x_s, resulting from a single SO_2 source having a known constant emission rate Q. It is important to appreciate that the diffusion equations are time-averaged, so that their proper application is the description of seasonal or annual concentration averages, certainly not daily ones. The solutions x_p and x_s, which are assumed to vary only with horizontal position, are zero order Bessel functions of the second kind. In addition to Q, x_p and x_s each depend on nine additional parameters: mixing height, wind speed and direction, horizontal diffusivity, first order rate constants for SO_2 conversion and wet and dry deposition, and first order rate constants for sulfate wet and dry deposition. All nine parameters are considered constant throughout the flow field.

Since the model is linear, the resultant prediction for the concentration of the primary or secondary pollutant at a receptor site is a linear superposition of the x's for the individual point sources. The model is optimized by a least squares criterion: the nine parameter values are chosen so as to minimize E^2,

$$E^2 = \sum (\text{observation} - \text{prediction})^2 / \sum (\text{observation})^2 \qquad (6)$$

where the summation is over all observations.

The most successful application of this approach has been the source apportionment of the wet sulfate deposition rate in Eastern North America (8). The parameter values resulting from the minimization of E^2 generally fall within the expected range for each one. The correlation coefficient between three year average predicted (using the optimized parameter set) wet deposition and observed values at 109 sites was 0.87. It is then a straightforward matter to calculate the percentage contribution from each source region at any chosen receptor site. For example, at Whiteface Mountain, New York, the three largest contributors to wet deposition were Ohio (11.9%), Pennsylvania (11.4%) and New York (7.8%). The apportionment of airborne sulfate was also accomplished using the same parameter values as obtained from the wet deposition problem.

The Deep Creek Lake Study

During August and September 1983 a field sampling study was conducted in rural Maryland at a site (Deep Creek Lake) which was anticipated to be heavily impacted by secondary sulfate from regional coal-fired power plants. When the analytical work in progress is completed (x-ray fluorescence, neutron activation analysis, ion chromatography), the resulting data base will consist of ambient aerosol measurements (130 six-hour intervals of size fractionated elemental and chemical concentration), ambient gas measurements (SO_2, O_3, and NO_x concentrations with 10 min time resolution), source measurements (size fractionated elemental aerosol composition and gaseous emission rates at 3 regional power plants expected to impact the receptor site), plume measurements (size fractionated aerosol composition at elevated points between sources and the receptor site), airborne aerosol regional signatures, and meteorologically-derived back trajectories. The unusually comprehensive content of this data set makes it a valuable resource for investigating various hybrid receptor model approaches.

Ambient Data Characteristics. Table I gives day and night averages of selected fine particle species and gaseous sulfur measured at the Deep Creek Lake ambient site.

Table I.   Fine Particle and Gaseous Sulfur Concentration
Averages at Deep Creek Lake, MD, August 1983

Species	10 AM-10 PM (ng/m^3) N = 48	10 PM-10 AM (ng/m^3) N = 47
Mass	52700	39800
S_p*	8570	6630
$SO_4^=$	25700	19900
Pb	42.5	46.8
Se	4.9	4.9
S_g**	14500	7950
S_g/S_p (dimensionless)	1.7	1.2

*fine particle sulfur
**gaseous sulfur (from SO_2)

The table shows substantial fine mass loadings, with sulfate representing about half of the total. Selenium, which is increasingly regarded as a good tracer species for coal combustion, also has a high concentration relative to that found in airsheds with little coal impact. Lead is traditionally a good indicator of mobile source emissions.   From the average lead concentration measured at the Deep Creek Lake site, a total mobile source impact of no more than 1-2 $\mu g/m^3$ can be inferred (9), a very small percentage of the measured mass concentration.

Table II shows the linear correlation coefficients of the species from Table I.   For 95 observations a correlation greater than 0.26 is significant at the 1% level.   Thus, the correlations involving lead are not significant (consistent with expectation), while the mutual correlations of fine particle sulfur, selenium and mass are impressively large.   Correlations involving gaseous sulfur are only slightly less large.

Table II.   Linear Correlation Coefficients (N = 95)

	Mass	S_p	S_g	Se	Pb
S_p	.94				
S_g	.60	.58			
Se	.75	.73	.71		
Pb	.16	.16	-.09	.03	
$S_p + S_g$	.75	.75	.98	.78	-.03

Tracer Hybrid Receptor Model Application.   Even though the Deep Creek Lake data base is not yet complete, in terms of all the chemical analyses that are anticipated to be included, it may be useful to give a simple illustration of how a hybrid receptor model can provide some insight into the data.

Table III shows ambient measurements obtained on August 5, 1983, between 10 AM and 4 PM.   The concentrations are all well above their average daytime values.   The S_g/S_p ratio is among the largest values seen during daytime sampling periods, indicating little gas to particle conversion has occurred, and suggestive of a short transport time.   During this period back trajectory calculations showed an average wind speed of 14 km/h, from the direction of the nearest major coal-fired power plant (Ft. Martin, 1150 MW) 45 km due west of Deep Creek Lake.   Table III also shows the measured S_g/Se ratio obtained at the Ft. Martin plant during September 1983.   Dilution source sampling was employed so that the distribution of selenium between its fine particle and gaseous phases should approximate that which is present in the ambient environment.

Under the assumption that the gaseous sulfur, fine particle selenium and secondary fine particle sulfur measured at an ambient site originates from a single point source the tracer hybrid receptor model can be expressed in terms of the two equations

$$S_p/S_g = [\exp((\overline{K}_r + \overline{K}_d)t)-1]\overline{K}_r t/(\overline{K}_r + \overline{K}_d)t \qquad (7)$$

$$S_g/Se = (S_g/Se)_0 \exp(-(\overline{K}_r + \overline{K}_d)t) \qquad (8)$$

Table III.   Ambient and Source Fine Particle
and Gaseous Sulfur Measurements

Deep Creek Lake, August 5, 1983, 10 AM–4 PM

S_g	37,100	ng/m^3 (28.3 ppb)
S_p	18,100	ng/m^3
S_e	7.9	ng/m^3
S_g/S_p	2.0	
S_g/S_e	4,690	

Ft. Martin Power Plant, September, 1983

S_g/S_e 16,000 $\pm$ 5,000

---

where t is the source to receptor transport time, $\overline{K}_r$ is the average gas to particle conversion rate, $\overline{K}_d$ is the average excess deposition rate for SO_2 relative to sulfate, and the zero subscript indicates a source measurement.   Inserting the three ratios from Table III, Equations 7 and 8 have the unique solution (most easily obtained graphically) 0.25 and 0.98 for $\overline{K}_r t$ and $\overline{K}_d t$, respectively.   Assuming the source to be the Ft. Martin plant, and thus a 3.2h transport time based on the back trajectory information, we have

$$\overline{K}_r = 7.8 \ \%/h \tag{9}$$

$$\overline{K}_d = 31 \ \%/h \tag{10}$$

The uncertainty in $\overline{K}_r$ is estimated to be 20%, while the uncertainty in $\overline{K}_d$ is at least 30%.
   The $\overline{K}_r$ value is similar to other measurements for dry summer daytime conditions.   The $\overline{K}_d$ value is larger than what is frequently assumed, but not implausible.   For example, in the Four Corners power plant plume study of Mamane and Pueschel (10), in complex terrain similar to that considered here, a particle dry deposition rate of 18%/h was found.   Since particles typically are dry-deposited at much lower rates than SO_2, a 31%/h excess deposition rate for SO_2 does not appear unreasonable.
   The results of Equations 9 and 10 do not take account of any "background" SO_2 and fine particle sulfur and selenium originating upwind of the Ft. Martin plant.   This omission is not expected to be a major source of error, since any such corrections occur in both numerator and denominator of measurement ratios.   In any

case the Deep Creek Lake data set includes upwind measurements whose analyses will allow this question to be quantitatively investigated.

Although the research described in this article has been supported by the United States Environmental Protection Agency, it has not been subjected to Agency review and therefore does not necessarily reflect the views of the Agency and no official endorsement should be inferred.

Literature Cited

1. Friedlander, S. Environ. Sci. Technol. 1973, 7, 235.

2. Friedlander, S. In Atmospheric Aerosol: Source/Air Quality Relationships; Macias, E. S.; Hopke, P. K., Eds.; ACS Symposium Series No. 167; American Chemical Society: Washington, DC, 1981; p. 1.

3. Lewis, C. W., Stevens, R. K. Atmos. Environ. 1985, 19, 917.

4. Gordon, G. E.; Olmez, I. In Receptor Methods for Source Apportionment; Pace, T. G., Ed.; APCA International Specialty Conference; Air Pollution Control Association: Pittsburgh, PA, 1986; p. 229.

5. Yamartino, R. J. In Fourth Symposium on Turbulence, Diffusion and Air Pollution; American Meteorological Society, Boston, MA, 1979; p. 84.

6. Yamartino, R. J. Proc. 77th Ann. Mtg. Air Pollut. Control Assoc., 1984, Paper No. 84-48.2.

7. Fay, J. A.; Rosenzweig, J. J. Atmos. Environ. 1980, 14, 355.

8. Fay, J. A.; Golomb, D.; Kumar, S. In Receptor Methods for Source Apportionment; Pace, T. G., Ed.; APCA International Specialty Conference; Air Pollution Control Association: Pittsburgh, PA, 1986; p. 105.

9. Lewis, C. W.; Baumgardner, R. E.; Stevens, R. K.; Russwurm, G. M. Environ. Sci. Technol. 1986, 20, 1126.

10. Mamane, Y.; Pueschel, R. F. J. Applied Meteorol. 1980, 19, 779.

RECEIVED January 12, 1987

Chapter 6

Trace Element Concentrations on Fine Particles in the Ohio River Valley

S. G. Tuncel[1], Glen E. Gordon[1], I. Olmez[1,3], J. R. Parrington[1,4], R. W. Shaw, Jr.[2,5], and R. J. Paur[2]

[1]Department of Chemistry and Biochemistry, University of Maryland, College Park, MD 20742
[2]Environmental Research Center, U.S. Environmental Protection Agency, Research Triangle Park, NC 27711

Atmospheric particles were collected from May, 1980 to Dec., 1981 at 3 sampling sites in the Ohio River Valley (ORV). The collected samples were analyzed by x-ray fluorescence (XRF) for elemental concentrations and their masses determined by β gauging. The XRF data and associated wind trajectories were used to select a subset (200) of ORV samples in the fine fraction for further analysis by instrumental neutron activation analysis (INAA). Combined XRF and INAA data provided concentration values for up to 40 elements. Chemical mass balances with 11 sources were used to fit trace element concentrations. About 90% of the predicted mass arises from the regional sulfate component, which accounts for most of the observed sulfur. Sulfate concentrations are nearly as high at the west station (in KY) as at the center (IN) and east (OH) stations in disagreement with the usual picture of build-up of sulfate in air masses as they move up the Valley, picking up SO_2, which is slowly converted to sulfate. Even when back trajectories are used to limit consideration to samples of air masses coming from the southwest, the picture remains despite the lack of strong sources upwind in MO, AK and OK. We find no reasonable way in which to fit observed sulfate concentrations and S/Se ratios with a simple hybrid receptor model.

[3]Current address: Nuclear Reactor Laboratory, Massachusetts Institute of Technology, Cambridge, MA 02139
[4]Current address: General Electric Co., Schenectady, NY 12301
[5]Current address: Army Research Office, Research Triangle Park, NC 27709

Trace element compositions of airborne particles are important for
determining sources and behavior of regional aerosol, as emissions
from major sources are characterized by their elemental composition
patterns. We have investigated airborne trace elements in a complex
regional environment through application of receptor models. A
subset (200) of fine fraction samples collected by Shaw and Paur
([1],[2]) in the Ohio River Valley (ORV) and analyzed by x-ray
fluorescence (XRF) were re-analyzed by instrumental neutron activation analysis (INAA). The combined data set, XRF plus INAA, was
subjected to receptor-model interpretations, including chemical
mass balances (CMBs) and factor analysis (FA). Back trajectories
of air masses were calculated for each sampling period and used
with XRF data to select samples to be analyzed by INAA.

Experimental Methods

The 3 ORV sampling sites (see Figure 1) were selected in rural
areas having minimal effects of local sources. The west site was
in a rural farming community in Union County, KY, the center site
in a similar area of Franklin County, IN, and the east site was in
a forest clearing in Ashland County, OH. The sites lie along a
590-km line with roughly equal spacings between them.

Samples were collected from May, 1980 to Aug., 1981 using
dichotomous samplers which separated particles into two size fractions (cut-point at 2.5-μm diam). Particles were collected on 1-
μm pore-diam Teflon membrane filters. Details of the sampling
protocol are discussed elsewhere ([1]). Sampling periods were 12 h
for some samples, but 24 h for most, with samples being changed at
noon and midnight for the former, and midnight for the latter.
Samples were β-gauged for mass determination and XRF analyses were
performed at Environmental Sciences Research Laboratory (ESRL) of
the U. S. Environmental Protection Agency (EPA).

At Maryland, back-trajectories of air masses were calculated
for each sampling period using the Air Resources Laboratory Branching Atmospheric Trajectory model ([3]). Sampling periods were classified according to the directions of their associated back-trajectories as was done previously with Shenandoah Valley samples ([4]).
Two hundred samples were selected for more detailed analysis by
INAA. Selection criteria included back-trajectories consistently
from certain directions during sampling durations (with SW trajectories heavily weighted) and some periods of stagnations to observe
high pollution build-ups. As fine particles travel over longer distances and carry more information than coarse particles, only fine
particle fractions were analyzed further. Results of XRF were also
used to select samples for subsequent INAA.

The selected samples were sent to the University of Maryland. They were opened in a Class 100 clean room and half of each
filter was cut from the holder with a stainless steel scalpel,
folded and transferred to an acid-washed polyethylene bag. The
bags were placed into pneumatic tube sample carriers ("rabbits")
along with standards and flux monitors, and irradiated in the
National Bureau of Standards (NBS) reactor at a flux of 5 x 10^{13}
n/cm^2-sec. Gamma-ray spectra of the irradiation products were
observed with Ge τ-ray detectors using procedures discussed by

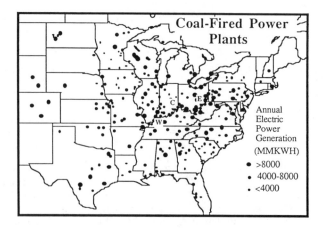

Figure. 1. Map of Ohio River Valley showing ORV sites and coal-fired power plants, with sizes of circles indicating plant capacities. West, Center and East sampling sites indicated as W, C and E, respectively.

Germani et al. (5). The final data selected are from INAA except
for Br, S, Si and Pb, taken from XRF. The combined methods yield
data for about 40 elements.

Results and Discussion

Average concentrations of selected elements and their standard
deviations for all samples analyzed by INAA from each station are
listed in Table I. With few exceptions, e.g., Mn at the west station, concentrations were remarkably similar at the 3 ORV sites.

Factor Analysis. A major objective of this project is to develop
regional scale receptor models which would use some of the 40-odd
observed species to determine sources or source regions of the
particles. As a first step we performed factor analysis (FA) on
all samples. In contrast to the rather good FA results obtained
from similar data from Shenandoah Valley (4), here the results
were poor. A 5-factor fit to 23 variables in 200 samples accounted
for only 57% of the variance. Factor 1 (Pb, Br, Sb, As and Se) is
a combined motor-vehicle and general anthropogenic component. Factor
2 (Fe, Si, Al, Sc, La, Sm) is crustal. Factor 3 (S, Se, mass and
south wind, with negative Zn) is the "regional sulfate" factor. Not-
ably, this factor contains negligible Mn, suggesting that the Mn
observed on this factor in Shenandoah Valley (4) and Watertown, MA
(6) results from both sulfate and Mn being brought into the East
by the same winds, but not originating from the same sources. As
shown in Table I, samples from the West often contain large amounts
of Mn. Only 7% of the Mn variation is accounted for by the 5 factors. Excess Mn in the Midwest arises from a few ferromanganese
plants. Other plants of this type have been shown to be large "hot
spots" for Mn (7). The origin of Factor 4 (Zn, some S, north wind)
is unclear. Factor 5 (V, La/Sm ratio and east wind) is the oil-
fired plant factor, perhaps with refinery contributions (8). The
FA results may be poor because samples were pre-selected for certain
wind trajectories and/or concentrations from XRF, whereas the entire
data set from Shenandoah Valley was used. Also, there were too few
samples to stratify them by season, whereas all Shenandoah samples
were collected during summer.

    Shaw and Paur performed FA of all elements observed by XRF
in all samples collected at the center site. The data from each
quarter were analyzed separately and data for fine and coarse particles were included in the same FAs. For consistency, four factors
were used for each quarter. The nature of the factors obtained
varied somewhat from quarter to quarter, but three factors emerged
consistently: (1) fine fraction S and Se, corresponding to our
Factor 3; (2) coarse fraction crustal elements, the coarse counter-
part of our Factor 2; and (3) fine fraction metals (Fe, Zn, Mn),
for which there is no direct analog among the FA of all samples in
this work. However, we also performed FA of the samples analyzed
from each station. For the center station, Factor 1 was heavily
loaded with As, Mn, Sb, Zn, Pb, Br, with smaller loadings of Fe
and Se, and the wind trajectories were from more northerly and
easterly directions than the average for all samples. Note that a
number of the elements on this factor are observable by INAA, but

Table I. Arithmetic Means and Standard Deviations of Concentrations
(ng/m^3) of Selected Elements Observed in a Subset of Samples
Analyzed by INAA and XRF from the Three ORV Sites

Element	Concentration (ng/m^3)		
	West Site	Center Site	East Site
Na	79 ±60(43)[a]	57 ±52 (55)[a]	84 ±113[b](96)[a]
Mg	81 ±43 (23)	88 ±43 (35)	98 ±91[b](56)
Al	98 ±124[b](44)	84 ±108 (56)	97 ±150 (98)
Si	330 ±430[b](43)	180 ±180 (52)	170 ±120 (95)
S	3500 ±3600 (44)	3800 ±2400[b](56)	2700 ±2300 (99)
Cl	14 ±14 (44)	37 ±32 (56)	39 ±37[b](97)
K	131 ±136[b](43)	82 ±46 (55)	79 ±53 (98)
Ca	80 ±59[b](44)	78 ±66 (55)	48 ±30 (95)
V	1.0 ±0.79[b](44)	0.87 ±0.55 (56)	0.80 ±0.60 (98)
Cr	0.93 ±1.3 (44)	0.95 ±0.77 (56)	1.5 ±1.7[b](95)
Mn	13 ±17[b](44)	4.6 ±2.7 (56)	8.3 ±9.8 (98)
Fe	82 ±85 (44)	72 ±50 (56)	94 ±150[b](97)
Co	0.11 ±0.09 (44)	0.10 ±0.10 (56)	0.23 ±1.4[b](94)
Cu	7.5 ±5.6 (39)	11 ±11 (53)	12 ±11[b](97)
Zn	28 ±82 (44)	18 ±14 (56)	30 ±25[b](97)
Ga	0.2 ±0.3 (39)	0.28 ±0.29 (38)	0.30 ±0.23[b](79)
As	1.1 ±0.8 (43)	0.98 ±0.54 (55)	1.6 ±1.4[b](98)
Se	2.0 ±0.9 (44)	2.3 ±1.3[b](56)	2.0 ±1.4[b](97)
Br	7.5 ±4.6 (44)	9.9 ±4.0 (55)	11 ±7[b](98)
Mo	0.56 ±0.45 (36)	0.46 ±0.56 (49)	1.6 ±3.5[b](82)
Cd	0.89 ±1.1 (27)	0.89 ±0.85[b](36)	1.0 ±0.68[b](62)
In	0.009 ±0.007 (39)	0.02 ±0.03 (54)	0.009 ±0.006[b](92)
Sb	0.59 ±0.38 (44)	0.63 ±0.35 (56)	0.69 ±0.49[b](97)
I	1.5 ±0.75 (39)	1.3 ±1.2 (51)	1.5 ±1.4 (91)
Cs	0.04 ±0.02 (43)	0.041 ±0.028 (54)	0.06 ±0.06[b](92)
La	0.18 ±0.21[b](43)	0.16 ±0.13 (55)	0.11 ±0.10 (96)
Sm	0.017 ±0.019[b](43)	0.016 ±0.019 (55)	0.016 ±0.021 (91)
W	0.073 ±0.082 (34)	0.13 ±0.27 (43)	0.16 ±0.26[b](85)
Pb	47 ±22 (43)	61 ±21[b](52)	60 ±31 (97)

[a] Number of samples are given in parentheses
[b] Highest station average for element

were not included in the XRF dat set, so there is good correspondence
between this factor and Factor 3 of the FA by Shaw and Paur (2).
Results from INAA/XRF data suggest a combined motor-vehicle and
industrial activities component from cities north and east of the
site.

Chemical Mass Balances. To attempt a quantitative resolution of
the ORV samples, we performed CMBs using 11 components from a source-
composition library developed at Maryland (9): coal, oil and refuse
combustion, soil and marine aerosol, emissions from refineries,
motor vehicles, iron and steel plants, copper plants and lime kilns,
and regional sulfate. Some components were modified for this use,
e.g., by an increase of Se on the coal component to account for
condensation of Se from the vapor phase after stack gases mix with
ambient air. Table II contains a brief summary of CMBs of ten samples
from the east site. The quality of fits is shown by comparison of
average predicted and observed concentrations, and by the average
larger/smaller (L/S) ratio where, for each sample, L/S for an element
is the predicted/observed ratio or its inverse, whichever is larger. A perfect fit for all samples yields an average L/S of 1.00.

Most previous CMBs, e.g., (10), were performed on whole-filter
data sets, for which about half of the mass is from coarse particles. In that case, many elements arise mainly from crustal dust,
making them easy to fit. By contrast, the fine fraction contains
little crustal material and many elements are highly enriched (relative to crustal abundances) because of passage through combustion
processes. Because of the sensitivity of enrichments to details of
the combustion sources and their pollution-control devices, these
elements are difficult to fit.

In view of these problems, the fits to the compositions of
the fine fractions are quite good. Only about 80% of the mass is
explained, nearly all of it as regional sulfate, but this is typical
for fits to fine fractions. The missing mass is probably condensed
water and carbonaceous material, nitrates, etc. Potassium is seriously underpredicted, partly because we included no wood-smoke component. The latter would account for residual K, but little else.
Several elements, including Cr, Co and Cd may have sources not
included in the CMBs, or the components used may be deficient in
these elements.

A major objective of these CMBs was to determine primary and
secondary contributions from coal-fired plants. Arsenic and Se are
often used as "markers" for primary emissions from coal-fired plants
(10), but Table II shows that substantial amounts of these elements
are associated with regional sulfate, most of which results from
transport from distant coal-fired plants. The regional sulfate
component was based largely on FA of fine particles collected in
Shenandoah Valley (4), which mainly represents material transported
into the area from the west. As previously discussed (11), broadly
similar components can be constructed from data of Thurston and
Spengler (6), Pierson et al. (12), and Rahn and Lowenthal (13). At
present, we don't know if this component is appropriate for samples
collected within the ORV. Also, industrial sources such as copper
plants and iron and steel mills interfere with some elements that
might otherwise be good markers for coal combustion. Gallium shows

Table II. CMB Fits to Selected Elements in Ten Fine Fraction
Samples from the East Site

Ele- ment	Conc.(ng/m^3) Avg Pred.	Obs.	L/S	Major Sources
Mass(μg/m^3)	23.6	30.8	1.7	RegS (22), MV(0.47),Cmt(0.42)
Na[b]	57	56	1.1	Mar (51), Cmt (3), Iron (3)
Al[b]	38	36	1.4	Coal (17), Soil (11), Cmt (9)
Si[b]	71	75	1.2	Soil (47), Coal (28), Cmt(19)
S[b]	2500	2310	1.1	RegS (2500), Iron(8), Oil(4)
K[b]	40	61	1.6	Cmt (21), Iron (9)
Ca[b]	57	46	1.4	Cmt (42), Iron (7)
V[b]	0.80	0.66	1.6	Oil (0.6), Iron (0.4)
Cr	0.22	0.54	3.6	Iron (0.11), Cmt (0.05)
Mn[b]	2.2	2.5	1.3	RegS (1.0), Iron (0.9)
Fe[b]	38	36	1.1	Iron (22), Coal (8), Soil (5)
Co	0.04	0.08	2.9	Oil (0.034), Iron (0.005)
Cu[b]	3.4	5.9	1.8	Cu (2.8), Iron (0.27)
Zn[b]	13	11	1.2	Incin (5), Cu (5)
Ga[b]	0.04	0.09	2.3	Coal(0.02),Cmt(0.014),Iron (0.012)
As[b]	0.34	0.5	1.9	Cu(0.11),RegS(0.11),Coal(0.07)
Se[b]	0.7	1.0	1.7	RegS (0.45), Coal (0.19)
Br[b]	7.8	7.7	1.3	MV (7)
Cd	0.22	0.85	3.4	MV (0.075),Incin(0.06),Cu (0.06)
In	0.004	0.004	3.2	RegS (0.004),Incin & Iron(0.001)
Sb[b]	0.23	0.43	2.1	Incin (0.09), RegS (0.05)
I	0.43	0.63	2.1	Mar (0.29), Coal (0.013)
La[b]	0.084	0.064	1.6	Ref (0.04)
Ce	0.70	0.08	1.4	Ref (0.034), Coal (0.021)
Sm[b]	0.006	0.008	1.4	MV (0.004), Coal (0.001)
Pb[b]	43	42	1.1	MV (32), Cu (5)

[a]Numbers in parantheses indicate contributions from indicated
source. Abbreviations: Incin = incinerators, Ref = refineries, MV
= motor vehicles, Mar = marine, Iron = iron and steel plants, Cu
= copper plants, Cmt = cement plants, RegS = regional sulfate.
[b]Included in CMB least-squares fit

promise as a marker, as does gas-phase B, discussed elsewhere (14).

If CMBs can be used to distinguish between primary and secondary emissions from coal-fired plants, the results can be used in hybrid receptor models to determine important parameters such as distance scales for transport and transformation of S species.

Hybrid Receptor Models

The meaning of the the term "hybrid receptor model" is not consistent in the literature. Following the definition proposed at the Quail Roost Receptor Modeling Workshop (15), we take it to be a combination of some meteorological aspects of traditional source-based models with some tracer aspects of receptor models. An important feature of such models is that one often works with ratios of species so that some of the most uncertain absolute parameters of classical models cancel out. As noted below, for example, one can calculate the concentration ratio of gas-phase SO_2 to gas-phase B as a function of distance from a common source more accurately than the absolute concentration of either species.

An important step towards treatment of SO_2 conversion to sulfate and deposition of both species that avoids absolute uncertainties of dispersion and deposition rates was taken by Lewis and Stevens, who investigated the mathematical basis of one form of hybrid receptor modeling (16). Their model assumes that one measures concentrations of SO_2 and SO_4 relative to that of some species borne by particles from the plant. They assumed that (1) dispersion, deposition and transformation of the three species (SO_2, SO_4 and fine primary particles) are linear or pseudo first-order processes, but may have complex dependences on time; (2) dispersion affects all three pollutants identically; (3) dry deposition is the only type of deposition which occurs; (4) deposition velocity is the same for all fine particles, but may be different for SO_2; (5) secondary sulfate is produced only by homogeneous oxidation of SO_2.

Lewis and Stevens' mathematical treatment is fairly general, as it allows the conversion rate and deposition velocities to vary with time, as expected. For example, the rate of SO_2 conversion is probably higher during daytime than at night. The value of their formulation is that the dispersion of both SO_2 and SO_4 and the deposition of SO_4 are handled by normalization to the concentration of fine primary particles from the SO_2 source. They made various assumptions about the time dependence of conversion and deposition rates and concluded that the errors are only about 10% or less if one assumes that the rates are equal to the time-averaged values.

As fine particles arise from many sources, it would be desirable to replace the fine particle mass concentration in the equations by the concentration of an element borne by the fine particles from coal combustion and no other source. The best candidate for such an element is Se (2,4,17). If coal-fired power plants were the only significant source of Se (probably a good assumption in many areas), one could measure emission rates of SO_2, SO_4 and Se from the source and their concentrations at a downwind location and plug the values into the equations and solve them to obtain the conversion and deposition rates averaged over the travel time of the plume. The model is a useful first step towards the use of receptor methods to determine transformation and deposition rates, but it is over-simplified, especially the assumption that one can follow the plume from a large source for many hours. There are few areas of the world in which that is possible. Also, the neglect of in-cloud processes is a serious problem; however, one could test the approach by selecting periods of dominant high pressure systems during which there is little cloudiness or rain.

To examine the first problem in more detail, Gordon and Olmez performed calculations that crudely simulated an air mass moving up the Ohio River Valley and into New England (14). They assumed that identical coal-fired plants were spaced at 50-km intervals over 1000 km and eliminated them for an additional 800 km. They assumed a ratio of Se/S = 0.00028 in the coal, and that 50% of the Se is released up the stack, of which 50% quickly becomes attached to particles, with the remainder staying in the gas phase. The atmosphere was assumed to be uniformly mixed up to 1.5 km and the wind speed, 10 km/hr. Selenium and sulfate particles were assumed to have the same deposition velocity, v_{g2}, and SO_2 a larger value, v_{g1}. Sulfur dioxide was also converted at a rate k_r = 1.0%/hr. Gordon and Olmez (14) also added a gas-phase tracer to the model, namely gas-phase B. In non-coastal areas, it seems to arise mainly from coal-fired plants. Fogg and Rahn suggest that B, mainly as H_3BO_3, has deposition properties similar to those of SO_2, but no chemical reaction similar to SO_2 conversion is known for gas-phase B (18). Thus, measurements and modeling of B/SO_2 ratios could add valuable additional constraints to hybrid receptor models. Fogg and Rahn used this approach to make rough estimates of SO_2 lifetimes (1-2 days) and oxidation rates (1-2%/hr) during transport from the Midwest to New England. Gordon and Olmez assumed the ratio of gas-phase B/SO_2 in stack emissions to be 0.00070 based on the results of Fogg and Rahn. Gas-phase B was assumed to have the same deposition velocity as SO_2, but no chemical decay. Calculations were performed, with v_{g1} = 2 cm/sec and v_{g2} = 0.5 cm/sec. As expected, just after each injection of fresh emissions, the particulate S/Se ratio drops because Se is added without new SO_4 until the new SO_2 has been converted to SO_4.

The predicted SO_2 concentration rises to 27 $\mu g/m^3$ at 500 km and remains almost constant to 1000 km, beyond which no new SO_2 is added, and drops rapidly beyond that point. The sulfate concentration rises to about 19 $\mu g/m^3$ at 1000 km and continues to rise a bit, as SO_2 is further converted, to a maximum at 1100 km, before slowly dropping. The particulate Se concentration increases to about 3 ng/m^3 at 1000 km and slowly decreases to 1800 km. The particulate S/Se ratio asymtotically approaches about 2100 up to 1000 km and increases beyond that point because additional particulate S is formed, while no more Se is added, reaching a value of about 3100 at 1800 km. The parameters were not chosen to attempt an exact fit to a particular data set, but the predicted concentrations of species were fairly reasonable. The B/SO_2 ratio remains fairly constant at about 0.0007 up to 1000 km, then increases by a factor of about 2.5 by 1800 km, as SO_2 is removed faster than gas-phase B. The latter is in reasonable agreement with the findings of Fogg and Rahn (18) The predictions were also in good agreement with measurements of gas-phase B and S and particulate B, S and Se in College Park, MD by Kitto and Anderson (19).

Tuncel et al. tabulated S/Se ratios for particles from many locations (4). The ratio is about 3000 at rural sites downwind, but outside of coal-burning areas. In the midst of the ORV, it is depressed to about 1700, in agreement with the model. In the midst of cities in which substantial coal is burned, the ratio is depressed to 1000 or less. Except for a few samples at Allegheny Mt. collected downwind from three power plants, Tuncel et al. did not see sudden drops in the S/Se ratio that one would expect to see occasionally in fresh plumes from coal-fired plants. A major flaw in the Gordon/Olmez model is the assumption of uniform vertical concentration profiles, which is surely a poor assumption just beyond a source. Most power plants have tall stacks, whereas, measurements are at ground level. The S/Se ratio will surely be depressed near the plume centerline, but the effect will usually be washed out before the plume hits ground level. However, around cities, there are probably some ground level sources.

We have performed more detailed hybrid-receptor calculations in an attempt to fit Shaw and Paur's gas-phase and particulate S data for three stations in the Ohio River Valley (1). Surprisingly, S concentrations do not increase strongly between the west station in Kentucky and the east station in Ohio. However, there was the possibility that high S levels occurred when air masses came back down the Valley from the east. Here we have eliminated this possibility by determining back-trajectories for all samples and found the same result when considering only air masses coming to the stations from the southwest.

To consider this point in more detail, we used XRF data because of the much greater amount of data available (and, thus, greater statistical significance) than from the samples analyzed by INAA. Sulfur is measured more accurately by XRF and the Se values from XRF agreed well with those from INAA for samples analyzed by both methods. Concentrations of S and Se, and the S/Se ratios for all samples with SW back-trajectories are listed in Table III. Southwest trajectories are more prominent during spring and summer than autumn and winter; however, recall that the sampling period (May, 1980 to Aug., 1981) contained two summers, but only one autumn, winter and spring. Particulate S levels are highest in summer (presumably because of highest SO_2 conversion rates), lowest in winter and intermediate in spring and autumn. Sulfur levels are nearly constant up the line of stations in spring, autumn and winter. Even in summer, the S concentration is highest at the center station, and the concentration at the west station is only about 30% below that at the east station. The fact that concentrations are highest at the center station may be related to the fact that the east station is more distant from the Ohio River and the highest density of coal-fired plants (see Figure 1). This suggests that there may be appreciable primary sulfate released by those plants, or that sulfate conversion is faster than we normally assume. In any case, there is clearly not a strong build-up of particulate S as air masses move up the ORV from the southwest.

There is considerable fluctuation of the Se values, much of it experimental uncertainty, as Se levels are close to the limit of detection for XRF. Thus, errors are of the order of ±30% for

Table III. Concentrations (ng/m^3) of S and Se and S/Se ratios for
fine particles borne by air masses from the southwest
in the Ohio River Valley for various seasons

Site		Sulfur				
		Spring	Summer	Autumn	Winter	Total
East	Avg	2200	3500	2200	1400	2600
	Std.Dev.	880	1900	890	600	1600
	No. pts.	15	21	7	6	49
Center	Avg	2100	3800	2300	1500	3000
	Std.Dev	1300	1500	1100	480	1600
	No. pts.	10	29	6	7	51
West	Avg	2200	2700	2200	1600	2400
	Std.Dev.	1200	1200	1400	330	1200
	No. pts.	16	39	9	7	71
Total	Avg	2200	3200	2200	1500	
	Std.Dev.	1100	1600	1200	490	
	No. pts.	41	88	22	20	
		Selenium				
East	Avg	1.3	1.7	1.4	1.6	1.5
	Std.Dev.	0.6	1.1	0.61	0.75	0.87
	No. pts.	15	21	6	6	48
Center	Avg	1.8	1.8	0.93	1.6	1.7
	Std.Dev.	0.67	0.59	0.35	0.56	0.64
	No. pts.	9	28	6	7	50
West	Avg	1.3	1.7	1.6	1.5	1.6
	Std.Dev.	0.79	0.71	0.66	0.57	0.73
	No. pts.	15	39	9	7	70
Total	Avg	1.4	1.7	1.3	1.6	
	Std.Dev.	0.73	0.77	0.63	0.63	
	No. pts.	39	88	21	20	
		S/Se				
East	Avg	1900	2700	2100	950	2100
	Std.Dev.	730	1500	1400	360	1300
	No. pts.	15	21	6	6	48
Center	Avg	1400	2200	2500	1000	1900
	Std.Dev.	540	750	950	300	860
	No. pts.	9	28	6	7	50
West	Avg	2200	1700	1400	1100	1700
	Std.Dev.	1100	560	540	250	770
	No. pts.	15	39	9	7	70
Total	Avg	1900	2100	1900	1000	
	Std.Dev.	930	1000	1100	320	
	No. pts.	39	88	21	20	

the analyses. There are enough data for spring and summer trajectories for these errors to cancel out, but there are so few data
for autumn and winter that the averages may not be very reliable.
Averaging over the whole year, we see that concentrations of Se
are slightly higher at the center station, but differences are not
very significant. Averaging over the three sites, Se concentrations are higher in summer and winter than in spring and autumn.
This agrees with source-emissions data (20) for SO_2 emissions:
there is a summer "air conditioning" peak, a winter "heating and
lighting" peak, and somewhat lower demands in transitional periods.

The qualitative behavior of the S/Se ratio during summer
agrees with the comments made above: it is lowest at the west station, where a lot of Se has been added, but conversion of SO_4 has
not come to steady state with removal. The value at the east station
is somewhat higher than the value of about 2200 predicted from the
simple hybrid model by Gordon and Olmez (14). There is a tendency
towards lower ratios in spring and autumn and clearly lower ratios
in winter, as expected from slower conversion when temperatures
and photochemical activities are low.

In our more detailed calculations to test hybrid receptor
modeling against these new data, we relaxed the assumption of a
constant SO_2 density vs. distance up the Valley, and put in estimates based on the SURE emissions inventory (21). Results from two
calculations are shown in Figures 2 and 3. We started the model
far to the SW, in Texas, to avoid boundary problems at the lower
end of the ORV. Except for a higher assumed conversion rate (1.5
vs. 1.0%/hr), parameters are the same as for the earlier calculations
(14). Note that the conversion rate is a 24-hr average, so it corresponds to a much higher value in the middle of the day, say 4-5%.
Here we are attempting to fit only data taken during summer.

Concentrations of pollutants remain rather low until we reach
the Mississippi River, as there are few strong sources to the southwest until Texas. The rise of concentrations is so fast that predicted levels of sulfate and Se are only about 30-40% low at the west
site. However, the predicted concentrations rise so high as we
move up the Valley that they greatly exceed the nearly constant
observed concentrations. The S/Se ratio rises to about 3500 as we
move away from SO_2 sources in Texas, because the SO_2 is mostly
converted to sulfate. This is about the expected value for an area
downwind from, but outside of areas of high SO_2 emissions (4). As
expected, the ratio drops sharply when we encounter heavy emissions
of SO_2 just upwind of the west station. There are large emissions
of Se, but the new sulfur is still mostly in the gas phase. Perhaps
fortuitously, the predicted S/Se ratios at the three sites are in
fairly good agreement with the experimental data.

The calculation of Figure 2 is rather poor because concentrations of the sulfur species rise so high in the ORV. It would
not help to increase deposition velocities, as the deposition fluxes
(not shown) are already too high. However, the vertical profiles
assumed by the model (constant to the mixing height) may be wrong.
Aircraft spirals were conducted routinely during the SURE project
(22). The concentration of SO_2 was found to drop off rather quickly
above the mixing height. Sulfate was not measured in real time,
but the light-scattering coefficient, b_{scat}, persisted to higher

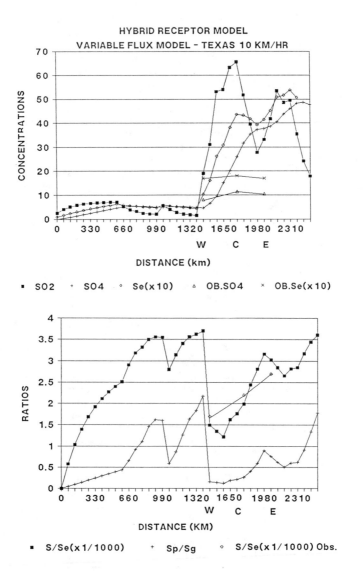

Figure. 2. Hybrid receptor model predictions of concentrations of SO_2, SO_4, particulate Se and the S/Se ratio from Texas up through the Ohio River Valley. Experimental data from XRF studies of Shaw and Paur (1) for southwest back-trajectories are connected by dashed lines.

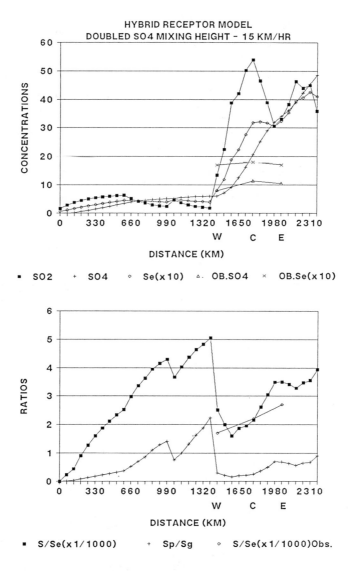

Figure. 3. Same as Figure 2 except sulfate allowed to mix uniformly to twice the mixing height and wind speed is increased from 10 to 15 km/hr.

altitudes. If b_{scat} is a measure of particulate sulfur, this result probably means that we should allow sulfate to mix to higher altitudes than the other pollutants. Figure 3 shows results of calculations in which we allowed the concentration of sulfate to be uniform to twice the mixing height and also increased the wind speed to 15 km/hr. Concentrations rise more slowly with distance up the Valley and don't reach as high levels as in Figure 2 (note different vertical scales). The changes cause concentrations at the west site to be more severely underpredicted, but bring the predictions down much closer to the observed values at the center and east stations. Except at the center site, the S/Se ratio predictions are worse than in Figure 2.

We could find no reasonable combination of parameters that fit the observed levels at the west station without grossly overpredicting them at the center and east stations. Among other things, we allowed up to 5% of the S to be released as primary sulfate. This increased the sulfate levels rather uniformly, but did not change the slope vs. distance up the Valley appreciably. The difficulty is that there are very few SO_2 sources to the southwest of the west site closer than Texas. Possibly the observations could be fitted by including a more specific treatment of wet deposition. The lower frequency of rainfall in Texas relative to the Ohio River Valley may allow sulfur to survive transport from Texas to Kentucky more easily than transport up the Valley. Calculations using another type of hybrid model, that of Samson et al. (23,24), which can explicitly handle the removal by precipitation, might be the most successful approach to understanding these data. Because of their unique and comprehensive nature, these data are some of the most important to be fitted by models. No model should be considered reliable unless it can do so!

Conclusion

Considerable progress is being made in the development of regional scale receptor modeling. There is surprisingly little variation of relative elemental concentration patterns of fine particles associated with various back-trajectory groups in the Ohio River Valley. The major exception to this is Mn, which is strongly influenced by emissions from one or more ferromanganese plants. Factor analysis did not yield much valuable information on ORVS samples, perhaps because of our pre-selection of samples to be analyzed by INAA and the lack of seasonal stratification. Chemical mass balances of fine-particle samples are quite promising, although concentration patterns are more difficult to fit accurately than for whole filter data or samples collected in urban areas. Various hybrid receptor modeling methods are potentially useful as an alternative to traditional source-based, "absolute" models for understanding sulfur transport, transformation and deposition. However, simple hybrid models do not seem capable of explaining the rather constant sulfate levels from KY to OH in the Ohio River Valley. Present knowledge of vertical concentration profiles of chemical species is very poor, which may greatly limit our ability to develop successful models of any type.

Acknowledgment

This work was in part supported by the U. S. Environmental Protection Agency under Grant R81-0403. We thank Robert K. Stevens and Charles W. Lewis for their encouragement and helpful discussions.

Literature Cited
1. Shaw, R. W., Jr.; Paur, R. J. Atmos. Environ. 1983, 17, 1431.
2. Shaw, R. W., Jr.; Paur, R. J. Atmos. Environ. 1983, 17, 2031.
3. Heffter, J. L., NOAA Tech. Memo. ERL ARL-121, 1983.
4. Tuncel, S. G.; Olmez, I.; Parrington, J. R.; Gordon, G. E.; Stevens, R. K. Environ. Sci. Technol. 1985, 19, 529.
5. Germani, M. S., et al. Anal. Chem. 1980, 52, 240.
6. Thurston, G. D.; Spengler, J. D. Atmos. Environ. 1985, 19, 9.
7. Dzubay, T. G.; Stevens, R. K.; Haagenson, P. L. Environ. Sci. Technol. 1984, 18, 873.
8. Olmez, I.; Gordon, G. E. Science 1985, 229, 966.
9. Sheffield, A. E.; Gordon, G. E., in Receptor Methods for Source Apportionment, T. G. Pace, editor (APCA, Pittsburgh, PA, 1986), pp. 9-22.
10. Kowalczyk, G. S.; Gordon, G. E.; Rheingrover, S. W. Environ. Sci. Technol. 1982, 16, 79.
11. Tuncel, S. G. et al.in Receptor Methods for Source Apportionment, T. G. Pace, editor (APCA, Pittsburgh, PA, 1986), pp. 116-126.
12. Pierson, W. R.; Brachaczek, W. W.; Truex, T. J.; Butler, J. W.; Korniski, T. J. Ann. NY Acad. Sci. 1980, 338, 145.
13. Rahn, K. A.; Lowenthal, D. H. Science, 1985, 228, 275.
14. Gordon, G. E.; Olmez, I., in Receptor Methods for Source Apportionment, T. G. Pace, editor (APCA, Pittsburgh, PA, 1986), pp. 229-238.
15. Stevens,R. K.; Pace, T. G. Atmos. Environ. 1984, 18, 1499.
16. Lewis, C. W.; Stevens, R. K. Atmos. Environ. 1985, 19, 917.
17. Stevens, R. K.; Dzubay, T. G.; Lewis, C. W.; Shaw, R. W., Jr. Atmos. Environ. 1984, 18, 261.
18. Fogg, T. R.; Rahn K. A. Geophys. Res. Lett. 1984, 11, 854.
19. M. E. Kitto and D. L. Anderson, "Simultaneous collection of particles and acidic gases for tracing emissions from coal-fired power plants," presented at the Amer. Chem. Soc. National Meeting, New York, April, 1986.
20. Toothman, D. A.; Yates, J. C.; Sabo, E. S. "Status report on the development on the NAPAP emission inventory for the 1980 Base Year and summary of preliminary data, Report to EPA, 1984.
21. Klemm, H. A.; Brennan, R. J. "Emissions inventory for the SURE region,"Electric Power Research Institute Report No. EA-1913, 1981.
22. Blumenthal, D. L.; Keifer, W. S.; McDonald, J. A. "Aircraft measurements of pollutants and meteorological parameters during the Sulfate Regional Experiment (SURE) program, Electric Power Research Institute Report No. EA-1909, 1981.
23. Samson, P. J.; Moody, J. L.; Kahl, J.; Keeler G., in Chemistry of Multiphase Atmospheric Systems, W. Jaeschke, editor (Springer-Verlag, Berlin, 1986) pp. 727-740.
24. Keeler, G.; Samson, P. J. "Meteorology of trace element receptor modeling," Draft Final Report to EPA, 1986.

RECEIVED May 15, 1987

CLOUD CHEMISTRY AND PHYSICS

Chapter 7

Simultaneous Collection of Particles and Acidic Gases for Tracing Emissions from Coal-Fired Power Plants

Michael E. Kitto and David L. Anderson

Department of Chemistry and Biochemistry, University of Maryland, College Park, MD 20742

Particulate and gaseous atmospheric components have been sampled using a multiple-filter system. A Teflon filter for particle collection preceded four ^{7}LiOH/ glycerol treated Whatman-41 filters in a stacked filter arrangement. Up to fifty elements were detected on the particulate filter, while ten elements (B, N, S, Cl, As, Se, Sb, Br, I and Hg) were observed on the base-treated filters using the combined techniques of PGAA, INAA and IC. The base-treated filters proved to be very efficient collectors of the acidic gas-phase species, but apparently allow some elemental and organic species to pass through as shown by studies with activated charcoal-impregnated filters. Application of observed concentrations of atmospheric particles and acidic gases are compared to the results predicted by a hybrid receptor model.

In this study we have employed the simultaneous collection of atmospheric particles and gases followed by multielement analysis as an approach for the determination of source-receptor relationships. A number of particulate tracer elements have previously been linked to sources (e.g., V to identify oil-fired power plant emissions, Na for marine aerosols, and Pb for motor vehicle contribution). Receptor methods commonly used to assess the interregional impact of such emissions include chemical mass balances (CMBs) and factor analysis (FA), the latter often including wind trajectories. With CMBs, source-strengths are determined (1) from the relative concentrations of marker elements measured at emission sources. When enough sample analyses are available, correlation calculations from FA and knowledge of source-emission compositions may identify groups of species from a common source type and identify potential marker elements. The source composition patterns are not necessary as the elemental concentrations in each sample are normalized to the mean value of the element. Recently a hybrid receptor model was proposed by Lewis and Stevens (2) in which the dispersion, deposition, and conversion characteristics of sulfur species in power-plant emissions

0097-6156/87/0349-0084$06.00/0

are related to a fine particulate tracer element (e.g., Se). In this study, we have tried to extend tracer techniques for coal-burning utility emissions to include gas-phase elements, and to relate receptor measurements to the hybrid receptor model, as modified by Gordon and Olmez (3).

Mass balance calculations (4,5) have accounted for only 30-50% of feed coal boron in the ashes, implying the rest was released in the gas phase. Analysis of size-fractioned fly-ash by PGAA showed an enrichment of B, as well as S and Cd, on the smaller particles (6), and recent stack measurements of gaseous B concentrations varied from 700 to 5000 $\mu g/m^3$ after a 20:1 dilution with ambient air (7). Fogg (8) has shown that, based on the chemical properties of boron compounds, the plausible gas-phase B species is $B(OH)_3$, boric acid. $B(OH)_3$ then presents itself as a possible gas-phase tracer for SO_2, as both should have similar dispersion and deposition characteristics, while $B(OH)_3$ will not undergo chemical conversion analogous to SO_2 to sulfate. By simultaneously measuring gas-phase $B(OH)_3$ and SO_2, and particulate Se and sulfate concentrations at a receptor site, we are able to test the hybrid receptor model with tracers in both phases.

Experimental

The sampling system was designed for efficient collection, high flow rates, and minimal analytical interferences. The optimum stacked-filter system consists of a Teflon-based (Zefluor or Fluoropore) particle filter placed prior to a series of ^{7}LiOH/glycerol treated Whatman-41 filters in the air-sample stream. Our studies have shown that Whatman-41 prefilters are inadequate to the extent that about 5% of some species (e.g., S, Br, I) may pass through the cellulose matrix. The choice of Zefluor or Fluoropore prefilter depends solely on blank-value preferences or availability. ^{7}LiOH is used as our analytical techniques are instrumental neutron activation (INAA) and neutron-capture prompt γ-ray activation (PGAA) analysis, therefore the use of NaOH or KOH would cause severe spectral interferences and "natural" Li contains enough ^{6}Li to cause significant neutron self-shielding in the sample. Normally, a Teflon filter followed by four treated 110-mm filters are contained in a single open-faced polyethylene filter holder with an exposed area of 75 cm^2 (Figure 1). Typical flow rates were 3.3 L/s, producing a face velocity of air at the filter surface of 44 cm/s and a residence time for gases on each treated filter of about 0.5 ms. Although they are simple and highly efficient, annular denuders were not used because they were unavailable when the sampling began and are only now being developed to accommodate higher flow rates. Also, they require additional preparation, with possible contamination, of the sample prior to analysis by nuclear techniques, whereas stacked-filter samples could be analyzed with very little handling or preparation.

In this study the filter samples were halved, bagged in cleaned polyethylene tubing, and first analyzed by PGAA using an external irradiation facility constructed by our group at the National Bureau of Standards (NBS) research reactor (9). PGAA provided determinations of the elements B, S, and Cl on the treated filters, and B, S, Cl, Si, Cd and often others on the particle filters. For analysis of short-lived isotopes by INAA, the bagged samples were

irradiated in the NBS reactor for 5 minutes. Subsequent accumulation
and analysis of each sample's γ-ray spectrum were performed at the
NBS reactor, using a procedure similar to that described by Germani
et al. (10). After 3-7 days of cooling the samples were
re-irradiated for 4 hours to produce intermediate-and long-lived
(n,γ) products, and two counts were performed at the University of
Maryland (~4 and ~12 hours after ~3 and ~30 day decay times,
respectively). Ion chromatography analyses of some of the other
filter halves were performed at the NBS Chemistry building to provide
a check of S and Cl values obtained by PGAA and INAA, as well as to
provide measurements of NO_x.

Results and Discussion

For a set of 14 filter samples taken in College Park, MD during May,
June, and July of 1984, 45-50 elements were routinely determined on
the particle filter by the combined techniques, and for the gas-phase
the concentrations of S, Cl, Br, I, As, Se, Sb and Hg (by INAA) and
B, S, and Cl (by PGAA) could be measured (Figure 2). The average
sampling period was about 3 days. The collection efficiency of the
first three ^7LiOH/glycerol stacked-filters (stages 2-4) can
be observed in Figure 3. In this typical sample (~800 m³), as for
others taken at various sites, the first three base-treated filters
collect virtually all the acidic gas-phase species. Blank or
insignificant levels are observed on stage 5. The percentage of the
total mass of elements detected by this system on the base-treated
filters were 78±11, 65±8, 75±26, 23±20, 5±3, 54±15, 0.5±0.8 and 91±3
for B, S, Cl, As, Se, Br, Sb and I, respectively. We do not report Hg
values as the particle data are unreliable due to potential losses
during irradiation. It is possible that some of the measured gas-
phase concentration is due to volatilization from particles collected
on the prefilter, and we are differentiating between particulate and
gaseous components with an operational definition. In this study, the
treated-filter ("acidic gas-phase") concentrations will include the
actual gaseous components in the air stream and artifacts due to
volatilization from or reaction with the particles on the prefilter,
and any very fine particulate material that pass through the
prefilter. Also, the "particulate" concentration includes actual
particle mass plus any gaseous component adsorbed by the prefilter.
This latter component is probably very small for Teflon-based
filters, but cannot be ruled out.
    For the particle filters we have determined enrichment factors
(EF) using Wedepohl's (11) crustal values and the equation:

$$EF = (X/Al)_{sample}/(X/Al)_{crust} \qquad (1)$$

As expected, B, S, V, Zn, As, Se, Sb, and the halogens were found to
be strongly enriched. The elements of interest in this study, B, S,
and Se have EF values of 35±22, 910±420, and 1940±980, respectively.
Preliminary results show the lowest B(g), SO_2, Se(p), and sulfate
concentrations during N to E winds and the highest values during SW
to NW winds. A summary of the data is shown in Figure 4, and periods
apparently affected by coal-derived aerosol are clearly seen.
    A series of experiments were conducted with activated-charcoal
impregnated filters being used in both side-by-side studies and in

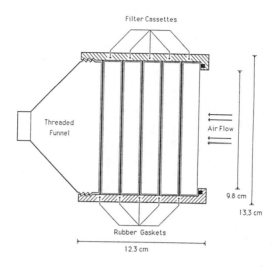

Figure 1. Schematic of stacked-filter sampler used for simultaneous collection of particles and acidic gases.

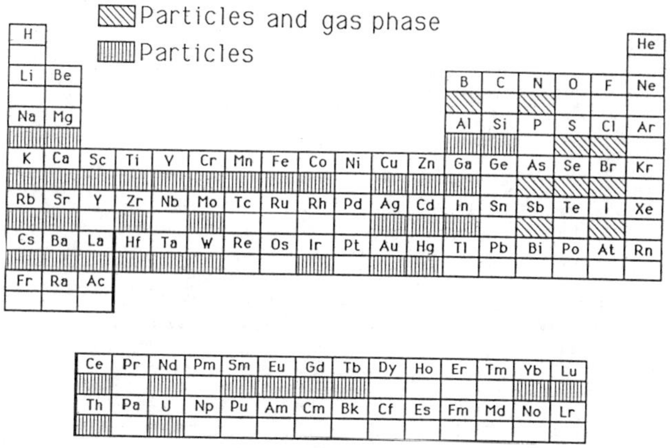

Figure 2. Atmospheric particulate and gas-phase elements, observed with INAA, PGAA and IC, collected by the stacked-filter method.

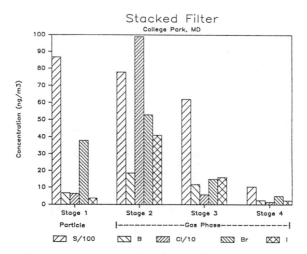

Figure 3.   Stage-by-stage atmospheric particulate and gas-phase
concentrations of typical College Park, MD sample.

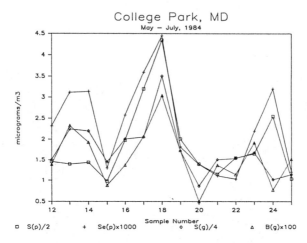

Figure 4.   Variations of atmospheric concentrations of trace
elements in the gas and particulate phase observed during a
continuous two-month sampling period.

series with ^{7}LiOH-treated filters. The results indicatd that the gaseous species containing B, S and As were efficiently trapped by the base-treated filters, as none was observed above blank levels on the charcoal filters when used in series behind the base-treated filters. Approximately equal amounts of acidic and nonacidic (i.e., organic) Cl, Br, and I were observed, while about twice as much Se was found to be acidic. Inconclusive evidence exist for Sb, as this element was observed only once on each filter type during the sampling period. Results for Hg indicate that only about 4% of the gaseous form of this element is trapped by the base-treated filters, assuming no loss during irradiation, and the gas-phase is dominated by nonacidic species. In agreement with Germani (12), charcoal filters apparently retain Hg during neutron irradiation. The conclusion from these experiments is that organic (e.g., CH_3Br) and elemental (e.g., Se^0) species in the atmosphere are not completely trapped by the ^{7}LiOH-treated filters. Charcoal-impregnated filters are not routinely used due to the significantly higher blank levels than the base-treated filters (10, 30, 15, 2, 2, and 10 times higher for B, Cl, As, Se, Br, and Sb, respectively), the spectral interference from the high amount of Mn present and the inability to analyze the filter matrix by IC.

A comparison of observed particulate concentrations from this study to one conducted about eight years ago at the same site (13) showed no measureable change for all the elements associated with a crustal component, with Al and La being representative (Table I). Other elements (e.g., S, Se) which showed enrichments in the earlier study continued to be enriched, but notable differences in elemental concentrations existed for V and Br, probably from decreased oil and leaded gasoline consumption (1), respectively. It should be noted that discrepancies between the two studies' concentrations maybe due to slight variations in sampling times (May-July vs Aug.-Sept.), methods (Teflon vs Nuclepore filters) and meteorology, though these are thought to be minor. While most of the elements have nearly identical concentrations between the two studies, and V and Br rarely reached the average levels of the previous study.

Table I.   Comparison of Some Elemental Concentrations (ng/m^3) Observed at the College Park, MD Site with Those Reported in Aug.-Sept., 1976 for the Same Site (13)

		This Study (n = 14) (1984)	Kowalczyk (n = 20) (1976)
Typical Crustal Elements:	Al	1200 ± 610	1250 ± 620
	La	1.3 ± 0.8	1.4 ± 0.9
Typical Enriched Elements:	S	3700 ± 1800	3100 ± 500
	Se	2.3 ± 1.0	2.3 ± 1.3
Notably Different Elements:	V	10 ± 6	20 ± 21
	Br	37 ± 17	150 ± 100

Application of Data to Receptor Modeling

Using both a hybrid receptor model, developed by Lewis and Stevens
(2) and modified by Gordon and Olmez (3), and a simple model of
emission from the Ohio River Valley, we compare the results of the
College Park (CP) samples as well as those of another continuous set
of samples taken from July 3-29, 1983 at Wallops Island, VA (WI), to
predicted results. Single-source differential equations (2) are used
to describe the time-varying concentrations of SO_2, $SO_4^=$ and a
particulate element characteristic of coal-fired power plant
emissions (chosen here as Se). An additional equation (3) can be
added to describe the concentration variation of $B(OH)_3$. The
following rate constants apply to the concentrations of the four
species in question:
     $k(t)$: dispersion and deposition (a rate assumed to be identical
             for all four species)
     $k_r(t)$: pseudo first-order SO_2 conversion rate (for the
             equations describing SO_2 and $SO_4^=$ concentrations)
and $k_d(t)$: additional deposition loss rate for the gases (SO_2 and
             $B(OH)_3$).
These two gaseous species are both acidic and the wet and dry
deposition characterics are assumed to be similar, yet $B(OH)_3$ does
not undergo conversion to another species, therefore the SO_2
conversion can be monitored by using gas-phase B as a tracer. In a
similar fashion, particulate Se is assumed to mimic sulfate and can
be used as a tracer of SO_2-to-sulfate conversion. The solutions to
the equations for the four species are as follows:

$$M_{SO2} = M_{SO2}(0)C(0)\exp[-(\overline{k}_r+\overline{k}_d)t] \tag{2}$$

$$M_B = M_B(0)C(0)\exp[-\overline{k}_d t] \tag{3}$$

$$M_{Se} = M_{Se}(0)\exp[-\overline{k}t] \tag{4}$$

$$M_{SO4} = (3/2)M_{SO2}(0)C(0)[\overline{k}_r/(\overline{k}_r+\overline{k}_d)][1-\exp(-(\overline{k}_r+\overline{k}_d)t)] \\ + M_{SO4}(0)C(0) \tag{5}$$

where $C(0) = M_{Se}/M_{Se}(0)$
       $\overline{k} = (1/t)\int k \, dt'$
       $\overline{k}_d = (1/t)\int k_d \, dt'$
and $\overline{k}_r = (1/t)\int k_r \, dt'$.
For our calculations, we assume that twenty identical power-plants
are spaced 50 km apart over 1000 km, as a simple simulation of the
Ohio River Valley region, and that coal-fired power plants are the
primary source of atmospheric B, S, and Se in continental regions.
Using the most reliable data available from the literature about
B(g), SO_2, and Se(p) release (3), and assuming atmospheric mixing to
1.5 km, an average wind velocity of 10 km/hr, a fine particulate (Se
and sulfate) deposition velocity of 0.5 cm/s, a gas phase (B and
SO_2) deposition velocity of 2 cm/s, and a SO_2 conversion rate of
1.0%/hr, we can predict the atmospheric concentrations and their
ratios as a function of distance (Table II). Fluctuations in the
model parameters will slightly change the predicted values, and shift
the model plots as a whole. The ratio values reported for the sites
represent the means of the individual sample ratios. The model input

parameters used were only a "first try" but concentrations observed at College Park agree reasonably well for such a simple model. We are in the process of attempting a more realistic representation of the Ohio River Valley based on actual power plant locations and outputs. The model was designed to predict ratios, yet the individual concentrations also agree quite well. For the Wallops Island study, the observed gas-phase B concentrations are exceptionally large, but this is not surprising as large concentrations of gaseous $B(OH)_3$ have been previously reported at marine sites ($\underline{8}$). Additional ambient measurements, identification of other sources of gas-phase B (if any), accompaning rain analysis, and a more rigorous definition of input parameters will help refine the model. Also, comparing sample-to-sample variations with wind back-trajectory information may help determine if such a model can be applied to large distance scales (~1500 km or more).

Table II.   Comparison of Hybrid Receptor Model with Observed Concentrations at College Park, MD (CP) and Wallops Is., VA (WI)

species	Concentration Predicted at Distance (km)				Observed CP (May–July, 1984)	Observed WI (July, 1983)
	100	700	1000	1800	14 samples	12 samples
gases						
SO_2 ($\mu g/m^3$)	16	27	28	0.2	14.0 ± 5.1	8.1 ± 4.9
B (ng/m^3)	12	22	23	0.53	15.7 ± 6.5	70 ± 50
particles						
$SO_4^=$ ($\mu g/m^3$)	1.0	14	19	11	11.2 ± 5.4	13.2 ± 7.5
Se (ng/m^3)	0.7	2.5	3.0	1.0	2.3 ± 1.0	1.76 ± 0.91
ratios						
S(p)/S(g)	0.04	0.35	0.46	26.0	0.56 ± 0.24	1.20 ± 0.38
$B(g)/SO_2$ x1000	0.75	0.81	0.82	1.80	1.11 ± 0.25	7.9 ± 2.7
S(p)/Se(p)	570	1900	2100	3100	1710 ± 530	3040 ± 770

Literature Cited

1. Kowalczyk, G. S.; Choquette, C. E.; Gordon, G. E. Atmos. Environ. 1978, 12, 1143.
2. Lewis, C. W.; Stevens, R. K. Atmos. Environ. 1985, 19, 917.
3. Gordon, G. E.; Olmez, I. APCA Specialty Conference on Receptor Methods for Source Apportionment: Real World Issues and Applications, Williamsburg, VA, 1985.

4.   Gladney, E.S.; Wangen, L. E.; Curtis, D. B.; Jurney, E. T.
     Environ. Sci. Technol. 1978, 12, 1084.
5.   Egarov, A. P.; Laktionova, N. V.; Popinako, N. V.; Novoselova,
     I. V. Therm. Engin. 1979, 26, 82.
6.   Kitto, M. E.; Anderson, D. L.; Gordon, G. E.; Ondov, J. M. 186th
     National ACS Meeting, Washington, D.C., 1983.
7.   Fogg, T. R.; Rahn, K. A. Geophys. Res. Let. 1984 1, 854.
8.   Fogg, T. R. Ph.D. Thesis, University of Rhode Island, Kingston,
     1983.
9.   Failey, M. P.; Anderson, D. L.; Zoller, W. H.; Gordon G. E.;
     Lindstrom, R. M. Anal. Chem. 1979, 51, 2209.
10. Germani, M. S.; Gokmen, I.; Sigleo, A. C.; Kowalczyk, G. S.;
     Olmez, I.; Small, A. M.; Anderson, D. L.; Failey, M. P.;
     Gulovali, M. C.; Choquette, C. E.; Lepel, E. A.; Gordon, G. E.;
     Zoller, W. H. Anal. Chem. 1980, 52, 240.
11. Wedepohl, K. H. In Origin and Distribution of the Elements,
     Ahrens, L. H., Ed.; Pergamon Press: London, 1968; p 999.
12. Germani, M. S. Ph.D. Thesis, University of Maryland, College
     Park, 1980.
13. Kowalczyk, G. S. Ph.D. Thesis, University of Maryland, College
     Park, 1979.

From a dissertation to be submitted to the Graduate School,
University of Maryland, by Michael E. Kitto in partial fulfillment of
the requirements for the Ph. D. degree in Chemistry.

Although the research described in this article has been funded
wholly or in part by the United States Environmental Protection
Agency under assistance agreement R-812503-01-0 to the University of
Maryland, it has not been subjected to the Agency's peer and
administrative review and therefore may not necessarily reflect the
views of the Agency and no official endorsement should be inferred.

RECEIVED March 10, 1987

Chapter 8

Aqueous-Phase Reactions in Clouds

Stephen E. Schwartz

Environmental Chemistry Division, Brookhaven National Laboratory,
Upton, NY 11973

Reaction of dissolved gases in clouds occurs by the
sequence gas-phase diffusion, interfacial mass transport, and concurrent aqueous-phase diffusion and
reaction. Information required for evaluation of
rates of such reactions includes fundamental data
such as equilibrium constants, gas solubilities,
kinetic rate laws, including dependence on pH and
catalysts or inhibitors, diffusion coefficients, and
mass-accommodation coefficients, and situational data
such as pH and concentrations of reagents and other
species influencing reaction rates, liquid-water content, drop size distribution, insolation, temperature, etc. Rate evaluations indicate that aqueous-
phase oxidation of $S(IV)$ by H_2O_2 and O_3 can be
important for representative conditions. No important aqueous-phase reactions of nitrogen species have
been identified. Examination of microscale mass-
transport rates indicates that mass transport only
rarely limits the rate of in-cloud reaction for
representative conditions. Field measurements and
studies of reaction kinetics in authentic precipitation samples are consistent with rate evaluations.

The composition of liquid-water clouds and processes responsible
for this composition are of obvious current interest in conjunction
with the so-called acid precipitation phenomenon since clouds con-
stitute the immediate precursor of precipitation. Additionally,
cloud composition is of interest because impaction of cloud droplets on surfaces may directly deliver dissolved substances onto
natural or artificial materials. In-cloud processes also influence
clear-air composition since dissolved substances resulting from
such reactions are released into clear air as gases or aerosol
particles upon cloud evaporation. It is thus desired to gain
enhanced description of the composition of clouds and the mecha-

0097-6156/87/0349-0093$06.00/0

nisms whereby clouds attain that composition. This paper outlines
methods of describing aqueous-phase reactions in liquid-water
clouds, with emphasis on processes involving dissolution and reaction of sulfur and nitrogen oxides to form sulfuric and nitric
acids.

Acid Incorporation Mechanisms

The processes by which clouds incorporate sulfuric and nitric acids
are conveniently distinguished into two categories depending upon
whether oxidation takes place in the gas phase or in the aqueous
phase, as illustrated schematically in Figure 1. For an examination of gas-phase atmospheric oxidation of SO_2 and NO_2 see ([1,2]).
Products of this oxidation, aerosol sulfuric acid and sulfate and
nitrate salts, and gas-phase nitric acid, are expected to be rapidly and to great extent incorporated into cloud droplets upon cloud
formation ([3,4]).
     Liquid-water clouds ([5]) represent a potentially important
medium for atmospheric chemical reactions in view of their high
liquid water content [10^4 to 10^5 times that associated with clear-
air aerosol ([6])] and high state of dispersion (typical drop radius
~10 μm). Clouds are quite prevalent in the atmosphere (fractional
global coverage ~50%) and persistent (lifetimes of a few tenths of
an hour to several hours). The presence of liquid water also contributes to thermochemical driving force for production of the
highly soluble sulfuric and nitric acids.
     At a microscopic level, the uptake and reaction of a gas in a
cloud droplet consists of the following steps, as illustrated in
Figure 2: (1) diffusion from the bulk gas phase to the air-water
interface, (2) transfer across the interface, (3) establishment of
any rapid aqueous-phase equilibria, and (4) aqueous-phase diffusion
concurrent with (5) aqueous-phase reaction. These steps define the
information necessary to evaluate the rates of such reactions.
Fundamental data, which must be determined by laboratory experiments, include equilibrium constants, gas solubilities, kinetic
rate laws, including any dependence on pH and concentrations of
other reagents catalysts, or inhibitors, gaseous and aqueous diffusion coefficients, and mass-accommodation coefficients. The
mass-accommodation coefficient is the fraction of gas kinetic collisions of a gaseous species upon an interface resulting in transfer of the species across the interface, and is expected to depend
on the identity of the solute gas and solvent, and the presence, if
any, of surface active materials. Situational data, which must be
measured in the field or else modeled or assumed, include pH and
concentrations of reagents and other species influencing reaction
rates, liquid-water content, drop size distribution, insolation,
temperature, etc. This paper takes the approach of evaluating
reaction rates for assumed representative values of these parameters. Inferences drawn from such evaluations can be examined for
consistency with field measurements.
     Oxidants present in the atmosphere thermochemically capable of
oxidizing SO_2 or NO_2 include not only molecular O_2 but also the
trace, highly reactive constituents O_3 and H_2O_2 that are the products of secondary atmospheric photochemical reactions. Despite

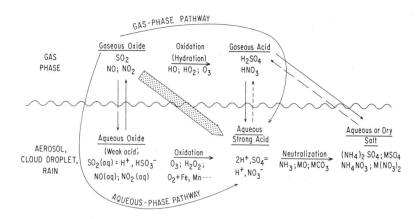

Figure 1.   Schematic representation of pathways for atmospheric
formation of sulfuric and nitric acids and their salts.
(Reproduced with permission from Ref. 28.   Copyright 1986
Lewis Publishers, Inc.)

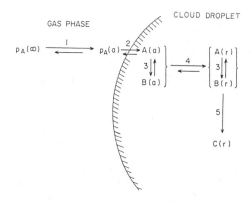

Figure 2.   Schematic illustration of the subprocesses compris-
ing a gas-aqueous reaction in a single cloud droplet.   A represents aqueous phase reagent species transferred from the gas
phase; B, species in rapid equilibrium with A; and C, product
species, at the surface of the drop (a) or in the interior (r);
p_A represents gas-phase partial pressure of A at the surface
of the drop (a) and at large distance from the drop (∞).

its great abundance, O_2 is not directly reactive with SO_2 or NO_2 in aqueous solution--the highly important industrial reactions producing H_2SO_4 and HNO_3 proceed by means of catalysts and/or reaction pathways involving intermediates.

Rate Evaluations

The rate of aqueous-phase in-cloud reaction can be evaluated, for specified reagent concentrations (including pH) and physical conditions, by means of the following assumptions:

1. Assumption of solubility equilibrium (Henry's law) for reagent gases in cloud droplets. Henry's law coefficients (H) of solute gases that do not react with water, e.g., O_3, H_2O_2, and PAN, can be measured by conventional techniques. A variety of techniques have been applied to determination of H_{NO_2} with fairly consistent results (7).

2. In the case of gases such as SO_2, which are anhydrides of weak acids (i.e., for SO_2, sulfurous acid), assumption also of pertinent hydration and acid dissociation equilibria, which, together with the cloud droplet pH, determine the total solubility. This pH-dependent total solubility is conveniently expressed as an effective Henry's law coefficient, H^*. Henry's law coefficients and effective Henry's law coefficients for gases of concern in cloud chemistry are summarized in Figure 3.

3. Assumption that laboratory-determined rate expressions are pertinent to evaluation of reaction rates in cloudwater, which inevitably contains substances that may be catalysts or inhibitors of reaction. Kinetic rate coefficients may themselves be pH dependent, reflecting the specific S(IV) moiety involved in reaction and/or acid catalysis. Laboratory kinetic studies of the H_2O_2-S(IV) reaction and the O_3-S(IV) reaction are summarized in Figures 4 and 5.

Such evaluations (e.g., 8-11) yield a pH-dependent instantaneous aqueous-phase oxidation rate and, for specified cloud liquid-water content, a rate that can be expressed as a fraction of the gas-phase reagent oxidized per unit time. Rate evaluations for aqueous-phase oxidation of SO_2 by O_3 and H_2O_2 are shown in Figure 6. The left-hand ordinate gives the aqueous-phase rate, per ppb gas-phase SO_2 concentration. In the context of rain acidification, for which a reaction rate of, say, 10^{-5} M h^{-1} is important, it is seen that the H_2O_2 reaction (for assumed H_2O_2 concentration of 1 ppb) is quite important, nearly independent of pH in over the relevant pH range (2-6). The pH independence results from the decreasing solubility of SO_2 with decreasing pH (Figure 3) in conjunction with the acid catalyzed reaction (Figure 4). While the instantaneous reaction rate is quite high, the extent of reaction may be limited by availability of H_2O_2, since the few available measurements to date of H_2O_2 concentrations in clear air (12-14) and in cloudwater (15) suggest that the concentration of this species rarely if ever exceeds a few parts per billion (gas-phase volume fraction) and is often less. The importance of the H_2O_2-S(IV) reaction suggested by these evaluations and the limited availability of H_2O_2 emphasize the need for enhanced understanding of the sources of H_2O_2, including gas-phase free-radical reactions and

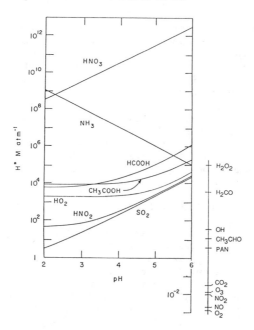

Figure 3. pH-Dependence of the effective Henry's law coefficient for gases which undergo rapid acid-base dissociation reactions in aqueous solution, as a function of solution pH. Buffer capacity of solution is assumed to greatly exceed incremental concentration from uptake of indicated gas. Also indicated at the right of the figure are Henry's law coefficients for non-dissociative gases. For references see (28).

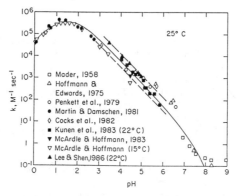

Figure 4. Second-order rate constant $k^{(2)}$ for oxidation of sulfur(IV) by hydrogen peroxide defined according to $d[S(VI)]/dt = k^{(2)}[H_2O_2][S(IV)]$, as a function of solution pH. Solid curve is fit to data by Overton (29). Dashed lines (slope = -1 corresponding to H^+ catalyzed oxidation of HSO_3^- in pH range 3 to 6) are arbitrarily placed to encompass most of the data. Temperature 25°C except as indicated. For references see (29).

possible aqueous-phase reactions involving O_3 and/or free radicals. The O_3-S(IV) reaction exhibits a very strong pH dependence that is due to the SO_2 solubility (Figure 3) and rate constant (Figure 5) both decreasing with decreasing pH. This reaction (for assumed O_3 concentration of 30 ppb) is important only at high pH ($\gtrsim 5$) and, in view of the formation of strong acid by this reaction, is self quenched.

The right-hand ordinate of Figure 6 expresses the reaction rate as percent of gas-phase SO_2 oxidized per hour, per unit liquid water content of the cloud. Oxidation rates in these units may be compared to clear-air oxidation rates (of order 1% h^{-1}), although this comparison should be tempered by the small fraction of the boundary layer that is occupied by clouds.

Authentic Precipitation Kinetic Studies. A recent study ($\underline{16}$) has examined the chemical kinetics of the H_2O_2-S(IV) reaction in rain-water and melt water of snow collected at our laboratory to ascertain whether the rate expression for this reaction determined with nominally "pure" water applies to such authentic precipitation samples, and by extension, to cloudwater. Kinetic studies were carried out on more than 300 precipitation samples obtained over a two-year period; sample collection was typically 30 min, and kinetic runs were usually made within the next 30 min. Reaction was initiated by adding typically no more than 4 µM of H_2O_2, HSO_3^-, or both, as necessary to a sample aliquot. Values of the effective second-order rate constant determined in these samples are shown in Figure 7. Although the data exhibit considerable scatter, they fall close to the "pure water" data for this reaction. Much of the scatter was attributed to uncertainty in pH; influence of ionic strength or of formaldehyde was excluded. We thus gain from this study considerable confidence in the applicability of laboratory studies of the kinetics of the H_2O_2-S(IV) reaction to evaluations in cloudwater. Similar studies of other reactions, however, are lacking and should be undertaken.

Mass-Transport Kinetics. The past several years have seen considerable progress in examining the problem of coupled mass transport and aqueous-phase chemical reaction applied to cloud droplets. The question that must be addressed is whether mass-transport coupling the bulk (large distance from drop) gas-phase concentration to, across, and within the drop surface is sufficiently rapid to maintain the Henry's law concentration of the dissolved reagent gas (relative to the bulk gas phase) in the face of aqueous-phase reaction that serves as a sink for this species. Hypothetical reagent concentration profiles in the vicinity of a drop are illustrated in Figure 8. If mass-transport in one or more of the regions (gas-phase, interface, aqueous-phase) is not sufficiently rapid to maintain a nearly uniform concentration profile, then the diminished aqueous-phase reagent concentration will result in a diminished reaction rate compared to that for assumed Henry's law equilibrium at the bulk gas-phase concentration. This situation would require that models evaluating gas-aqueous reactions in clouds treat different drop sizes separately, reflecting differing reaction rates and resultant differing concentrations. Techniques

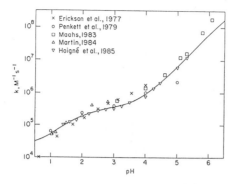

Figure 5. Second-order rate constant $k^{(2)}$ for oxidation of sulfur(IV) by ozone defined according to $d[S(VI)]/dt = k^{(2)}[O_3(aq)][S(IV)]$, as a function of solution pH at 25°C. Curve represents a three-component (SO_2, HSO_3^-, $SO_3^=$) rate expression due to Hoigné (30). For references see (30,31).

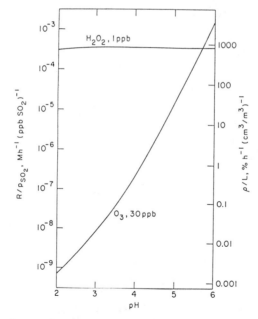

Figure 6. Rate of aqueous-phase oxidation of S(IV) by O_3 (30 ppb) and H_2O_2 (1 ppb), as a function of solution pH. Gas-aqueous equilibria are assumed for all reagents. R/p_{SO_2} represents aqueous reaction rate per ppb of gas-phase SO_2. ρ/L represents rate of reaction referred to gas-phase SO_2 partial pressure per $cm^3 \cdot m^{-3}$ liquid water volume fraction. Temperature 25°C. Modified from Ref. (10).

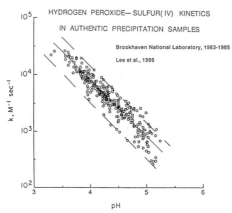

Figure 7. Second-order rate constant $k^{(2)}$ of H_2O_2-$S(IV)$ reaction determined in freshly collected rainwater samples. The solid line is a regression line constrained to slope of -1. Dashed lines, transferred from Figure 4, represent envelope of results from studies in purified water in various laboratories. Data from Ref. (16).

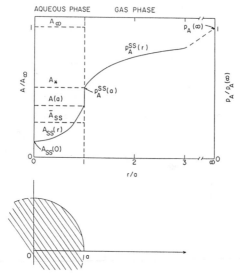

Figure 8. Hypothetical concentration profiles in gas and aqueous phases indicating gradient in reagent concentration due to flux of material into and within drop. Concentration scales of aqueous-phase ($r < a$) left ordinate and gas-phase ($r > a$) right ordinate are chosen so that the same coordinate on each scale represents the condition of phase equilibrium. Departure from the uniform profile at the "bulk" ($r = \infty$) value represents the inability of mass transport to maintain the reagent concentration as the reagent is consumed by aqueous-phase reaction. (Reproduced with permission from Ref. 28. Copyright 1986 Lewis Publishers, Inc.)

for such treatment are outlined in Ref. (17). Alternatively, if
mass-transport limitation is absent, model evaluations would be
greatly simplified.

From the above outline, the mass-transport problem is seen to
consist of coupled boundary value problems (in gas and aqueous
phase) with an interfacial boundary condition. Cloud droplets are
sufficiently sparse (typical separation is of order 100 drop radii)
that drops may be treated as independent. For cloud droplets
(diameter ~5 µm to ~40 µm) both gas- and aqueous-phase mass-
transport are dominated by molecular diffusion. The flux across
the interface is given by the molecular collision rate times an
accommodation coefficient ($\alpha \leq 1$) that represents the fraction of
collisions leading to transfer of material across the interface.
Magnitudes of mass-accommodation coefficients are not well known
generally and this holds especially in the case of solute gases
upon aqueous solutions. For this reason α is treated as an adjust-
able parameter, and we examine the values of α for which interfacial mass-transport limitation is significant. Values of α in
the range 10^{-6} to 1 have been assumed in recent studies (e.g.,
18). As noted below, recent experimental studies have yielded
measurements of this important quantity for systems of interest in
cloud chemistry.

Solution of the coupled mass-transport and reaction problem
for arbitrary chemical kinetic rate laws is possible only by numer-
ical methods. The problem is greatly simplified by decoupling the
time dependence of mass-transport from that of chemical kinetics;
the mass-transport solutions rapidly relax to a pseudo steady state
in view of the small dimensions of the system (19). The gas-phase
diffusion problem may be solved parametrically in terms of the net
flux into the drop. In the case of first-order or pseudo-first-
order chemical kinetics an analytical solution to the problem of
coupled aqueous-phase diffusion and reaction is available (19).
These solutions, together with the interfacial boundary condition,
specify the concentration profile of the reagent gas. In turn the
extent of departure of the reaction rate from that corresponding to
saturation may be determined. Finally criteria have been developed
(17,19) by which it may be ascertained whether or not there is
appreciable (e.g., 10%) limitation to the rate of reaction as a
consequence of the finite rate of mass transport. These criteria
are listed in Table 1.

Examination of Mass-Transport Limitation. The availability of
criteria for mass-transport limitation allows examination of the
importance of such limitation in representative situations. This
is conveniently achieved by means of graphs, as shown in Figures 9
and 10 for the S(IV)-O$_3$ and S(IV)-H$_2$O$_2$ reactions, respectively.
Here the inequalities in Table 1 are represented as lines in a
plane whose coordinates are log $k^{(1)}$ and log H (or log H*).
Each of the several criteria thus appears as a straight line in
this plane. The sense of the figure is that mass-transport limitation is absent (i.e., <10%) for points ($k^{(1)}$, H) below and/or to
the left of the lines denoting the inequalities. In the figure,
two lines are indicated for each inequality, corresponding to 10
and 30 µm diameter, since the inequalities are parametrically
dependent on drop size. Also, for interfacial mass-transport, the

Table I

Criteria for Absence of Mass-Transport
Limitation

Gas Phase $\qquad Hk^{(1)} \leq \varepsilon \dfrac{3\ D_g}{RT\ a^2}$

Interface $\qquad Hk^{(1)} \leq \varepsilon \dfrac{3\ \bar{v}\alpha}{4a\ RT}$

Aqueous Phase $\qquad k^{(1)} \leq 15\varepsilon \dfrac{D_a}{a^2}$

- ε: Maximum tolerable mass-transport limitation
- H: Henry's law or effective Henry's law coefficient
- $k^{(1)}$: Pseudo first-order rate coefficient
- a: Drop radius
- $\bar{v}$: Mean molecular speed
- α: Mass accommodation coefficient
- D_g: Gas-phase diffusion coefficient
- D_a: Aqueous-phase diffusion coefficient

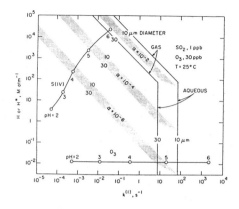

Figure 9. Examination of mass-transport limitation in O_3-S(IV) reaction. Solid lines indicate onset of appreciable (10%) gas- and aqueous-phase mass transport limitation for 10 µm and 30 µm diameter drops; hatched bands indicate onset of appreciable interfacial mass-transport limitation, also for 10 to 30 µm diameter drops. Mass-transport limitation is absent for points $(k^{(1)}, H)$ below and to the left of indicated bounds.

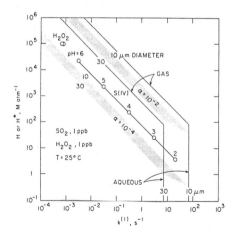

Figure 10. Examination of mass-transport limitation in H_2O_2-S(IV) reaction. As in Figure 9.

several bands represent different assumed values of mass-accommodation coefficient α.

For a given reaction, e.g., the O_3-S(IV) reaction, Figure 9, mass-transport limitation must be examined for each reagent and, since SO_2 solubility and reaction rate coefficients are pH-dependent, as a function of pH. We first consider mass-transport limitation of O_3. For this we assume an SO_2 concentration of 1 ppb. This concentration, together with S(IV) solubility (Figure 3) and second order rate coefficient $k^{(2)}$ (Figure 5) defines a pH-dependent $k^{(1)} = k^{(2)}H^*_{S(IV)}$ p_{SO_2} that constitutes the abscissa of the point to be plotted. The ordinate of the point is H_{O_3}, which is independent of pH. The points $(k^{(1)}, H_{O_3})$ as a function of pH generate a curve in the plane, in this case a horizontal line. These points can be compared to the several bounds indicative of the occurrence of appreciable mass-transport limitation. This comparison indicates mass-transport limitation for 10 μm drops at pH ≥ 5.3 and for 30 μm drops at pH ≥ 4.7. Interfacial mass-transport limitation also is indicated at about the same pH for α as low as 10^{-6}. Thus, one must take cognizance of this mass-transport limitation (by the methods of Ref. 17) in evaluations pertinent to these circumstances, but can assume saturation of O_3 at pH values lower than 4.7. Note, however, that for higher values of SO_2 concentration the values of $k^{(1)}$ shift to the right, shifting the onset of mass-transport limitation to lower pH values. A similar analysis for SO_2 is also shown on the figure. In this case (assumed O_3 concentration 30 ppb) gas-phase mass-transport limitation is indicated only for pH ≥ 5.9. However, if α is as low as 10^{-6} or 10^{-4} interfacial mass-transport limitation would become appreciable at pH 4 and 5, respectively.

Examination of mass-transport limitation to the H_2O_2-S(IV) reaction is given in Figure 10 for assumed concentration of each reagent of 1 ppb. This examination indicates no gas-phase limitation, and aqueous-phase limitation only at quite low pH (≤ 2.5). Interfacial limitation would be appreciable only for values of α $\leq 10^{-3}$.

The conclusions drawn from this analysis may be summarized as follows:

1. Gas- and aqueous-phase mass-transport limitation to the rate of either the O_3-S(IV) or the H_2O_2-S(IV) reaction is for the most part not appreciable but may be appreciable under some conditions of pH and/or reagent concentration.

2. Interfacial mass-transport limitation may or may not be substantial depending on values of the pertinent mass-accommodation coefficients. However, for mass-accommodation coefficients $\geq 10^{-3}$, little or no mass-transport limitation is indicated for most conditions.

Accommodation Coefficient Measurements. Recently Lee and Tang (20) have presented measurements of the accommodation coefficients of O_3 and SO_2 on aqueous solution. In the case of O_3 a value of 5 x 10^{-4} is reported. It is seen by examination of Figure 9 that an accommodation coefficient of this magnitude is well above the value that would lead to interfacial mass-transport limitation under circumstances of interest, intersecting the O_3 line only at pH >6, well

beyond the onset of aqueous-phase mass-transport limitation. For
SO_2 only a lower limit to the accommodation coefficient has been
determined, viz., $\alpha \geq 2 \times 10^{-3}$. However even this value is sufficiently great to rule out mass-transport limitation under most
circumstances of interest. Thus, the $S(IV)$ curve in Figure 9 (O_3
reaction) crosses the $\alpha = 2 \times 10^{-3}$ interfacial bound only at pH
5.7, and in Figure 10 (H_2O_2 reaction) lies entirely below this
bound.

Evidently no information is available pertinent to the mass-
accommodation coefficient of H_2O_2 on aqueous solution that would
permit assessment of the role of interfacial mass-transport limitation of this important reaction.

Nitrogen Oxide Reactions. Examination of possible aqueous-phase
reactions of nitrogen dioxide and peroxyacetyl nitrate has revealed
no reactions of importance to cloud chemistry ([21,22]). This situation is a consequence of the low solubilities and/or low reactivities of these gases with substances expected to be present in
cloudwater, although studies with actual precipitation samples
would be valuable in confirming this supposition. NO_2 has been
shown ([23]) to react with dissolved $S(IV)$, but the details of the
mechanism and rate of this reaction remain to be elucidated.

An in-cloud reaction of importance at night and possible also
during the day is the uptake of nitric acid by gas-phase reactions
$$NO_2 + O_3 \longrightarrow NO_3 + O_2$$
$$NO_3 + NO_2 \longrightarrow N_2O_5$$
followed by uptake of N_2O_5 and/or NO_3 by cloudwater and aqueous-
phase reaction ([24,25]). Quantitative evaluation of the rate of
this process awaits determination of the solubility and reactivity
of NO_3 and N_2O_5 as well as determination of mass-accommodation
coefficients.

Field Measurements

Field measurements, in addition to providing concentrations and
other situational data necessary for kinetic evaluations, also
allow inferences to be drawn about the occurrence of chemical reactions in clouds. Such inferences include the following:
1. Greater acidity of cloudwater (measured by the ratio
   $[H^+]/([NO_3^-] + 2[SO_4^=])$ or $[H^+]/[NH_4^+]$) than in corresponding
   clear-air ([26]) is indicative of the occurrence of acid formation by in-cloud reaction.
2. Greater fractional conversion of SO_2 to cloudwater sulfate than
   of NO_2 to cloudwater nitrate ([27]) is indicative of more extensive in-cloud oxidation of SO_2 than of NO_2.
3. An apparent mutual exclusivity of gas-phase SO_2 and aqueous
   H_2O_2 observed in non-precipitating liquid-water stratiform
   clouds, i.e., one or the other species present but never both
   at appreciable concentrations ([27]), is consistent with the
   H_2O_2-$S(IV)$ reaction proceeding to completion in such clouds.
These inferences from field measurements provide support for the
applicability of evaluations of cloud chemistry based upon laboratory studies.

Conclusions

Techniques are at hand to evaluate the rates of aqueous-phase acid formation reactions in clouds. Such evaluations indicate that oxidation of SO_2 by H_2O_2 and O_3 can be important in-cloud reactions for assumed representative reagent concentrations and other conditions. Rapid aqueous-phase reactions do not appear to be indicated for oxidation of nitrogen oxides to nitric acid.

Acknowledgments

This work was supported by the National Acid Precipitation Assessment program through the PRECP project funded by the U.S. Department of Energy and was performed under the auspices of the United States Department of Energy under Contract No. DE-AC02-76CH00016.

Literature Cited

1. Calvert, J. G.; Stockwell, W. R. Acid generation in the troposphere by gas-phase chemistry. Environ. Sci. Technol. 1983, 17, 428A-442A.
2. Calvert, J. G.; Stockwell, W. R. Mechanism and rates of the gas-phase oxidations of sulfur dioxide and nitrogen oxides in the atmosphere. In SO_2, NO and NO_2 Oxidation Mechanisms: Atmospheric Considerations; Calvert, J. G., Ed.; Butterworth: Boston, 1984; pp. 1-62.
3. Twomey, S. Atmospheric Aerosols; Elsevier: Amsterdam, 1977; pp. 143-164.
4. Levine, S. Z.; Schwartz, S. E. In-cloud and below-cloud scavenging of nitric acid vapor. Atmos. Environ. 1982, 16, 1725-1734.
5. For a discussion of cloud microphysical properties see e.g. Pruppacher, H. R. and Klett, J. D. Microphysics of Clouds and Precipitation; D. Reidel: Dordrecht, 1978.
6. Ho, W. W.; Hidy, G. M.; Govan, R. M. Microwave measurements of the liquid water content of atmospheric aerosols. In Advances in Environmental Science and Technology; Hidy, G. M. et al., Eds.; Wiley: New York, 1980; Vol. 9, pp. 215-236.
7. Schwartz, S. E.; White, W. H. Kinetics of reactive dissolution of nitrogen oxides into aqueous solution. In Advances in Environmental Science and Technology; Schwartz, S. E., Ed.; Wiley: New York, 1983: Vol. 12, pp. 1-116.
8. Penkett, S. A.; Jones, B. M. R.; Brice, K. A.; Eggleton, A. E. J. The importance of atmospheric ozone and hydrogen peroxide in oxidising sulphur dioxide in cloud and rainwater. Atmos. Environ. 1979, 13, 123-137.
9. Erickson, R. E.; Yates, L. M.; Clark, R. L.; McEwen, D. The reaction of sulfur dioxide with ozone in water and its possible atmospheric significance. Atmos. Environ. 1977, 11, 813-817.
10. Schwartz, S. E. Gas-Aqueous Reactions of Sulfur and Nitrogen Oxides in Liquid-Water Clouds. In SO_2, NO and NO_2 Oxidation Mechanisms: Atmospheric Considerations; Calvert, J. G., Ed.; Butterworth: Boston, 1984; pp. 173-208.

11. For a recent review see Calvert, J. G.; Lazrus, A.; Kok, G. L.; Heikes, B. G.; Walega, J. G.; Lind, J.; Cantrell, C. A. Chemical mechanisms of acid generation in the troposphere. Nature 1985, 317, 27-38.

12. Kok, G. L.; Heikes B. G.; Lazrus, A. L. Gas and aqueous phase measurements of hydrogen peroxide. Symposium on Acid Rain: I. Sources and Atmospheric Processes, Division of Petroleum Chemistry, Inc.; American Chemical Society, preprints, 1986, Vol. 31, No. 2, pp. 541-544.

13. Heikes, B. G.; Kok, G. L.; Lazrus, A. L.; Walega, J. G. H_2O_2, O_3 and SO_2 measurements in the lower troposphere over the eastern U.S.A. during fall. J. Geophys. Res. 1987, in press.

14. Tanner, R. L.; Markovits, G. Y.; Ferreri, E. M.; Kelly, T. J. Sampling and determination of gas-phase hydrogen peroxide following removal of ozone by gas-phase reaction with nitric oxide. Anal. Chem. 1986, 58, 1857-1865.

15. Kelly, T. J.; Daum, P. H.; Schwartz, S. E. Measurements of peroxides in cloudwater and rain. J. Geophys. Res. 1985, 90, 7861-7871.

16. Lee, Y.-N.; Shen, J.; Klotz, P. J.; Schwartz, S. E.; Newman, L. Kinetics of the hydrogen peroxide-sulfur(IV) reaction in rainwater collected at a northeastern U.S. site. J. Geophys. Res. 1986, 91, 13264-13274.

17. Schwartz, S. E. Mass-transport considerations pertinent to aqueous-phase reactions of gases in liquid-water clouds. In Chemistry of Multiphase Atmospheric Systems; Jaeschke, W., Ed.; Springer: Heidelberg, 1985; pp. 415-471.

18. Chameides, W. L. The photochemistry of a remote marine stratiform cloud. J. Geophys. Res. 1984, 89, 4739-4755.

19. Schwartz, S. E. and Freiberg, J. E. "Mass-transport limitation to the rate of reaction of gases in liquid droplets: Application to oxidation of SO_2 in aqueous solutions. Atmos. Environ. 1981, 15, 1129-1144.

20. Tang, I. N.; Lee, J. H. Accommodation coefficients of ozone and sulfur dioxide: Their implications on SO_2 oxidation in cloud water. American Chemical Society Symposium Series, 1987; this volume.

21. Lee, Y.-N.; Schwartz, S. E. Evaluation of the rate of uptake of nitrogen dioxide by atmospheric and surface liquid water. J. Geophys. Res. 1981, 86, 11971-11983.

22. Lee, Y.-N. Atmospheric aqueous-phase reactions of nitrogen species; Kinetics of some aqueous-phase reactions of peroxyacetyl nitrate. Conference on Gas-Liquid Chemistry of Natural Waters; Brookhaven National Laboratory, 1984; BNL 51757, Papers 20, 21.

23. Lee, Y.-N.; Schwartz, S. E. Kinetics of oxidation of aqueous sulfur(IV) by nitrogen dioxide. In Precipitation Scavenging, Dry Deposition, and Resuspension; Pruppacher, H. R., Semonin, R. G., Slinn, W. G. N., Eds.; Elsevier: New York, 1983; pp. 453-470.

24. Heikes, B. G.; Thompson, A. M. Effects of heterogeneous processes on NO_3, HONO, and HNO_3 chemistry in the troposphere. J. Geophys. Res. 1983, 88, 10883-10895.

25. Chameides, W. L. The possible role of NO₃ in the nighttime
     chemistry of a cloud. J. Geophys. Res. 1985, 91, 5331-5337.
26. Daum, P. H.; Schwartz, S. E.; Newman, L. Acidic and related
     constituents in liquid water stratiform clouds. J. Geophys.
     Res. 1984, 89, 1447-1458.
27. Daum, P. H.; Kelly, T. J.; Schwartz, S. E.; Newman, L.
     Measurements of the chemical composition of stratiform clouds.
     Atmos. Environ. 1984, 18, 2671-2684.
28. Schwartz, S. E. Chemical conversions in clouds. Aerosols:
     Research, Risk Assessment and Control Strategies; Lee, S. D.,
     Schneider, T., Grant, L. D., Verkerk, P. J., Eds.; Lewis:
     Chelsea, MI, 1986; pp. 349-375.
29. Overton, J. H., Jr. Validation of the Hoffmann and Edwards'
     S(IV)-H₂O₂ Mechanism. Atmos. Environ. 1985, 19, 687-690.
30. Hoigné, J.; Bader, H.; Haag, W. R.; Staehelin, J. Rate con-
     stants of reactions of ozone with organic and inorganic com-
     pounds in water-III. Water Res. 1985, 19, pp. 993-1004.
31. Martin, L. R. Kinetic studies of sulfite oxidation in aqueous
     solution. In SO₂, NO and NO₂ Oxidation Mechanisms: Atmo-
     spheric Considerations; Calvert, J. G., Ed.; Butterworth:
     Boston, 1984; pp. 63-100.

RECEIVED May 15, 1987

Chapter 9

Accommodation Coefficients of Ozone and SO₂: Implications on SO₂ Oxidation in Cloud Water

I. N. Tang and J. H. Lee

Environmental Chemistry Division, Brookhaven National Laboratory, Upton, NY 11973

Interfacial mass transfer of trace gases into aqueous pnase is investigated in a UV absorption-stop flow apparatus. For the first time, the mass accommodation coefficients are determined for O_3 (5.3×10^{-4}) and for SO_2 ($> 2 \times 10^{-2}$). The results are incorporated into a simple model considering the coupled interfacial mass transfer and aqueous chemistry in cloud drops. It is shown that dissolution of O_3 into a drop is fast compared with its subsequent oxidation of dissolved SO_2. In addition, the conversion rate of $S(IV)$ to $S(VI)$ in aqueous drops by ozone reactions is not limited by interfacial resistance.

Interfacial mass transfer is an important consideration in many dynamic processes involving the transport of a gaseous species across a gas-liquid interface. In particular the rate of trace gas incorporation into aqueous drops in the atmosphere has recently received much attention because of its relevance to acid precipitation (1,2). In the present paper, mass accommodation coefficient measurements are reported for O_3 and SO_2 on water surfaces, using an UV absorption-stop flow technique. The results are incorporated into a simple model considering the coupled interfacial mass transfer and aqueous chemistry in aqueous drops. Some implications of the measured accommodation coefficients on the oxidation of SO_2 by O_3 in cloud water are discussed.

Experimental

A detailed description of the apparatus shown in Figure 1 and the experimental procedure will be given elsewhere. Here, it suffices to summarize as follows. The experiments were carried out in a thermostated reaction cell constructed of a rectangular Pyrex tube, 4 cm x 8 cm in cross section and 38 cm in length, and placed with its

length in a horizontal position. The cell was equipped with an optical window on either end, gas inlet and outlet on the top, and liquid
inlet and outlet on the bottom. Liquid water was circulated through
the lower portion of the cell by an all-Teflon diaphragm pump,
whereas trace quantities of O_3 or SO_2 in a humidified carrier gas was
flowing concurrently in the upper space. The system was designed to
operate at low pressure, therefore, very precise flow and pressure
controls were essential to maintain the required stability during an
experiment.

An UV light beam, obtained with an intensity-regulated deuterium
lamp and a narrow-slit monochromator, passed through the gas phase
between two perfectly aligned pin holes mounted in front of the optical windows. An EMR 541-N PM tube, with an appropriate interference
filter placed immediately before it, was used in conjunction with
associated electronics to continuously monitor the UV intensity as a
means of measuring changes in concentration of the reagent gas.

In a typical experiment, the system was pumped down to a specified total pressure, and at the same time the flow rates of the
aqueous phase and the humidified carrier gas were carefully adjusted
to maintain a stable flow. O_3 or SO_2 from a reservoir was leaked
into the carrier gas through a precision needle valve. As soon as a
steady light intensity was obtained, two solenoid valves on the gas
inlet and outlet of the reaction cell were closed and a third solenoid valve on the by-pass line opened. The gas phase in the reaction
cell became stagnant and the light intensity increased with time as
the reagent gas was being absorbed into the aqueous phase.

Results and Discussion

System Analysis. Because of the simplified cell geometry and well-
defined operating conditions, a one-dimensional mathematical model is
adequate for describing the mass transport in the gas phase. The
differential equation is given by

$$\frac{\partial C}{\partial t} = D \frac{\partial^2 C}{\partial y^2} \tag{1}$$

where C is the reagent gas concentration at time t, y the vertical
coordinate expressing the distance between the glass wall ($y = 0$) and
the gas-liquid interface ($y = \ell$). The initial condition is represented by

$$C = C_0, \text{ at } t = 0; \ 0 \leq y \leq \ell \tag{2}$$

and the boundary conditions are

$$\frac{\partial C}{\partial y} = 0, \text{ at } y = 0; \ t > 0 \tag{3}$$

and

$$-D \frac{\partial C}{\partial y} = (\frac{\alpha \bar{v}}{4})C, \text{ at } y = \ell; \ t > 0 \tag{4}$$

Here, D is the diffusivity of the reagent gas in the gaseous medium, $\bar{V}$ the mean molecular speed of a Maxwell-Boltzmann gas, and α the mass accommodation coefficient. The standard solution is readily obtained (3) as follows:

$$\frac{C(t,y)}{C_o} = \sum_{n=1}^{\infty} \frac{2L\cos(\beta_n y/\ell)}{(L^2 + L + \beta_n^2)\cos\beta_n} \exp\left(-\frac{\beta_n^2 D}{\ell^2}\right) t \tag{5}$$

where β_n are positive roots of the equation

$$\beta\tan\beta = L = \frac{\alpha \bar{V} \ell}{4D} \tag{6}$$

Equation (5) indicates that by monitoring the gas concentration change as a function of time, the accommodation coefficient may be deduced using a computer program. However, precautions must be undertaken to satisfy the boundary condition that the surface concentration of the dissolved gas must be negligible at all times. This can be accomplished in principle by agitation and by addition of proper chemical reagents in the aqueous phase to remove the dissolved gas as quickly as it is absorbed. In addition, the system must be operated at sufficiently low pressure so that the gas-phase resistance is much smaller than interfacial resistance.

Results. For O$_3$, experiments were made with both nitrogen and helium as carrier gas in the pressure range of 29 to 85 torr, covering an effective diffusivity range of 1.46 to 5.61 cm^2/sec. Data were taken at three different temperatures, namely, 0, 10 and 19°C. The effects of added chemical reagent on the apparent accommodation coefficient, α_a, were studied using pure water, NaOH and Na$_2$SO$_3$ solutions. As shown in Figure 2, the decay of O$_3$ with time under a given condition behaves as expected from the mathematical solution and is quite reproducible.

In pure water, as shown in Figure 3, α_a has a small value of 1.7×10^{-7} as a result of the water surface being quickly saturated by O$_3$. It increases only slightly to a value of 6×10^{-7} by the addition of 0.05N NaOH, indicating the slow reaction of OH$^-$ with dissolved O$_3$. However, α_a increases dramatically to a value of 4.5×10^{-5} upon adding only 8×10^{-4}M Na$_2$SO$_3$. It continues to increase with increasing Na$_2$SO$_3$ concentrations until it levels off at a value of $(5.3 \pm 0.4) \times 10^{-4}$, where the errors represent one standard deviation evaluated from a total of 79 measurements in the plateau region as shown in Figure 3. The fact that α_a no longer changes with sulfite concentration indicates that an ultimate or true value of accommodation coefficient for O$_3$ on water surfaces has now been reached.

Similar experiments were carried out with SO$_2$ in helium carrier gas. Preliminary results indicated that α_a increased from ∼5×10^{-5} in pure water to ∼2×10^{-4} in 0.05N NaOH solution. These values of α_a are about two orders of magnitude larger than those of O$_3$ under identical experimental conditions. When 0.2% H$_2$O$_2$ solution (at pH = 13) was used, α_a increased to about 1×10^{-3}. Further experiments with solutions of higher H$_2$O$_2$ concentrations showed that the mass accommodation coefficient of SO$_2$ would be greater than 2×10^{-3}. No higher

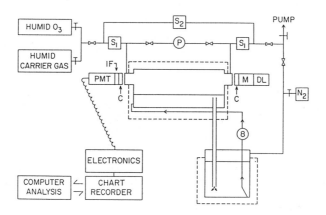

Figure 1. Schematic Diagram of the Apparatus.

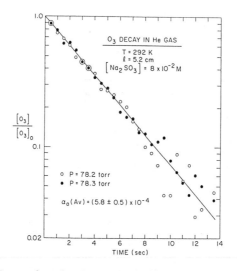

Figure 2. O_3 decay in helium carrier gas.

values could be obtained for SO_2 since H_2O_2 at high concentrations decomposed excessively on vessel walls, thereby interfering with the measurement. However, it was discovered that NaClO was a very effective reagent for SO_2 oxidation in aqueous solutions. Using NaClO, the value of α_a for SO_2 increased to 2×10^{-2} and possibly higher. The final value could not be measured with good precision since diffusional processes also became important in controlling mass transport rates at such high α_a values. Therefore, 2×10^{-2} represents the lower bounds of α_a for SO_2.

Model Studies. The oxidation of dissolved SO_2 in water has been the subject of numerous studies in the past decade, and its atmospheric significance regarding acid precipitation needs no further elaboration here. However, most of the earlier studies (4-7) have been devoted to aqueous chemistry only. Recently, Schwartz and Freiberg (8) have considered the importance of mass transfer processes in limiting the S(IV) oxidation rates in aqueous drops. Chameides (9) has made a rather comprehensive model study of the photochemistry of a stratiform cloud in a remote region of the marine atmosphere. He concludes that the rate of SO_2 conversion to sulfuric acid is sensitive to a variety of parameters including the accommodation coefficients of the reagent gases such as SO_2, H_2O_2, HO_2 and OH. Unfortunately, however, no accommodation coefficient measurements have been reported in the literature for these gases.

It would, therefore, be interesting to examine how important the newly measured accommodation coefficients would be in the conversion of S(IV) to S(VI) in a water droplet. A simple model is set up, which considers only aqueous chemistry and gas-phase mass transfer of O_3 and SO_2 to a cloud droplet. At $t = 0$, the droplet is exposed to an atmosphere containing constant concentrations of SO_2 and O_3. The aqueous concentrations of S(IV) and S(VI) are then calculated as a function of time.

The chemical reactions considered in the model are listed in Table I, together with the appropriate constants used in the calculation. The rate expression for gas-phase mass transfer is given by

$$\frac{dC}{dt} = \frac{3D\gamma}{a^2RT} (p_s - p_a) \tag{7}$$

where a is the droplet radius, R the gas constant, T the absolute temperature, p_s the partial pressure of the reagent gas in the bulk gas phase and p_a at the droplet surface. Here, p_a is related to the Henry's law constant, H, by

$$p_a = \frac{C}{H} \tag{8}$$

and γ, a kinetic correction factor to the Maxwell's equation ($\gamma = 1$), can be evaluated by one of the several expressions proposed in the literature (10). For practical purposes, however, these expressions yield very similar values. Consequently, the following expression due to Fukuta and Walter (11) was used in the present study:

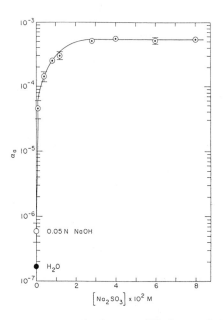

Figure 3. Apparent accommodation coefficient of O_3 as a function of Na_2SO_3 concentration in aqueous solution.

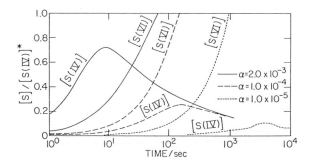

Figure 4. Conversion of S(IV) to S(VI) in droplet by ozone oxidation.

Table I. SO2 Oxidation by Ozone in Droplet

Reactions	Equilibrium, Rate, Solubility Constants	References
$O_3(g) \rightleftharpoons O_3(aq)$	$H_1 = 1.15\times10^{-2} \exp[2360(1/T - 1/298)]$ M atm^{-1}	NBS
$O_3(aq) + HSO_3^- \;\text{-->}\; HSO_4^- + O_2$	$k_2 = 1.0\times10^{14} \exp(-11000/RT)M^{-1}$ sec^{-1}	(4)
$O_3(aq) + SO_3^= \;\text{-->}\; SO_4^= + O_2$	$k_3 = 1.0\times10^{17} \exp(-10,500/RT)M^{-1}$ sec^{-1}	(4)
$SO_2(g) \rightleftharpoons SO_2(aq)$	$H_4 = 1.23 \exp[3120(1/T - 1/298)]M$ atm^{-1}	NBS
$SO_2(aq) + H_2O \rightleftharpoons HSO_3^- + H^+$	$K_5 = 1.7\times10^{-2} \exp[2090(1/T - 1/298)]M$	NBS
$HSO_3^- \rightleftharpoons SO_3^= + H^+$	$K_6 = 6\times10^{-8} \exp[1120(1/T = 1/298)]M$	NBS
$HSO_4^- \rightleftharpoons SO_4^= + H^+$	$K_7 = \exp[2.3026(-475.14/T + 5.0435 - 0.018222T)]M$	ES
$H_2O \rightleftharpoons H^+ + OH^-$	$K_w = 1\times10^{-14} \exp[-6716(1/T - 1/298)]M$	NBS

NBS: National Bureau of Standards Technical Note 270-1, 1965.
ES: "Electrolyte Solutions" by R.A. Robinson and R.H. Stokes," Butterworth and Co., Ltd., 1959.

$$\gamma = \frac{a}{a + (4D/\bar{V}\alpha)} \qquad (9)$$

Note that the term containing α in the denominator accounts for interfacial resistance.

Equation (7) was combined with appropriate chemical reaction rate expressions to yield a set of coupled differential equations expressing rates of change in the dissolved O_3 and S(IV) concentrations. The equations were then solved numerically with the usual constraints of electroneutrality and the appropriate ionic equilibria given in Table I.

Figure 4 shows the results of a case calculation performed for the following conditions: $a = 10$ μm; $T = 283$ K; $p(O_3) = 300$ ppb; $p(SO_2) = 1$ ppb; $\alpha(O_3) = 5 \times 10^{-4}$; $\alpha(SO_2) = 2 \times 10^{-3}$, 1×10^{-4}, 1×10^{-5}; and initial droplet pH = 7. In Figure 4 [S(IV)]* is the saturation molar concentration of S(IV) in the absence of O_3 and, therefore, the curves represent the time evolution of [S(IV)] and [S(VI)] normalized to [S(IV)]* solely for the convenience of comparing and plotting the calculated results.

It is interesting to observe that in all cases [S(IV)] always rises to a peak and then falls off gradually. In contrast, [S(VI)] continues to increase as the oxidation reaction goes on. It indicates a dynamic process in which the stationary-state concept does not seem to apply to the sulfur species. On the contrary, the calculation (results not shown here) indicates that the droplet quickly becomes saturated with dissolved O_3 and, shortly after, maintains a steady-state $[O_3]$ close to saturation for a long time, even though the accommodation coefficient of O_3 used in the calculation is as low as the measured value, 5×10^{-4}. In addition, the effect of interfacial SO_2 mass transfer on oxidation is not considered appreciable since the curves calculated for $\alpha(SO_2) = 1$ are almost identical to those calculated for $\alpha(SO_2) = 2 \times 10^{-3}$. Only when $\alpha(SO_2)$ is substantially smaller than the measured lower limit of 2×10^{-2} is there a noticeable difference between curves. Note that the time scales shown in Figure 4 depend upon the gas-phase concentrations chosen for a particular case study.

Conclusion

The mass accommodation coefficients have been measured for the first time for O_3 and SO_2 on water surfaces. Model studies using the measured accommodation coefficients indicate that the conversion rate of S(IV) to S(VI) in aqueous drops by ozone reactions is not limited by interfacial resistance.

Acknowledgments

The authors would like to thank Dr. S. E. Schwartz for many helpful comments and suggestions. The encouragement and enthusiasm expressed by Dr. L. Newman throughout the work are deeply appreciated. This research was performed under the auspices of the U.S. Department of Energy under Contract No. DE-AC02-765CH00016.

Literature Cited

1. Chameides, W. L.; Davis, D. D. J. Geophy. Res. 1982, 87, 4863-77.
2. Schwartz, S. E. In Chemistry of Multiphase Atmospheric Systems; Jaeschke, W., Ed.; Springer-Verlag; Berlin, 1986; p. 415.
3. Carslaw, H. S.; Jaeger, J. C. Conduction of Heat in Solids, 2nd Ed., Oxford University Press; Oxford, 1959, p. 491.
4. Erickson, R. E.; Yates, L. M.; Clark, R. L.; McEwen, D. Atm. Environ. 1977, 11, p. 813-17.
5. Larson, T. V.; Horike, N. R.; Harrison, H. Atm. Environ. 1978, 12, 1597-611.
6. Penkett, S. A.; Jones, B. M. R.; Brice, K. A.; Eggleton, A. E. J. Atm. Environ. 1979, 13, 123-37.
7. Moller, D. Atm. Environ. 1980, 14, 1067-76.
8. Schwartz, S. E.; Freiberg, J. E. Atm. Environ. 1981, 15, 1129-44.
9. Chameides, W. L. J. Geophy. Res. 1984, 89, 4739-55.
10. Wagner, P.E. In Aerosol Microphysics II; Marlow, W. H. Ed.; Springer-Verlag; Berlin, 1986; p. 129.
11. Fukuta, N.; Walter, L. A. J. Atm. Sci. 1970, 27, 1160-72.

RECEIVED May 13, 1987

KINETICS

Chapter 10

Photocatalytic Formation of Hydrogen Peroxide

Detlef W. Bahnemann[1], Michael R. Hoffmann, Andrew P. Hong,
and Claudius Kormann

W. M. Keck Laboratories, California Institute of Technology, Pasadena, CA 91125

The two-electron reduction of molecular oxygen to
hydrogen peroxide can be catalyzed by metal oxide
semiconductor particles in the presence of visible
and near-UV light. Even though very high quantum
yields for this process are observed, rather low
steady-state concentrations of H_2O_2 are reached.
Detailed mechanisms are presented to explain these
experimental findings. Metal oxide particles are
found in atmospheric and surface waters. The
environmental significance of photocatalytic
formation of H_2O_2 on these particles in natural
systems is discussed.

Hydrogen peroxide, H_2O_2, is one of the most powerful oxidants in
haze aerosols, clouds, and hydrometeors at low pH ([1]). A major
pathway for the formation of sulfuric acid in humid atmospheres
below pH 5 seems to be the oxidation of sulfur dioxide by H_2O_2
([2-4]). Hydrometeor concentrations of hydrogen peroxide as high as
50 μM have recently been reported by Kok and co-workers ([5-7]),
while typical atmospheric H_2O_2 levels up to 5 ppb have been
predicted from Henry's law calculations ([8,9]). Various sources
for the production of H_2O_2 in the atmosphere have been proposed:
it can be generated in the gas phase by the combination of
hydroperoxyl radicals, $HO_2 \cdot$ ([10]), at the air-water interface due
to photoinduced redox processes ([11]), and in the aqueous phase via
photo-catalyzed reactions with humic/fulvic acid and green algae
as mediators (Zepp, R. G., EPA Environmental Research Laboratory
at Athens, personal communication). Furthermore , $HO_2 \cdot$ radicals

[1]Permanent address: Hahn-Meitner Institut, Bereich Strahlenchemie,
Glienicker Straße 100, D 1000 Berlin 39, Federal Republic of Germany

0097-6156/87/0349-0120$06.00/0

which are produced in the gas phase can be scavenged by the water droplets where they then form H_2O_2. This *in situ* generated hydrogen peroxide together with the H_2O_2 scavenged from the gas phase is thought to be the main source for the H_2O_2 accumulated in cloudwater droplets (10,12,13). Another very likely possibility for H_2O_2 production, however, has so far been neglected in the design of models for aerosol-, fog-, and cloudwater chemistry. Various metal oxides, some of which are very abundant in natural environments, have been shown to act as photocatalysts for a large variety of reactions (14), e.g., the photolysis of desert sands resulted in the production of ammonia from dinitrogen (15). Atmospheric particulate matter originates mainly from natural sources (721-1850 Tg yr^{-1} in 1979 globally) but also from man-made emissions (125-385 Tg yr^{-1} in 1982 in the USA) with iron, titanium, and zinc being some of the most abundant transition metals detected in ambient samples (16). These metals are present as hydroxides but also frequently as the respective oxides, depending upon the environmental conditions (17). Hence the present work addresses the question of hydrogen peroxide formation in aqueous solutions as catalyzed by metal oxides upon irradiation with visible and near-UV light.

Photocatalysis with Semiconductors

Many metal chalcogenides and oxides are known to be semiconductors. These materials can act as sensitizers for light-induced redox processes due to their electronic structure consisting of a valence band with filled molecular orbitals (MO's) and a conduction band with empty MO's. Absorption of a photon with an energy above the bandgap energy Eg generally leads to the formation of an electron/hole pair in the semiconductor particle (18):

$$\text{semiconductor} \quad \overset{h\nu}{\to} \quad e^-(cb) \quad + \quad h^+(vb) \tag{1}$$

In the absence of suitable scavengers, recombination occurs within a few nanoseconds (19). Valence band holes ($h^+(vb)$) have been shown to be powerful oxidants (20-23) whereas conduction band electrons ($e^-(cb)$) can act as reductants (24,25). The redox potentials of both, e^- and h^+, are determined by the relative position of the conduction and valence band, respectively. Bandgap positions are material constants which have been determined for a wide variety of semiconductors (26). Most materials show "Nernstian" behavior which results in a shift of the surface potential by 59 mV in the negative direction with a pH increase of $\Delta pH = 1$. Consequently electrons are better reductants in alkaline solutions while holes have a higher oxidation potential in the acid pH-range (26). Thus, with the right choice of semiconductor and pH, the redox potential of the $e^-(cb)$ can be varied from +0.5 to -1.5 V (vs. NHE) and that of the $h^+(vb)$ from +1.0 to more than +3.5 V. This sufficiently covers the full range of redox chemistry of the H_2O/O_2 system (27).

H_2O_2 can therefore be formed via two different pathways in an aerated aqueous solution provided $e^-(cb)$ and $h^+(vb)$ are generated:

$$O_2 + 2e^-(cb) + 2H^+_{aq} \rightarrow H_2O_2 \qquad (2)$$

$$2H_2O + 2h^+(vb) \rightarrow H_2O_2 + 2H^+_{aq} \qquad (3)$$

Reaction 2 has been studied in great detail (28–44) since Baur and Neuweiler (28) in 1927 observed the formation of H_2O_2 when they illuminated aqueous zinc oxide suspensions in the presence of glycerin and glucose which in turn were oxidized. Appreciable yields of hydrogen peroxide are detected only when appropriate electron donors, D, are added prior to illumination. This strongly indicates that it is the electron donor, D, which is adsorbed on the catalyst's surface and hence sacrificed via Reaction 4.

$$D + h^+(vb) \rightarrow D^+\cdot \qquad (4)$$

The presence of surficial D interferes with the e^-/h^+ recombination leaving $e^-(cb)$ (conduction band electrons) behind which then react with dioxygen via Reaction 2. Small quantities of H_2O_2 detected in the absence of added donors contained only oxygen atoms from O_2 as shown by labelling studies (34) which indicates the presence of contaminants in the semiconductor that are able to fill the $h^+(vb)$. Cadmium sulfide, CdSe, and ZnO showed the highest catalytic activity for dioxygen reduction (35,38). Titanium dioxide, on the other hand, which seems to be the material with the greatest potential for water splitting is reported to have negligable activity (35,41–43). The oxidation of water via Reaction 3, however, has not yet been demonstrated unambiguously. While Rao et al. (45) reported the formation of H_2O_2 in water splitting experiments on ZnO and TiO_2, Salvador and Decker (46) could not verify this observation. The intermediate production of H_2O_2 as the first molecular step of the four-hole oxidation of water to dioxygen has been predicted (46,47) and a variety of free radical intermediates have already been detected (48–50). Whenever the oxidation of H_2O is found to proceed with high yields there is no indication of hydrogen peroxide formation (51–54), but the dioxygen production seems to proceed via different intermediate peroxides as shown by Baur and Perret (51,52); they studied the photocatalytic formation of O_2 on ZnO in the presence of silver nitrate and observed the intermediate production of silver peroxides. In the case of TiO_2, the absence of detectable amounts of H_2O_2 and O_2 during water photoelectrolysis experiments has been explained with the well-documented adsorption and photo-uptake of these oxo-species by the material (55–71) and their incorporation into the molecular structure as peroxytitanates (68,72,73).

The above discussion indicates that a detailed study of the mechanism of the light-induced hydrogen peroxide production on various oxide surfaces is warranted in order to judge its potential environmental implications. Using a newly developed polarographic technique for the kinetic analysis of hydrogen peroxide concentrations with a sensitivity of 10^{-7} M, we present further insight into the photocatalytic formation and destruction of H_2O_2.

Experimental Details

Several catalysts were prepared from chemicals of highest available grade. Mechanistic studies were performed using colloidal dispersions of zinc oxide, ZnO, which contained particles with a mean diameter of 5 nm (Bahnemann, D. W.; Kormann, C.; Hoffmann, M. R. J. Phys. Chem. submitted 11/3/86). Suspensions of such small aggregates exhibit negligible light scattering properties and conventional spectroscopic techniques can be used to study ongoing reactions (74). The preparation of titanium dioxide particles, TiO_2, coated with cobalt(II)tetrasulfophthalocyanine, Co(II)TSP, has recently been reported (Hong, A. P.; Bahnemann, D. W.; Hoffmann, M. R. J. Phys. Chem. accepted for publication 12/12/86). These particles have a mean diameter of 30 nm with 30% of the surface area covered with Co(II)TSP. Desert sand obtained from Death Valley has been treated with several acid washing cycles and selected by size and weight (Kormann, C.; Bahnemann, D. W.; Hoffmann, M. R. unpublished data). The H_2O_2 concentration was measured continuously with a YSI-Clark 2510 Oxidase Probe connected to a YSI model 25 oxidase meter. The surface of the electrode was covered with a dialysis membrane (molecular weight cutoff 12,000 - 14,000) to prevent any interference caused by the catalyst particles. Equilibration times between 30 and 60 minutes were allowed to ensure a stable signal once the electrode was immersed into the reaction solution. Following equilibration, changes in H_2O_2 content were monitored at a sensitivity of 10^{-7} M and a time constant of 1 s. The electrode was calibrated following each kinetic experiment using a standard addition method; linear response was obtained between 10^{-7} and $2 \cdot 10^{-5}$ M H_2O_2. Since this polarographic method is sensitive to any species with a redox potential of 700 mV, different methods were used to verify the formation of hydrogen peroxide. Following the illumination an aliquot of the solution was taken and titrated with iodide in the presence of a catalyst (75,76) to form the I_3^- anion which was quantitatively measured by spectrophotometry ($\epsilon(352nm) = 26400$ M^{-1} cm^{-1}) (77). As a second check and when very small concentrations of H_2O_2 were detected with the polarographic method a very sensitive fluorometric determination (detection limit: $1.2 \cdot 10^{-8}$ M H_2O_2) was employed. This latter procedure involves the reaction of H_2O_2 with p-hydroxyphenylacetic acid in the presence of horseradish peroxidase to yield a product which fluoresces at 400 nm ($\lambda(ex) = 320$ nm) (78,79). Even though the polarographic method can not differentiate between H_2O_2 and other species with a similar electrochemical half-wave potential, the use of two alternative chemical analysis techniques eliminates such artifacts. Interferences by other chemicals such as ozone can also be excluded in this study since it is extremely unlikely that they should occur with all three methods to the same extend.

Figure 1 shows the expermental set-up for the photolysis studies. White light of a 450 W Xe lamp (Osram XBO) passes through a water filter, a monochromator (PRA B102) and an appropriate UV-filter before the continuously stirred sample is irradiated. The analog signal of the oxidase meter is amplified to give the right amplitude for the input of the A/D converter (MBC Dash 8) which digitizes the data and feeds them into an IBM PC/AT for kinetic analysis. Aberchrome 540 is used for the determination of the light flux to enable an absolute measurement of the quantum yields (80).

Results and Discussion

The formation of hydrogen peroxide upon the illumination of an air-saturated aqueous colloidal suspension of zinc oxide particles is shown in Figure 2. No H_2O_2 is produced when light energies below the bandgap energy of ZnO where employed (Eg(ZnO)= 3.4 eV or λ(ex) = 365 nm), e.g., λ(ex) = 400 nm. As the irradiation was performed at lower wavelengths, e.g., λ(ex) = 366 and 320 nm, the sudden increase of the signal from the polarographic analyzer indicated H_2O_2 formation with a wavelength-independent quantum yield of 6%. No hydrogen peroxide is formed or depleted in the absence of light. Prolonged illumination leads to the formation of a steady-state in $[H_2O_2]$ of $1.2 \cdot 10^{-4}$ M in irradiated samples. The quantum-yields ϕ determined from the initial slope of the $[H_2O_2]$ vs. time plots depended strongly on the oxygen-content of the solution: ϕ increased to 10% in O_2-saturated samples and decreased sharply below $2 \cdot 10^{-5}$ M O_2. No H_2O_2 is produced when anoxic solutions were irradiated. The following mechanism explains these observations. Electrons and holes are formed in the zinc oxide particles under bandgap irradiation (Reaction 1). Their recombination is prevented by the presence of 2 mM acetate ions which are strongly adsorbed onto the ZnO surface and are oxidized via:

$$CH_3COO^- \quad + \quad h^+(vb) \quad \rightarrow \quad (CH_3COO)^{\bullet} \tag{5}$$

$$(CH_3COO)^{\bullet} \quad \rightarrow \quad {}^{\bullet}CH_2COO^-/H^+_{aq} \quad and/or \quad {}^{\bullet}CH_3/CO_2 \tag{6}$$

The fate of the radicals produced via Reaction 6 is currently being investigated. Initial results indicate the formation of organic peroxides and suggest the intermediate formation of peroxy-radicals (Kormann, C.; Bahnemann, D. W.; Hoffmann, M. R. unpublished results). With the inhibition of charge recombination conduction band electrons are now available to reduce molecular oxygen yielding H_2O_2 (Reaction 2). The observed steady-state concentration of hydrogen peroxide can be understood as a competition between Reactions 2 and 7.

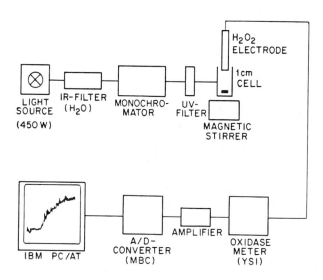

Figure 1.   Experimental configuration used for irradiations and hydrogen peroxide detection.

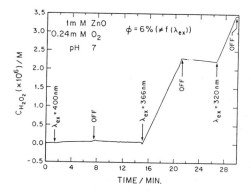

Figure 2. H_2O_2 formation upon illumination of an aqueous colloidal suspension of zinc oxide in the presence of 2 mM acetate (other exp. cond. are given in the figure).

$$H_2O_2 \qquad 2e^-(cb) \quad + \quad 2H^+_{aq} \quad \rightarrow \quad 2H_2O \qquad\qquad (7)$$

The value $[H_2O_2](ss) = 1.2 \cdot 10^{-4}$ M measured in air-saturated solutions ($[O_2](ss) = 2.4 \cdot 10^{-4}$ M) suggests that Reaction 7 is about twice as efficient as the initial dioxygen reduction.

H_2O_2 is also produced in the absence of hole scavengers provided the right catalyst is used. Figure 3 shows the formation of hydrogen peroxide upon bandgap illumination of an oxygenated aqueous suspension of TiO_2 coated with Co(II)TSP which acts as an electron relay to transfer $e^-(cb)$ onto O_2 (Hong, A. P.; Bahnemann, D. W.; Hoffmann, M. R. J. Phys. Chem. accepted for publication 12/12/86). It is clearly obvious from Figure 3 that the same steady-state concentration of H_2O_2 is reached once the system is perturbed by the addition of H_2O_2 during prolonged irradiation. As in the case of ZnO no formation or depletion of hydrogen peroxide is observed in the absence of light. An octahedrally coordinated surface complex, e.g., $Ti-O^--Co(III)TSP-O_2^-\cdot$, has been identified as the catalytically active species in the TiO_2-Co(II)TSP system. With dioxygen being bound in the form of superoxide, $O_2^-\cdot$, this complex proved to be extremely stable but acts as an effective acceptor for conduction band electrons produced upon irradiation of the bulk TiO_2:

$$Ti-O^--Co(III)TSP-O_2^-\cdot + e^-(cb) \rightarrow Ti-O^--Co(III)TSP-H_2O + H_2O_2 \quad (8)$$
$$+ 2 H^+_{aq}$$

The aquo complex formed in Reaction 8 readily accepts another $e^-(cb)$ to form a reduced metal center which then quickly reacts with O_2

$$Ti-O^--Co(II)TSP-H_2O + O_2 \rightarrow Ti-O^--Co(III)TSP-O_2^-\cdot \qquad (9)$$

yielding again the stable $O_2^-\cdot$ complex.

H_2O_2 is formed in quantum yields close to 50% by this reaction sequence. The observed net formation of H_2O_2 indicates that the valence band holes, $h^+(vb)$, are able to oxidize water via Reaction 3. The low steady-state concentrations $[H_2O_2](ss)$ which are reached during these experiments (5 - 25 μM depending on the nature of the catalyst) suggest that oxidation of H_2O_2 via

$$H_2O_2 \quad + \quad 2h^+(vb) \quad \rightarrow \quad O_2 \quad + \quad 2H^+_{aq} \qquad\qquad (10)$$

efficiently competes with Reaction 3. When present at high concentrations, hydrogen peroxide can also compete with molecular oxygen (Reaction 9) for the open coordination site on Co(II)TSP:

$$Ti-O^--Co(II)TSP-H_2O + H_2O_2 \rightarrow Ti-O^--Co(III)TSP-OH + OH^- \quad (11)$$

Reaction 11 is analogous to Reaction 8 in that it leads to the overall reduction of H_2O_2 by two $e^-(cb)$. The major difference between the zinc oxide and the TiO_2–Co(II)TSP systems is that the surface complex (Co(II)TSP) acts as an electron relay in one case while sacrificial electron donors such as acetate are a prerequisite for interruption of the e^-/h^+ recombination in the other case.

Following the studies of these rather well-defined model systems aerated aqueous suspensions of desert sand particles were irradiated (λ(ex) = 350 nm) in the presence of sodium acetate. The very rapid formation of a steady-state concentration of 0.2 μM H_2O_2 upon illumination is shown in Figure 4. This, however, decays very quickly when the light is turned off. A similar depletion is apparent when H_2O_2 is added in the dark. If the light is turned on during this decay period a steady-state of 0.2 μM is again established. These cycles can be repeated many times without any apparent loss in activity. It has already been demonstrated (15) that desert sand contains minerals such as hematite, α-Fe_2O_3, and anatase, TiO_2, and can thus be photocatalytically active. We envision a mechanism similar to that proposed for the model systems above to account for the observed formation of H_2O_2 on desert sands. In this case the e^-/h^+ pair (Reaction 1) is intercepted by the donor acetate (Reactions 5 and 6) leaving e^-(cb) behind to reduce O_2 via Reaction 2. The efficient destruction of H_2O_2, on the other hand, might be caused by metal ion contaminants (M^{x+}) adsorbed on the sand particles (81–85). Hydrogen peroxide can thus react with M^{x+} in a Fenton type reaction (86),

$$M^{x+} \quad + \quad H_2O_2 \quad \rightarrow \quad M^{(x+1)+} \quad + \quad OH^- \quad + \quad OH\cdot \tag{12}$$

followed by the free radical Reactions 13 to 17 (87,88).

$$H_2O_2 \quad + \quad OH\cdot \quad \rightarrow \quad H_2O \quad + \quad HO_2\cdot \tag{13}$$

$$HO_2\cdot \quad \rightleftharpoons \quad O_2^-\cdot \quad + \quad H^+_{aq} \tag{14}$$

$$HO_2\cdot + O_2^-\cdot + H^+_{aq} \quad \rightarrow \quad H_2O_2 \quad + \quad O_2 \tag{15}$$

$$HO_2\cdot \quad + \quad OH\cdot \quad \rightarrow \quad H_2O \quad + \quad O_2 \tag{16}$$

$$OH\cdot \quad + \quad OH\cdot \quad \rightarrow \quad H_2O_2 \tag{17}$$

This reaction sequence results in the overall disproportionation of H_2O_2 and thus explains its rapid disappearance in the dark. Finally, a word of caution should be added regarding other possibilities to photogenerate hydrogen peroxide in such an ill-defined natural system. In spite of the rigorous pre-treatment it is possible that trace amounts of organic adsorbates are still present on the desert sand samples employed in this study. On the other hand, it is well documented that naturally occurring humic type materials can also be photochemically active (89). Thus we cannot exclude the possibility that part of the observed rather low steady-state

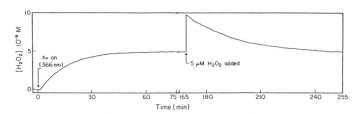

Figure 3.   Formation and depletion of H_2O_2 upon irradiation ($\lambda(ex)$ = 366 nm) of an oxygenated aqueous suspension of 0.3 g TiO_2-Co(II)TSP/l at pH 12.

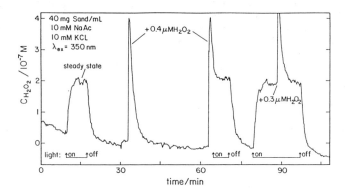

Figure 4.   Formation and depletion of H_2O_2 upon illumination and in the dark observed in an aerated aqueous suspension of Death Valley desert sand (other exp. cond. are given in the figure).

concentration of H_2O_2 is formed via the direct excitation of such molecules. Further experiments are currently being performed to differentiate between these pathways.

Concluding Remarks

We have shown that hydrogen peroxide can be produced photocatalytically in the presence of semiconductor particles. Quantum yields up to 50% and steady-state concentrations between 0.2 and 120 μM H_2O_2 have been observed. While the reduction of molecular oxygen by e^-(cb) seems to be the most likely process for H_2O_2-formation, oxidation of water by h^+(vb) should in principle yield the same products.

It is the observation of hydrogen peroxide production upon the illumination of an aerated aqueous suspension of desert sand particles that presents the most intriguing result of this study. Submicron sand particles are very abundant in the atmosphere where they act as condensation nuclei (90). Their involvement as catalysts and/or photocatalysts in chemical transformations occurring in natural environments has so far been neglected even though they are rather persistent in the atmosphere with half-lives of several days before precipitation takes place. We propose the surface reaction of photocatalytically formed H_2O_2 with sulfur dioxide (SO_2) and nitrous oxides (NO_x) as an additional pathway for the formation of acid rain. Even though due to its metal-catalyzed dismutation the steady-state concentration of H_2O_2 observed in the desert sand experiment was rather low, it may nevertheless be high enough to yield reasonable quantities of oxidation products like H_2SO_4 or HNO_3. Further experiments are in progress to study the photocatalytic activity of natural systems.

Acknowledgment

We gratefully acknowledge the financial support of the U.S. EPA (CR812356-01-0 and R811612-01-0) and in particular we want to thank Drs. Donald Carey and Marcia Dodge for their support.

Literature Cited

1. Hoffmann, M. R.; Kerr, J. A.; Calvert, J. G. Chemical Transformation Modules for Eulerian Acid Deposition Models. Vol.II: The Aqueous-Phase Chemistry; NCAR, Boulder, CO, 1984.
2. Hoffmann, M. R.; Boyce, S. D. Advances in Environmental Science and Technology; Schwartz, S. E., Ed.; Wiley, New York, 1983, 12, 147.
3. Hoffmann, M. R.; Jacob, D. J. SO_2, NO, and NO_2 Oxidation Mechanisms: Atmospheric Considerations; Calvert, J. G., Ed.; Acid Precipitation Series - Vol. 3; Teasley, J. I., Series Ed.; Butterworth, Boston, MA, 1984, 101.
4. Jacob, D. J.; Hoffmann, M. R. J. Geophys Res. 1983, 88, 6611.

5. Kok, G. L.; Darnall, K. R.; Winer, A. M., Pitts, J. N., Jr.; Gay, B. W. Environ. Sci. Tech. 1978, 12, 1077.
6. Kok, G. L. Atmos. Environ. 1980, 14, 653.
7. Richards, L. W.; Anderson, J. A.; Blumenthal, D. L.; McDonald, J. A.; Kok, G. L. Atmos. Environ. 1983, 17, 911.
8. Schwartz, S. E. Annals of the New York Academy of Sciences, Section of Environmental Sciences 1985, xx, xxx.
9. Seinfeld, J. H. Atmospheric Chemistry and Physics of Air Pollution; John Wiley & Sons, New York, NY, 1986, 236.
10. Chameides, W. L.; Davis, D. D. J. Geophys Res. 1982, 87, 4863.
11. Zika, R. G.; Saltzman, E.; Chameides, W. L.; Davis, D. D. J. Geophys. Res. 1982, 87, 5015.
12. Graedel, T. E.; Goldberg, K. I. J. Geophys. Res. 1983, 88, 865.
13. Chameides, W. L. J. Geophys. Res. 1984, 88, 4739.
14. Fendler, J. H. J. Phys. Chem. 1985, 89, 2730.
15. Schrauzer, G. N.; Strampach, N.; Hui, L. N.; Palmer, M. R.; Saleshi, J. Proc. Natl. Acad. Sci. USA 1983, 80, 3873.
16. Seinfeld, J. H. Atmospheric Chemistry and Physics of Air Pollution; John Wiley & Sons, New York, NY, 1986, 26.
17. Stumm, W.; Morgan, J. J. Aquatic Chemistry; John Wiley & Sons, New York, NY, 1981, 238.
18. Bard, A. J. Science 1980, 207, 139.
19. Rothenburger, G.; Moser, J.; Grätzel, M.; Serpone, N.; Sharma, D. K. J. Am. Chem. Soc. 1985, 107, 8054.
20. Izumi, I.; Dunn, W. W.; Wilbourn, K. O.; Fan, F. F.; Bard, A. J. J. Phys. Chem. 1980, 84, 3027.
21. Harvey, P. R.; Rudham, R.; Ward, S. J. Chem. Soc. Faraday Trans. 1 1983, 79, 2975.
22. Herrmann, M.-M.; Mozzanega, M.-N.; Pichat, P. J. Photochem. 1983, 22, 333.
23. Fox, M. A.; Chen, C.-C.; Park, H.-H.; Younathan, J. N. ACS Symp. Ser. 1985, 278, 69.
24. Brown, G. T.; Darwent, J. R. J. Chem. Soc. Faraday Trans. 1 1984, 80, 1631.
25. Bahnemann, D.; Henglein, A.; Spanhel, L. Faraday Discuss. Chem. Soc. 1984, 78, 151.
26. Gerischer, H. Topics in Applied Physics 1979, 31, 115.
27. Latimer, W. M. Oxidation Potentials, 2nd Edition; Prentice-Hall, New York, NY, 1952, 38-50.
28. Baur, E.; Neuweiler, C. Helv. Chim. Acta 1927, 10, 901.
29. Böhi, J. Helv. Chim. Acta 1929, 12, 121.
30. Chari, C. N.; Qureshi, M. J. Indian Chem. Soc. 1944, 21, 97.
31. Chari, C. N.; Qureshi, M. J. Indian Chem. Soc. 1944, 21, 297.
32. Markham, M. C.; Laidler, K. J. J. Phys. Chem. 1953, 57, 363.
33. Rubin, T. R.; Calvert, J. G.; Rankin, G. T.; MacNevin, W. M. J. Am. Chem. Soc. 1953, 75, 2850.
34. Calvert, J. G.; Theurer, K.; MacNevin, W. M. J. Am. Chem. Soc. 1954, 76, 2575.
35. Stephens, R. E.; Ke, B.; Trivich, D. J. Phys. Chem. 1955, 59, 966.

36. Kuriacose, J. C.; Markham, M. C.   J. Catalysis 1962, 1, 498.
37. Morrison, S. R.; Freund, T.   J. Chem. Phys. 1967, 47, 1543.
38. Harbour, J. R.; Hair, M. L.   J. Phys. Chem. 1977, 81, 1791.
39. Harbour, J. R.; Hair, M. L.   J. Phys. Chem. 1979, 83, 652.
40. Hair, M. L.; Harbour, J. R.   Adv. Chem. Ser. 1980, 184, 173.
41. Pappas, S. P.; Fischer, R. M.   J. Paint Technology 1974, 46, 65.
42. Cundall, R. B.; Rudham, R.; Salim, M. S.   J. Chem. Soc. Faraday Trans. 1 1976, 72, 1642.
43. Harbour, J. R.; Hair, M. L.   "Magnetic Resonance in Colloid and Interface Science", Fraissard, J. P.; Resing, H. A., Eds.; Riedel Publ. Co. 1980, 431.
44. Harbour, J. R.; Tromp, J.; Hair, M. L.   Can. J. Chem. 1985, 63, 204.
45. Rao, M. V.; Rajeshwar, K.; Pal Verneker, V. R.; DuBow, J.   J. Phys. Chem. 1980, 84, 1987.
46. Salvador, P.; Decker, F.   J. Phys. Chem. 1984, 88, 6116.
47. Rives-Arnau, V.   J. Electroanal. Chem. 1985, 190, 279.
48. Jaeger, C. D.; Bard, A. J.   J. Phys. Chem. 1979, 83, 3146.
49. Anpo, M.; Shima, T.; Kubokawa, Y.   Chem. Lett. 1985, 1799.
50. Serwicka, E.   Colloids and Surfaces 1985, 13, 287.
51. Baur, E.; Perret, A.   Helv. Chim. Acta 1924, 7, 910.
52. Perret, A.   J. Chim. Phys. 1926, 23, 97.
53. Hada, H.; Yonezawa, Y.; Saikawa, M.   Bull. Chem. Soc. Jpn. 1982, 55, 2010.
54. Nishimoto, S.-I.; Ohtani, B.; Kajiwara, H.; Kagiya, T.   J. Chem. Soc. Faraday Trans. 1 1983, 79, 2685.
55. Kennedy, D. R.; Ritchie, M.; MacKenzie, J.   Trans. Faraday Soc. 1958, 54, 119.
56. McLintock, I. S.; Ritchie, M.   Trans. Faraday Soc. 1965, 61, 1007.
57. Stone, F. S.   Anal. Real. Soc. Espan. Fis. Quim. 1965. 61, 109.
58. Boonstra, A. H.; Mutsaers, C. A. H. A.   J. Phys. Chem. 1975, 79, 1694.
59. Boonstra, A. H.; Mutsaers, C. A. H. A.   J. Phys. Chem. 1975, 79, 1940.
60. Boonstra, A. H.; Mutsaers, C. A. H. A.   J. Phys. Chem. 1975, 79, 2025.
61. Munuera, G.; Rives-Arnau, V.; Saucedo, A.   J. Chem. Soc. Faraday Trans. 1 1979, 75, 736.
62. González-Elipe, A. R.; Munuera, G.; Soria, J.   J. Chem. Soc. Faraday Trans. 1 1979, 75, 748.
63. Munuera, G.; González-Elipe, A. R.; Soria, J.; Sanz, J.   J. Chem. Soc. Faraday Trans. 1 1980, 76, 1535.
64. Munuera, G.; Navio, A.   Stud. Surf. Sci. Catal. Pt. B, New Horiz. Catal. 1981, 7, 1185.
65. Munuera, G.; González-Elipe, A. R.; Rives-Arnau, V.; Navio, A.; Malet, P.; Soria, J.; Conesa, J. C.; Sanz, J.   "Adsorption and Catalysis on Oxide Surfaces", Che M.; Bond, G. C., Eds.; Elsevier Sci. Publ. 1985, 113.
66. Tanaka, K.; White, J. M.   J. Phys. Chem. 1982, 86, 4708.

67. Tatsumi, K.; Shiotani, M.; Freed, J. H. J. Phys. Chem. 1983, 87, 3425.
68. Yesodharan, E.; Grätzel, M. Helv. Chim. Acta 1983, 66, 2145.
69. Duonghong, D.; Grätzel, M. J. Chem. Soc. Chem. Comm. 1984, 1597.
70. Oosawa, Y.; Grätzel, M. J. Chem. Soc. Chem. Comm. 1984, 1629.
71. Che, M.; Gianello, E.; Tench, A. J. Colloids and Surfaces 1985, 13, 231.
72. Mühlebach, J.; Müller, K.; Schwarzenbach, G. Inorg. Chem. 1970, 9, 2381.
73. Schwarzenbach, D. Inorg. Chem. 1970, 9, 2391.
74. Bahnemann, D.; Henglein, A.; Lilie, J.; Spanhel, L. J. Phys. Chem. 1984, 81, 709.
75. Patrick, W. A.; Wagner, H. B. Anal. Chem. 1949, 21, 1279.
76. Savage, D. J. Analyst (London) 1951, 76, 224.
77. Mönig, J. Diplomathesis, Technical University of Berlin, Germany, 1980, pp. 38-40.
78. Guilbault, G. G.; Brignac, P. J.; Juneau, M. Anal. Chem. 1968, 40, 1256.
79. Lazrus, A. L.; Kok, G. L.; Gitlin, S. N.; Lind, J. A.; McLaren, S. E. Anal. Chem. 1985, 57, 917.
80. Heller, H. G.; Langan, J. R. J. Chem. Soc. Perkin Trans. 2, 1981, 341.
81. James, R. O.; Healy, T. W. J. Coll. Interface Sci. 1972, 40, 42.
82. James, R. O.; Healy, T. W. J. Coll. Interface Sci. 1972, 40, 53.
83. Huang, C.-P.; Stumm, W. J. Coll. Interface Sci. 1973, 43, 409.
84. Davis, J. A.; Leckie, J. O. J. Coll. Interface Sci. 1978, 67, 90.
85. Elliott, H. A.; Huang, C. P. J. Coll. Interface Sci. 1979, 70, 29.
86. Fenton, H. J. H. J. Chem. Soc. 1894, 65, 899.
87. Haber, F.; Weiss, J. Proc. R. Soc. London Ser. A 1934, 147, 332.
88. Weinstein, J.; Bielski, B. H. J. J. Am. Chem. Soc. 1979, 101, 38.
89. Zafiriou, O. C.; Joussot-Dubien, J.; Zepp, R. G.; Zika, R. G. Environ. Sci. Technol. 1984, 18, 359A.
90. Pruppacher, H. R.; Klett, J. D. Microphysics of Clouds and Precipitation; D. Riedel Publ. Co., Dordrecht, Holland, 1978.

RECEIVED March 16, 1987

Chapter 11

Direct Kinetic and Mechanistic Study of the OH-Dimethyl Sulfide Reaction Under Atmospheric Conditions

A. J. Hynes and P. H. Wine

Molecular Sciences Branch, Georgia Tech Research Institute, Georgia Institute of Technology, Atlanta, GA 30332

A pulsed laser photolysis-pulsed laser induced fluorescence technique was employed to study the OH + CH_3SCH_3 reaction in N_2, air, and O_2 buffer gases. Complex kinetics were observed in the presence of O_2. A four step mechanism involving hydrogen abstraction, reversible addition to the sulfur atom, and scavenging of the (thermalized) adduct by O_2 is required to explain all experimental observations. In one atmosphere of air, the effective bimolecular rate constant decreases monotonically from 1.58×10^{-11} to $5.2 \times 10^{-12} cm^3$ $molecule^{-1}s^{-1}$ over the lower tropospheric temperature range 250-310K. Over the same temperature range the branching ratio for hydrogen abstraction increases monotonically from 0.24 to 0.87.

On a global scale, natural emissions of reduced sulfur compounds account for about 50% of the total sulfur flux into the atmosphere (1-3). Hence, it is important to understand the natural sulfur cycle in order to establish a "base line" for assessing the significance of anthropogenic perturbations (primarily SO_2 emissions). Dimethylsulfide (DMS) is the predominant reduced sulfur compound entering the atmosphere from the oceans (4-9), and DMS oxidation represents a major global source of S(VI). The atmospheric oxidation of DMS can be initiated by reaction with either OH or NO_3. In marine environments, however, NO_3 levels are typically very low and DMS is destroyed primarily by OH:

$$OH + CH_3SCH_3 \longrightarrow CH_3SCH_2 + H_2O \qquad (1a)$$

$$\xrightarrow{\quad M \quad} CH_3S(OH)CH_3 \qquad (1b)$$

0097–6156/87/0349–0133$06.00/0
© 1987 American Chemical Society

A number of kinetics studies of Reaction 1 have been reported
(10-17). In addition, several steady state photolysis-end product
analysis studies have recently been reported where conclusions were
drawn concerning the relative importance of hydrogen abstraction and
addition to the sulfur atom as reaction pathways (18-20). Despite
the rather large data base, neither the rate constant nor the branching ratio for Reaction 1 is well defined. Values for k_1 have been
measured directly using both flash photolysis (10,11,13,17) and discharge flow (14,16) techniques, with reported 298K rate constants
ranging from 3.2 to 9.8 x $10^{-12}cm^3molecule^{-1}s^{-1}$ and reported activation energies ranging from -352 to +274 cal mole^{-1}. All direct
measurements were carried out in the absence of the potentially
reactive gas O_2. Two competitive kinetics studies (12,15), both of
which employed one atmosphere of air as the buffer gas, report 298K
rate constants in agreement with the higher values reported in the
direct studies. While there seems to be general agreement that the
branching ratio for Channel 1a is significant, the contribution from
Channel 1b remains poorly defined.

We have employed a pulsed laser photolysis - pulsed laser
induced fluorescence technique to carry out direct, real time
studies of OH reactions with DMS and DMS-d$_6$ in N_2, air, and O_2 buffer
gases. Both temperature and pressure dependencies have been investigated. We find that the observed rate constant ($k_{obs} \equiv d[OH]/[OH]$
[DMS]dt) depends on the O_2 concentration. Our results are consistent
with a mechanism which includes an abstraction route, a reversible
addition route, and an adduct + O_2 reaction which competes with adduct decomposition under atmospheric conditions.

Experimental

A schematic of the apparatus is shown in Figure 1. OH was produced
by 248 nm (or 266 nm in some experiments) pulsed laser photolysis of
H_2O_2 and detected by observing fluorescence excited by a pulsed tunable dye laser. Fluorescence was excited in the OH($A^2\Sigma^+ - X^2\pi$) 0-1
band at 282 nm and detected in the 0-0 and 1-1 bands at 309±5 nm.
Kinetic data was obtained by electronically varying the time delay
between the photolysis laser and the probe laser. Sulfide concentrations were measured in situ in the slow flow system by UV photometry
at 228.8 nm.

Results

All experiments were carried out under pseudo-first order conditions
with DMS in large excess over OH. Exponential OH decays were observed under all experimental conditions investigated. Plots of k'
(the pseudo-first order OH decay rate) versus DMS concentration were
linear. Values for k_{obs} were obtained from linear least squares
determinations of the slopes of k' versus [DMS] plots. Measured
values for k_{obs} as a function of temperature, pressure, and O_2 concentration are summarized in Table I.

Important observations concerning the data reported in Table I
are summarized below

1. In the absence of O_2, DMS reacts significantly more rapidly
with OH than does DMS-d$_6$. This suggests that under these experimental conditions (no O_2) hydrogen abstraction is the dominant reaction

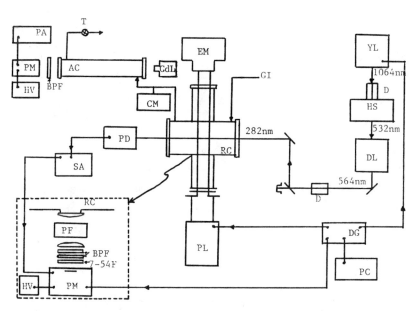

Figure 1. Schematic of the apparatus. AC-absorption cell, BPF-bandpass filter, CdL-cadmium lamp, CM-capacitance manometer, D-frequency doubler, DG-three channel delay generator, DC-dye laser, EM-emergy monitor, GI-gas inlet, HS-harmonic separator, HV-high voltage, PA-picoammeter, PD-photodiode, PM-photomultiplier, PL-photolysis laser, RC-reaction cell, SA-signal averager, T-chrottle, YL-Nd:YAG laser, 7-54F-Corning 7-54 glass filter.

Table I. Observed Bimolecular Rate Constants as a Function of Temperature, Pressure, and O_2 Concentration

Sulfide	T(K)	P(Torr)	M	Range of $k'(s^{-1})$	$k_{obs} \pm 2\sigma$ [a] $(10^{-12}cm^3mole$-$cule^{-1}s^{-1})$
CH_3SCH_3	262	700	air	498–24900	12.5 $\pm$ 1.7
	279	700	air	372–24200	9.53 $\pm$ 0.28
	298	40	N_2	160–13700	4.80 $\pm$ 0.11
	298	500	SF_6	53–7500	4.75 $\pm$ 0.15
	298	50	air	151–8610	4.68 $\pm$ 0.08
	298	130	air	1960–21800	5.04 $\pm$ 0.14
	298	340	air	310–28900	5.18 $\pm$ 0.34
	298	590	air	596–56100	5.80 $\pm$ 0.16
	298	750	air	1850–65700	6.28 $\pm$ 0.10
	321	700	air	420–22300	5.43 $\pm$ 0.30
CD_3SCD_3	261	700	air	1080–50500	11.6 $\pm$ 1.1
	266	700	O_2	854–48500	13.5 $\pm$ 1.2
	275	700	O_2	606–54200	11.9 $\pm$ 2.0
	276	700	air	1650–47300	9.63 $\pm$ 0.63
	287	700	air	777–20100	5.29 $\pm$ 0.44
	287	700	O_2	593–23100	6.99 $\pm$ 0.53
	298	450	N_2	1520–18900	1.82 $\pm$ 0.11
	298	100	air	193–19800	2.10 $\pm$ 0.15
	298	300	air	336–17300	2.68 $\pm$ 0.09
	298	500	air	804–11700	2.97 $\pm$ 0.13
	298	700	air	672–18900	3.40 $\pm$ 0.13
	298	700	O_2	1290–21200	6.50 $\pm$ 0.72
	317	700	air	817–16500	3.02 $\pm$ 0.18
	321	700	O_2	620–13600	3.72 $\pm$ 0.27
	340	700	air	1030–11470	2.32 $\pm$ 0.11
	340	700	O_2	547–7880	2.30 $\pm$ 0.28
	361	700	air	1110–15200	2.66 $\pm$ 0.11

(a) errors are 2σ and represent precision only

pathway. We have carried out conventional FP-RF kinetic studies of
OH reactions with a series of sulfides in argon buffer gas (21);
reactivity trends and activation energies observed in these experiments support the dominance of Channel 1a when no O_2 is present.

2. At 298K, k_{obs} increases as a function of air pressure for
both DMS and DMS-d_6 reactions with OH. The slopes of k_{obs} versus
P_{air} plots are virtually equal for the two sulfides.

3. In both air and O_2 at 700 Torr total pressure, k_{obs} increases dramatically with decreasing temperature.

All experimental observations are consistent with the following
mechanism (written for CH_3SCH_3 but identical for CD_3SCD_3):

$$OH + CH_3SCH_3 \longrightarrow CH_3SCH_2 + H_2O \tag{1a}$$

$$OH + CH_3SCH_3 + M \longrightarrow CH_3S(OH)CH_3 + M \tag{1b}$$

$$CH_3S(OH)CH_3 + M \longrightarrow OH + CH_3SCH_3 \tag{-1b}$$

$$CH_3S(OH)CH_3 + O_2 \longrightarrow products \tag{2}$$

$$OH \longrightarrow \text{loss by reaction with } H_2O_2 \text{ and} \atop \text{diffusion from the detector field} \atop \text{of view} \tag{3}$$

As mentioned above, in the absence of O_2 all observed OH removal appears to be via the abstraction route, i.e. Reaction 1a. Apparently,
Reaction -1b is very fast compared to the time scale of our experiments. However, the adduct lifetime must be long enough that it can
be scavenged by O_2 in competition with decomposition back to reactants. The dramatic dependence of k_{obs} on temperature is qualitatively consistent with the above mechanism. The activation energy
for Reaction -1b is expected to be quite large, so the fraction of
adduct molecules scavenged by O_2 can increase dramatically over a
relatively small temperature range.

At high O_2 levels, the adduct can be assumed to be in steady
state. Applying the steady state approximation to the above mechanism, one obtains:

$$k_{obs} = \frac{k_{1a}(T) + X(T)\{k_{1a}(T) + k_{1b}(T)\}[O_2]}{1 + X(T)[O_2]} \quad , \quad X(T) \equiv \frac{k_2(T)}{k_{-1b}(T)} \tag{4}$$

We assume that over the limited temperature range 260 - 360K, all
rate constants can be expressed in Arrhenius form:

$$k_i(T) = A_i \exp(-E_i/RT). \tag{5}$$

We have taken the 13 rate constants for OH + DMS-d_6 measured in 700
Torr air and 700 Torr O_2 (Table I) and fit $k_{obs}^D(T,[O_2])$ to Equation
4 using a least squares fitting criterion. The superscript D indicates the CD_3SCD_3 analog of equations 1-4. Values for $k_{1a}^D(T)$ were

taken from the FP-RF results ($\underline{21}$). A_{1b}^D, $A_X^D(\equiv A_2^D/A_{-1b}^D)$ and
$E_X^D(\equiv E_2^D-E_{-1b}^D)$ were taken as independent variables. By analogy with
known activation energies for OH addition to CH_3SH ($\underline{22}$), CH_3SD ($\underline{22}$),
and CH_3SSCH_3 ($\underline{13}$), E_{1b}^D was fixed at -0.7 kcal/mole. As shown in
Figure 2, equation 4 fits the experimental data very well (median
residual = 5.3%); we conclude, therefore, that the proposed mechanism
does include all important reactions. Best fit parameters are $A_{1b}^D =$
$3.04 \times 10^{-12} cm^3 molecule^{-1}s^{-1}$, $A_X^D = 5.53 \times 10^{-31} cm^3 molecule^{-1}$, and
$E_X^D/R = 7460K$.

Implications for Atmospheric Chemistry

Our results demonstrate that both the effective rate constant (k_{obs})
and the branching ratio (addition versus abstraction) for reaction
(1) change dramatically as a function of temperature over the lower
tropospheric temperature range 250-310K. It should be be kept in
mind that, for purposes of atmospheric modeling, addition followed by
decomposition back to OH + CH_3SCH_3 is treated as no reaction. The
"effective" addition pathway represents only those adduct molecules
which are scavenged by O_2.

A majority of our experiments employed DMS-d_6 as the sulfide
reactant because more information concerning elementary reaction
rates could be obtained in this matter (this aspect of our study is
not discussed in detail in this paper). However, enough experiments
were carried out with DMS to demonstrate that, within experimental
uncertainty, k_{obs} values for OH reactions with DMS and DMS-d_6 differ
only by the difference in the abstraction rates. The pressure
dependence data in air at 298K strongly supports this approximation.
Substituting the appropriate Arrhenius parameters into equation 4
leads to the following expression for the temperature dependence of
k_{obs} for the OH + DMS reaction in 760 Torr air (units are cm^3
molecule^{-1}s^{-1}):

$$k_{obs} = \frac{Texp(-234/T) + 8.64\times10^{-10}exp(7230/T) + 2.68\times10^{-10}exp(7810/T)}{1.04\times10^{11}T + 88.1exp(7460/T)}$$

(6)

Values for k_{obs} at ten degree intervals have been calculated
from equation 6, as have branching ratios for abstraction (B_{abs}) and
addition (B_{add}). The branching ratios were calculated from the
relationships

$$B_{abs} = k_{1a}/k_{obs} = 9.6\times10^{-12}exp(-234/T)/k_{obs}$$

(7)

$$B_{add} = 1 - B_{abs}$$

(8)

The results are tabulated in Table II.

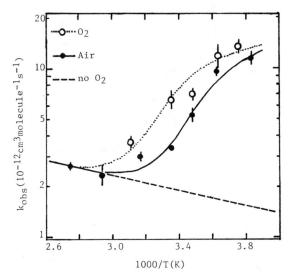

Figure 2.   Results obtained from using equation 4 to simulate the dependence of k_{obs} on $\lfloor O_2 \rfloor$ and temperature for the OH + CD_3SCD_3 reaction.   All bimolecular rate constants were measured at a total pressure of 700 Torr.   The best fit parameters A_{1b}^D, A_X^D, and E_X^D/R are given in the text.   Error bars are 2σ, precision only.

Table II.   Values for K_{obs}, B_{abs}, and B_{add}

$T(K)$	$10^{12}k_{obs}$ $(cm^3molecule^{-1}s^{-1})$	B_{abs}	B_{add}
250	15.8	0.24	0.76
260	14.5	0.27	0.73
270	12.5	0.32	0.68
280	9.8	0.42	0.58
290	7.4	0.58	0.42
300	5.9	0.75	0.25
310	5.2	0.87	0.13

Under atmospheric conditions the abstraction route is thought to result in production of $CH_3S + H_2CO$ via the following reaction sequence (17,20):

$$OH + CH_3SCH_3 \longrightarrow H_2O + CH_3SCH_2 \tag{1a}$$

$$CH_3SCH_2 + O_2 + M \longrightarrow CH_3SCH_2O_2 + M \tag{9}$$

$$CH_3SCH_2O_2 + NO \longrightarrow CH_3SCH_2O + NO_2 \tag{10}$$

$$CH_3SCH_2O + M \longrightarrow CH_3S + CH_2O + M \tag{11}$$

The ultimate fate of CH_3S is unknown, although Balla, et al. (23) report direct kinetic evidence that this radical reacts very rapidly with NO and NO_2 but negligibly slowly with O_2. Possible routes for the adduct + O_2 reaction include the following:

$$
\begin{array}{l}
\qquad\qquad\qquad\qquad \underset{\text{(DMSO)}}{CH_3\overset{O}{\overset{\|}{S}}CH_3 + HO_2} \tag{12a}\\[2em]
\underset{CH_3\underset{|}{\overset{OH}{S}}CH_3 + O_2}{} \\[2em]
\qquad\qquad\qquad\qquad CH_3O_2 + CH_3SOH \tag{12b}
\end{array}
$$

CH_3SOH is probably converted to CH_3SO_3H (methanesulfonic acid) by reaction with O_2 while the atmospheric fate of DMSO is unclear. DMSO has a very low vapor pressure and may be rapidly removed via heterogeneous processes.

At 298K our results demonstrate that reaction 1 in one atmosphere of air proceeds 70% via abstraction and 30% via (irreversible) addition. Photooxidation studies have been reported by Niki, et al. (18) and Hatakeyama and Akimoto (19), where 298K SO_2 yields from OH initiated oxidation of CH_3SCH_3 were reported to be 22% and 21%, respectively. Large yields of methanesulfonic acid were observed in both studies. At present, there is insufficient information to allow SO_2 production to be associated with either the abstraction route or the addition route. However, it should be noted that our results suggest that abstraction is the dominant reaction pathway for T > 300K while addition is the dominant pathway for T < 270K. Hence, temperature dependent product analysis studies should shed some light on the detailed pathways for SO_2 and CH_3SO_3H production.

Acknowledgment

This work was supported by the National Science Foundation through grant no. ATM-82-17232.

Literature Cited

1. Cullis, D. F.; Hirschler, M. M. Atmos. Environ. 1980, 14, 1263.
2. Moller, D. Atmos. Environ. 1984, 18, 19.
3. Moller, D. Atmos. Environ. 1984, 18, 29.
4. Barnard W. R.; Andreae, M. O.; Watkins, W. E.; Bingemer, H; Georgii, H.-W. J. Geophys. Res. 1982, 87, 8787.
5. Andreae, M. O.; Barnard, W. R.; Ammons, J. M. Ecol. Bull. 1983, 35, 167.
6. Andreae, M. O.; Raemdonck, H. Science 1983, 221, 744.
7. Cline, J. D.; Bates, T. S. Geophys. Res. Lett. 1983, 10, 949.
8. Turner, S. M.; Liss, P. S. J. Atmos. Chem. 1985, 2, 223.
9. Andreae, M. O.; Ferek, R. J.; Bermond, F.; Byrd, K. P.; Engstrom, R. T.; Hardin, S.; Houmere, P. D.; Le Marres, F.; Raemdonck, H.; Chatfield, R. B. J. Geophys. Res. 1985, 90, 12891.
10. Atkinson, R.; Perry, R. A.; Pitts, Jr., J. N. Chem. Phys. Lett. 1978, 54, 14.
11. Kurylo, M. J. Chem. Phys. Lett. 1978, 58, 233.
12. Cox, R. A.; Sheppard, D. Nature 1980, 289, 330.
13. Wine, F. H.; Kreutter, N. M.; Gump, C. A.; Ravishankara, A. R. J. Phys. Chem. 1981, 85, 2660.
14. MacLeod, H.; Poulet, G.; LeBras, G. J. Chem Phys. 1983, 80, 287.
15. Atkinson, R.; Pitts, Jr., J. N.; Aschmann, S. M. J. Phys. Chem. 1984, 88, 1584.
16. Martin, D.; Jourdain, J. L.; LeBras, G. Int. J. Chem. Kinet. 1985, 17, 1247.
17. Wallington, T. J.; Atkinson, R.; Tuazon, E. C.; Aschmann, S. M. Int. J. Chem. Kinet. 1986, 18, 837.
18. Niki, H.; Maker, P. D.; Savage, C. M.; Breitenbach, L. P. Int. J. Chem. Kinet. 1983, 15, 647.
19. Hatakeyama, S.; Akimoto, H. J. Phys. Chem. 1983, 87, 2387.
20. Grosjean, D. Environ. Sci. Tech. 1984, 18, 460.
21. Hynes, A. J.; Wine, P. H.; Semmes, D. H. J. Phys. Chem. 1986, 90, 4148.
22. Wine, P. H.; Thompson, R. J.; Semmes, D. H. Int. J. Chem. Kinet. 1984, 16, 1623.
23. Balla, R. J.; Nelson, H. H.; McDonald, J. R. Chem. Phys. 1986, 109, 101.

RECEIVED June 2, 1987

Chapter 12

SO$_2$ Oxidation by Hydrogen Peroxide in Suspended Droplets

W. A. Jaeschke and G. J. Herrmann

Center for Environmental Research, J. W. Goethe-University, P.O. Box 11 19 32, D-6000 Frankfurt am Main, Federal Republic of Germany

One of the most significant reactions in the context of acidity in rainwater is the SO_2-oxidation by hydrogen peroxide in aqueous solution. Therefore a dynamic flowreactor was constructed, where SO_2 removal rates could be investigated in the presence of H_2O-containing droplets. The diameter of the suspended droplets was in the size range between 1 μm and 25 μm which is comparable to size distributions observed in atmospheric clouds or fogs. Pseudo first order rate constants of the SO_2-Oxidation were measured at different pH-values. The H_2O_2-concentration in the droplets was varied between 2×10^{-5}m and 10^{-2}m. The obtained second order rate constants were strongly pH-dependent ($1,48 \times 10^5$ l mol^{-1} sec^{-1} at pH 2 and $1,3 \times 10^2$ l mol^{-1} sec^{-1} at pH 5,5). At H_2O_2-concentrations above 10^{-3} m the microphysical transfer of SO_2 via droplet interface became the rate determining step. From the experiments an accomodation-coefficient for SO_2 could be calculated which was greater than 10^{-1}.

Recent measurements of gas- and liquid-phase concentrations of hydrogen peroxide in the troposphere (1,2) substantiate the notion that H_2O_2 is the major oxidant leading to the generation of sulfuric acid in atmospheric multiphase systems like fogs and clouds. The oxidation of $S(IV)_{aq}$ requires a phase transfer of gaseous SO_2 into the suspended droplets. This transfer represents a chain of consecutive processes including transport of $(SO_2)_g$ to the droplets, phase-transfer through the gas-liquid interface, transport of dissolved $S(IV)_{aq}$ in the liquid phase and subsequent oxidation of $S(IV)_{aq}$ to $S(VI)_{aq}$ by dissolved H_2O_2. Because of the consecutive nature of this multiphase oxidation process the slowest step of the chain determines the overall rate. Commonly the overall rates of such processes occuring in atmospheric fog and clouds are calculated by linear extrapolations from kinetic data gained in bulk-solution experiments. It is doubtful whether the assumed linear relations are existing in atmospheric systems, especially with respect to the liquid water content (LWC) of fogs and clouds because this parameter is the result of the integral over a spectrum

0097–6156/87/0349–0142$06.00/0

of droplets in the range of 1 μm $<$ r $<$ 20 μm. In this size range of droplets both gas-phase and aqueous-phase mass transport of S(IV)aq may become the rate-determining step because the oxidation reaction of S(IV)aq by H$_2$O$_2$ is assumed to be very fast. In addition at SO$_2$-mass-accommodation-coefficients below 10^{-2} the interfacial transport of S(IV)-species may also govern the rate of the multiphase oxidation reaction (3).

Experimental

In this study the rate of the oxidation of gaseous SO$_2$ by H$_2$O$_2$ containing droplets in a multiphase simulation experiment was investigated. For this purpose a dynamic flow reactor was designed in which the removal of (SO$_2$)g in the gas-phase and the formation of S(VI)aq in the liquid phase could be determined. The experimental setup (Figure 1) was similar to that described in previous publications (4-5). Clean air, humidified to 94 % r.H., was mixed with certain amounts of (SO$_2$)g at the top of the dynamic tubular flow reactor. The reaction mixture was led through the reactor with a flow rate of 25 l/min. Droplets containing H$_2$O$_2$ were generated by an ultrasonic droplet generator and injected into the reactor. The droplet diameters ranged from 0.5 to 12.5 μm radius (r) (Figure 2). A compilation of experimental details is given in Table I.

Table I: Experimental details

Parameter	Provided by	Range		Monitored
SO$_2$	Cylinder	300 - 8500	ng/m^3	Fluorescence
H$_2$O$_2$	Stok solution	2 $\cdot$ 10^{-5} - 10^{-2}	mol/l	Titration
pH	HCl	2 - 5.5		Titration
Droplet size (radius)	Ultra sonic droplet	0,5 - 12,5	μm	Light scattering (Partoscope)
Liquid Water content	generator	8 $\cdot$ 10^{-3} - 7,5	ml/m^3	Calculated
Rel. Humid.	Water vapour source	94	%	Hum. indicator (Veisala)
Temperature	Thermostat. system	25	°C	"

In order to avoid wall effects by condensation of water vapour at r.H. $<$ 100 % it was necessary to lower the vapour pressure of the generated droplets using a neutral salt. Sodium chloride (high purity) was chosen and the concentration of the diluted reservoir solution of this salt was set to 1.5 mol l^{-1} so that the droplets generated from this solution were in thermodynamic equilibrium with the surrounding moist air of 94 % r.H. in the reactor. The pH-value of the solution was altered by addition of different ml-amounts of HCl (25%, reagent grade).

Each measuring point in the flow reactor corresponds to a fixed transport time of the multiphase mixture in the reactor. The transport

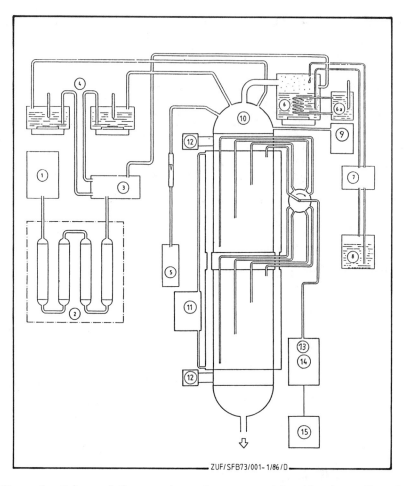

ZUF/SFB73/001-1/86/D

Figure 1.   Scheme of the experimental set up used for kinetic studies of the SO_2-oxidation in the presence of H_2O_2-containing droplets.
1. Compressor, 2. Air Cleaner, 3. Mass Flow Controller, 4. Vaporizer, 5. SO_2-source, 6. Nebulizer, 7. Pump, 8. Stock solution, 9. Partoscope A, 10. Reaction chamber, 11. Thermostat, 12. Humidity Sensor, 13. SO_2 Detection, 14. $SO_4^=$-Sampling, 15. Recorder.

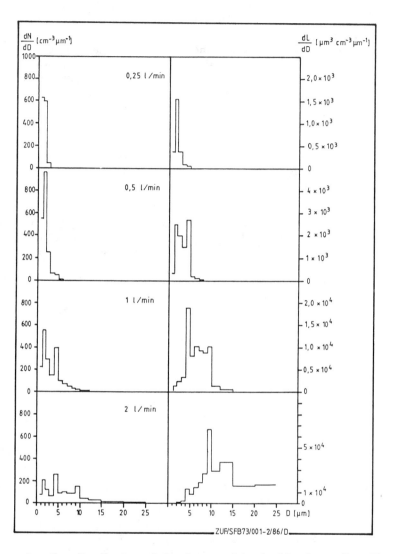

Figure 2.   Size distribution of droplets used in the kinetic studies. The size distribution was measured by a PARTOSCOPE A at three different flow rates in the nebulizer.

time is identical with the period of time in which the $(SO_2)g$ could react with the H_2O_2-containing droplets. Considering the flow rate and the geometry of the flow reactor, the total transport time was 340 sec.

When dissolved $S(IV)_{aq}$ is oxidized in the droplets, the absorption equilibrium between the $S(IV)_{aq}$-concentration and the $(SO_2)g$-concentration is disturbed. It is continuously re-established following Henry's law and the well-known dissolution equilibria of $S(IV)$ in the liquid phase. Thus a $(SO_2)g$-concentration-gradient between the inlet and the outlet of the reactor is formed, which is related to the travel time of the mixture.

Theory

For kinetic calculations only the $S(IV)_{aq}$ concentration is considered

$$S(IV)_{aq} = SO_2 \cdot H_2O + HSO_3^- + SO_3^= \tag{1}$$

The ratio of the three $S(IV)_{aq}$ species is pH-dependent. It can be calculated from the measured $(SO_2)g$ by Henry's law equilibrium constant H_{SO_2} and the well known first and second ionization constants K_{D1} and K_{D2}.

$$S(IV)_{aq} = (SO_2)_g \cdot H_{SO_2} + \frac{(SO_2)_g H_{SO_2} K_{D1}}{[H^+]} + \frac{(SO_2)_g H_{SO_2} K_{D1} K_{D2}}{[H^+]^2}$$

$$S(IV)_{aq} = (SO_2)_g \cdot H_{SO_2} (1 + \frac{K_{D1}}{[H^+]} + \frac{K_{D1} K_{D1}}{[H^+]^2})$$

$$S(IV)_{aq} = (SO_2)_g \cdot H^*_{SO_2} \tag{2}$$

$H^*_{SO_2}$ in Equation 2 is defined as a pseudo Henry's law coefficient that depends on the hydrogen ion concentration and encompasses the totality of the dissolved $S(IV)_{aq}$ species (3).

The ratio between the spatial difference of $S(IV)_{aq}$ in the reactor, which can be calculated from the $(SO_2)g$-gradient, and the corresponding travel-time interval is equal to the removal rate R:

$$R = - \frac{d[S(IV)]_{aq}}{dt} = \frac{d[S(VI)]_{aq}}{dt} \tag{3}$$

As the gradient of $S(IV)_{aq}$ is related to the oxidation product $S(VI)_{aq}$ appearing in the droplets an inverse gradient of the $S(VI)_{aq}$-concentration must be noticeable. The relation between $S(IV)$- and $S(VI)$-concentration gradients at any given travel time of the mixture can be expressed by the following general Equation:

$$R = - \frac{d[S(IV)]_{aq}}{dt} = \frac{d[S(VI)]_{aq}}{dt} = k_1 [S(IV)_{aq}]^{\alpha} \quad (4)$$

k_1 = 1st proportionality factor
α = const.

In order to determine k_1 and the exponent α in Equation 4 the removal of $S(IV)_{aq}$ and the formation of $S(VI)_{aq}$ should be measured during the experiments. The rate-coefficient k_1 was investigated as a function of different experimental conditions which are listed below:
- concentration of liquid water in the reactor (L)
- concentration of hydrogen peroxide in the droplets ($[H_2O_2]_{aq}$)
- pH of the droplets ($[H^+]_{aq}$)
These parameters have been varied during several separate experimental runs. The relative humidity always was kept constant at 94 % and the temperature in the reactor was set to 25°C.
The dependence of the overall transformation rate R in Equation 4 from the liquid water content L can be expressed by an exponential dependence of k_1 from L:

$$k_1 = k_2 \times L^{\beta} \quad (5)$$

k_2 = 2nd proportionality factor
β = const.

The exponent β represents a possible non-linear relationship between the removal rate R and the liquid water content which could be caused by mass-transport-limitations.
More precisely L is defined by the integral over the size distribution of the droplets used in the experiments.

$$L = \frac{\pi}{6} \int D^3 (\frac{dN}{dD}) dD$$

The dependence of R from the concentration of H_2O_2 in the droplets can also be expressed by an exponential equation:

$$k_2 = k_3 \times [H_2O_2]_{aq}^{\gamma} \quad (6)$$

k_3 = 3rd proportionality factor
γ = const.

were γ represents the reaction order with respect to the concentration of the oxidant. k_3 represents the rate coefficient of the oxidation reaction in the multiphase system at a certain pH-value.

The influence of the proton concentration $[H^+]$ in the droplets on the oxidation of $S(IV)_{aq}$ can be expressed as:

$$k_3 = k_4 \times [H^+]_{aq}^{\delta} \qquad (7)$$

k_4 = 4th proportionality factor
δ = const.

where δ represents the reaction order with respect to the concentration of hydronium-ions in the individual droplets. k_4 represents the rate coefficient of the multiphase reaction in the pH-range under investigation.

In summary the dependence of the transformation of $S(IV)aq$ to $S(VI)aq$ in the system can be expressed by combining Equation 2, 4, 5, 6 and 7 as:

$$\frac{-dS[(IV)]_{aq}}{dt} =$$

$$\frac{d[S(VI)]_{aq}}{dt} = k_4 [(SO_2)_g H^*_{SO_2}]^{\alpha} \times L^{\beta} \times [H_2O_2]_{aq}^{\gamma} [H^+]_{aq}^{\delta} \qquad (8)$$

In this equation the brackets indicate molar concentrations for liquid phase species. The concentration of $(SO_2)_g$ must be given as partial pressure and $H^*_{SO_2}$ represents the effective Henry's law constant of SO_2 considering the dissolution equilibria reactions of $S(IV)_{aq}$. As to be seen from Equation 8 the transformation of $(SO_2)_g$ to $S(VI)_{aq}$ in a multiphase system must be measured as a function of $(SO_2)_g$, L, $[H_2O_2]aq$ and $[H^+]aq$ in order to determine the constant k_4 and the exponents α, β, γ and δ.

Results and Discussion

In Figure 3 the decays of the $S(IV)_{aq}$-concentrations at various liquid water contents are plotted in a semi-logarithmic scale against the reaction time. The experiments were performed at pH = 4 and $[H_2O_2]aq = 10^{-3}$ mol l^{-1}.

The formation of $S(VI)aq$ is plotted using transformation variables in order to gain comparable values with the inverse gradient of $S(VI)aq$. In all cases linear dependences are obtained which means that the exponent α in Equation 8 is equal to one. Thus the $S(IV)_{aq}$-removal can be considered kinetically as a pseudo-first-order reaction with respect to $S(IV)aq$. The different slopes of the straight lines in Figure 3 correspond to different values of the liquid water content. These slopes directly represent values of k_1 since α =1. They are compiled together with the respective values of the liquid water content in the table beyond Figure 3.

In order to determine the value of the exponent β in Equation 5 the values of k_1 are plotted in a log-log diagram versus the corresponding liquid water content (L) (Figure 4). From the slope of the linear

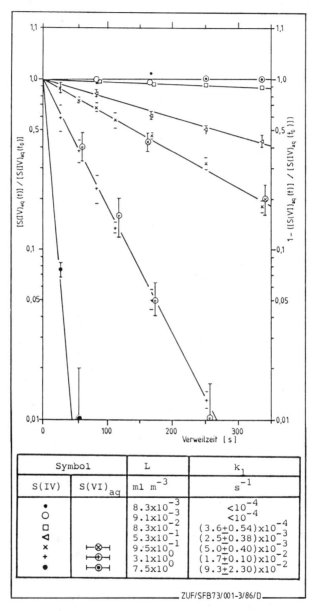

Symbol		L	k_1
S(IV)	S(VI)$_{aq}$	ml m^{-3}	s^{-1}
●		8.3×10^{-3}	$< 10^{-4}$
○		9.1×10^{-3}	$< 10^{-4}$
□		8.3×10^{-2}	$(3.6 \pm 0.54) \times 10^{-4}$
◁		5.3×10^{-1}	$(2.5 \pm 0.38) \times 10^{-3}$
×	⊢⊗⊣	9.5×10^{-1}	$(5.0 \pm 0.40) \times 10^{-3}$
+	⊢⊕⊣	3.1×10^{0}	$(1.7 \pm 0.10) \times 10^{-2}$
●	⊢⊙⊣	7.5×10^{0}	$(9.3 \pm 2.30) \times 10^{-2}$

ZUF/SFB73/001-3/86/D

Figure 3.   Semilogarithmic plot of S(IV)-decay and [S(VI)]$_{aq}$-increase versus reaction time. [S(VI)]$_{aq}$ plotted with circled symbols as transformation variable.

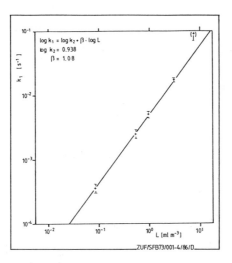

Figure 4. Pseudo-first-order rate constant k_1 as function of the liquid water content (L); $[H_2O_2]aq = 10^{-3}$ mol l^{-1}; pH = 4.0.

regression line the value of the exponent can be calculated to be $\beta = 1.08$. Because of the minor deviation from one (within the experimental errors) the dependency of the transformation of $S(IV)_{aq}$ to $S(VI)_{aq}$ from the liquid water content can be stated as linear. A remark must be given on this linear relationship of R from L: The linear dependency holds only for the used drop size spectra with radii between 0.5 and 12.5 μm representing L (Figure 2). In the presence of droplets with a larger size, (> 12.5 μm) mass transport limitations are to be expected and thus the relationship between R and L will no longer be linear. This phenomenon will be investigated in the near future.

In a second serie of experiments the concentration of hydrogen peroxide in the droplets was varied in the range from 2×10^{-5} to 5×10^{-3} mol l^{-1} while the other experimental conditions were kept constant. The pH of the droplets was set to 4.0. Again the $S(IV)_{aq}$ decay showed a pseudo-first-order kinetic. The measured rate constants are plotted in a log-log diagram in Figure 5 in dependence of the respective H_2O_2-concentration.

The slope of the log-log line in Figure 5 gives a value for the exponent $\gamma = 1.12$ in Equation 6. This indicates a nearly linear dependency between the overall $S(IV)_{aq}$ removal rate and the H_2O_2 concentration in the range of 2×10^{-5} to 5×10^{-3} mol l^{-1} at pH = 4.0 in the presence of droplets between 0.5 and 12.5 μm radius. The value of k_3 can be calculated from the regression analysis to be equal to $(8.89 \pm 1.51) \times 10^3$ l mol^{-1}s^{-1}.

Investigations concerning the pH-dependence of the transformation of $S(IV)_{aq}$ to $S(VI)_{aq}$ were performed between pH 2.0 and 5.5 because pH-values in that range may occur in atmospheric multiphase systems. The results of these experiments are shown in Figure 6 for pH-values 2.0, 3.0, 4.0 and 5.5. In the table in Figure 6 the values of the exponent γ and the second order rate constants k_3 are listed for the different pH-values of the droplets. The reaction of $S(IV)_{aq}$ with droplets containing H_2O_2 shows a linear dependency from the oxidant over the pH-range under investigation. The slopes of the lines in Figure 6 are nearly one and the deviations are within the limits of the experimental error. The values of the k_3 measured in suspended droplets range from $(1.21 \pm 0.29) \times 10^2$ l mol^{-1}s^{-1} at pH = 5.5 up to $(1.97 \pm 0.35) \times 10^5$ l mol^{-1}s^{-1} showing a surprisingly good correspondence with rate coefficients measured in bulk-solution experiments (6).

From the log-log plot (Figure 7) of k_3 against the H^+-concentration the dependence of R from the pH of the droplets can be calculated. The slope of the straight line indicates that the value of exponent δ equals 0.93. Thus a nearly linear relationship from the pH-value over the pH-range 2.0 to 5.5 is existing and the value of the 3rd order rate constant k_4 in Equation 8 can be calculated to $(2.43 \pm 0.73) \times 10^7$ l2 mol^{-2}s^{-1}. In order to give an impression of the errors connected with these kinds of measurement in multiphase simulation experiments the k_3-values in Figure 7 are given with error bars. The vertical error bars reflect the uncertainties of the measurement techniques and the deviation of k_3-values during repeated experiments. The horizontal error bars represent changes in the pH-value of the droplet solution due to the formation of sulfuric acid in the droplets and subsequent dissociation of H_2SO_4. The value of k_3 at pH 5.5 represents a mean value in the pH-range of 4.5 to 5.5. At pH-values below 4.5 the increase of the H^+-concentration due to sulfate formation was of minor importance.

A final set of experiments was performed in order to investigate the

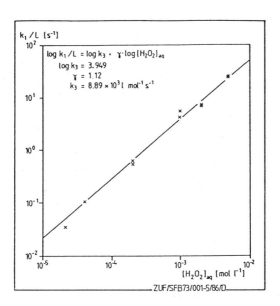

Figure 5. Normalized pseudo-first-order rate constants k_1/L versus $[H_2O_2]_{aq}$-concentration of the droplets (pH = 4.0).

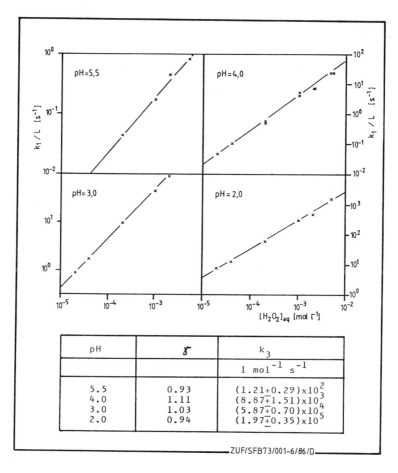

Figure 6. Normalized pseudo-first-order rate constants k₁/L as functions of the [H₂O₂]aq-concentration for pH = 5.5, 4.0, 3.0, 2.0.

influence of mass-transport limitations at the used droplet distributions. Figure 8 shows the results of these experiments performed at pH 2.0 and with H_2O_2-concentrations up to 10^{-1} mol l^{-1}. The crosses represent values of rate coefficients gained at $L = 9.1 \times 10^{-3}$ ml m^{-3} and the circles show the respective coefficients at $L = 2.5 \times 10^{-3}$ ml m^{-3}. The decrease of L from 9.1×10^{-3} ml m^{-3} to the lower value caused a shift in the droplet distribution from a mean radius of 1 μm to 0.7 μm. At H_2O_2 concentrations above 5×10^{-3} mol l^{-1} a deviation from the first order relationship with respect to H_2O_2 was observed and a nearly zero order dependence of the transformation at H_2O_2-concentrations between 10^{-2} and 10^{-1} mol l^{-1} was observed. A comparison of characteristic times for the consecutive processes (3) shows that a combinatory effect of interface transport and liquid phase transport limitation is probably the explanation for this phenomenon. When the liquid water content was decreased by a reduction of the droplet diameter an increase of the rate constants occured. However the linear relationship also was lost at $L = 2.5 \times 10^{-3}$ and H_2O_2-concentrations of 10^{-2} mol l^{-1}. An analysis of the characteristic times showed, that only for the highest H_2O_2-concentration (10^{-1} mol l^{-1}) mass transport limitations in the liquid phase occured. Since gas phase diffusion of SO_2 could not account for the limitations (characteristic time 10^2 times faster) the interface transport must be the rate determining step of the multiphase SO_2-reaction. A qualitative estimation could be performed regarding values for the accommodation coefficient of SO_2 between 10^{-1} and 10^{-4}. The resulting value for SO_2 gives a range for the accommodation coefficient between 10^{-3} and 10^{-2}.

Together with the limitations shown above, i.e. drop size distributions between 0.5 and 12.5 um, H_2O_2-concentrations below 5×10^{-3} mol l^{-1} and pH-values between 2.0 to 5.5 the results of this study can be applied to atmospheric multiphase systems such as fogs and clouds. k_1-values for different atmospheric relevant H_2O_2-concentrations and liquid water contents representative for cumulus (1 ml m^{-3}), stratus (10^{-1} ml m^{-3}) and fogs (10^{-2} ml m^{-3}) can be calculated. In Figure 9 results of such calculations are shown for stratus clouds with a H_2O_2-concentration of 10^{-3} mol l^{-1} and different pH-values in the droplets. The rising values of k_1 with decreasing pH show the influence of the acid catalyse of the H_2O_2-$S(IV)$-reaction on the transformation rates (7).

The experiments with suspended droplets show that the lower solubility of SO_2 at lower pH-values is of no influence on the SO_2-removal rate, as long as the transfer of $(SO_2)_g$ from the gas-phase into the droplet is faster than the chemical reaction. This can also be seen theoretically from Equation 9 which is the integrated version of Equation 8 using the experimental results that $\alpha = \beta = \gamma = \delta = 1$.

$$[(SO_2)_g \ H^*_{SO_2}]t = [(SO_2)_g \cdot H^*_{SO_2}]t_0 e^{-2,43 \times 10^{-7} L [H_2O_2] \ [H^+] t} \quad (9)$$

(L is given as mass mixing ratio.)

The pseudo-Henry's law coefficient has no influence on the rate constant of the reaction because it is not a rate-but an equilibrium-constant. The rate constant in the multiphase system is only governed by the liquid water content and the concentrations of the oxidant and the H^+ lons.

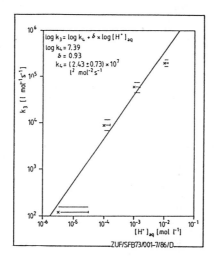

Figure 7. Log-log plot of the second-order rate constants k₃ versus the respective concentration of [H⁺]aq in the droplets.

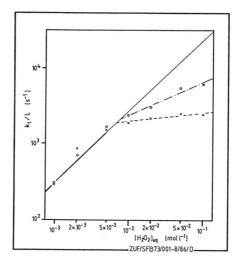

Figure 8. Pseudo-first-order rate constants as function of the [H2O2]aq-concentration for high H2O2-concentrations (> 10-3 mol l-1) at pH = 2.0. Symbols: x: L = 9.1 x 10-3 ml m-3; o: L = 2.5 x 10-3 ml m-3.

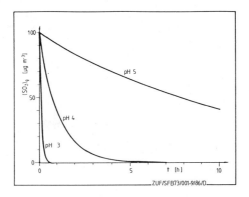

Figure 9. SO₂-Removal at a simulated concentration of L = 0,1 [ml/m3] and [H₂O₂] = 10⁻³ mol l⁻1 and 3 different pH-Values.

Acknowledgments

This work was performed within the program of the DFG Sonderfor-schungsbereich 73 (Atmospheric Trace Components) - Project E1 'Physico chemistry of precipitation' -

Literature Cited

1.   Heikes, B.G., Lazrus, A.L. and Kok, G.L. Presented at the Seventeenth International Symposium on Free Radicals, 1985.
2.   Lind, J. NCAR private communication, 1985.
3.   Schwartz, S.E. In Chemistry of Multiphase Atmospheric Systems; W. Jaeschke, Ed; Springer-Verlag, Berlin, 1986; pp. 415-472.
4.   Jaeschke, W. Toxicol. and Env. Chem., 1985, 10, 4, 265.
5.   Berresheim, H., Jaeschke, W. J. Atm. Chem. 1986, 4, 311-334.
6.   Martin, L.R. In SO_2, NO and NO_2 oxidation mechanisms: Atmospheric Considerations; J.G. Calvert, Ed.; Acid Precipitation Series, Butterworth Publishers, Ann Arbor, 1984, Vol. 3, pp. 63 - 100.
7.   Hoffmann, M.R. and Jacob, D.J. In SO_2, NO and NO_2 oxidation mechanisms: Atmospheric Considerations; J.G. Calvert, Ed.; Acid Precipitation Series, Butterworth Publishers, Ann Arbor, 1984, Vol. 3, pp. 101 - 172.

RECEIVED March 10, 1987

Chapter 13

Measurement of Concentration and Oxidation Rate of S(IV) in Rainwater in Yokohama, Japan

Shigeru Tanaka, Kazuo Yamanaka, and Yoshikazu Hashimoto

Department of Applied Chemistry, Keio University, Hiyoshi, Yokohama 223, Japan

Sulfite and bisulfite in rain water are rapidly oxidized to sulfate by the catalytic effect of metallic ions such as Fe(III) and Mn(II). The rates of oxidation of S(IV) in test solutions were measured using ion chromatography. The rate constant, k, measured for a 12.5 μM S(IV) solution was found to be 0.6-10.4 hr^{-1} at pH 3-6 in the presence of 1.8 μM Fe(III) and 0.18 μM Mn(II) catalysts, and 0.4-5.9 x 10^{-3} hr^{-1} without the catalysts. Triethanolamine (TEA) was used to stabilize actual rain water samples prior to analysis. TEA masks the catalytic effect of metallic impurities found in the rain water. The concentrations and the rates of oxidation of S(IV) in rain waters from Yokohama, Japan measured by this method were 0.8-23.5 μM (16 samples) and 0.12-3.3 hr^{-1} (8 samples), respectively.

In recent years, the effects of acid rain on lake water, heavy metals contaminated soils and structural materials have been widely discussed (1). Sulfur and nitrogen contained in fossil fuels are released into the atmosphere by combustion. Sulfur and nitrogen oxides dissolve in rain drops as bisulfite, sulfite and nitrite ions. These components are further oxidized into sulfate and nitrate ions. Since these species lower pH, it is important to accurately determine them in rain water. However, these ions are difficult to analyze because they rapidly oxidize in the presence of catalysts such as ferric and manganous ions. Light, temperature, and pH also affect the oxidation rate of S(IV).

In this study, the rate of S(IV) oxidation in test solutions was measured as a function of the concentration of metallic ions. The relations between the rate of oxidation of S(IV) and the metallic ions were also investigated using actual rain samples. The effect of pH on the oxidation of S(IV) to S(VI) was also examined.

Experimental

The oxidation of S(IV) is a first order reaction with respect to S(IV) (2,3). This reaction is accelerated by the presence of metallic ions such as ferric and manganous ions which act as catalysts (4-8). Therefore, the effect of the metallic ions on the oxidation of S(IV) was investigated by using test solutions. Table I shows experimental conditions for the oxidation of S(IV) in test solutions. The pH values of synthetic rain water samples were adjusted between 3 and 6. S(IV) concentration in the test solutions was adjusted to 12.5 μM; most of S(IV) existed as bisulfite at pH 3-6 (9). The rate of S(IV) oxidation was measured using ion chromatographic analysis. The pH of each test solution was adjusted by using a buffer.

In this study, a Model IC 100 ion chromatograph made by Yokogawa Co. was used for determination of S(IV) in the solution. A 2 mM Na_2CO_3/4 mM $NaHCO_3$ eluent was used to separate chloride, nitrate, sulfate, and sulfide ions.

Table I. Experimental Conditions for
the Oxidation of S(IV) in Test Solutions

pH	3, 4, 5, 6
Catalyst	Fe^{3+}, 1.8 μM
	Mn^{2+}, 0.18 μM
	Fe^{3+}, 1.8 μM; Mn^{2+}, 0.18 μM
	Fe^{3+}, 18 μM; Mn^{2+}, 1.8 μM
S(IV)	12.5 or 125 μM
Temp.	25°C

Results and Discussion

The result of measurements of the rate constant and half life of S(IV) in the test solutions are shown in Table II. The rate of oxidation of S(IV) in the solution without a catalyst was 0.4-5.9 x 10^{-3} hr^{-1}. The rate increases by 2 to 4 orders of magnitude in the presence of metallic ions, and a significant catalytic effect of ferric and manganous ions was found in these experiments. In the test solution containing both ferric and manganous ions, the rate enhancement was additive.

In the presence of these metallic ions, different oxidation rates were observed for each pH value. The maximum rate of oxidation occurred at pH 4 to 5. This is due to the change of the chemical form of each metallic ion with changing pH.

Table II. Rate Constant and Half Life of S(IV)
Oxidation in Test Solutions; 25°C, 12.5 μM S(IV)

pH	Pure Water		$1.8 \ \mu M \ Fe^{3+}$		$0.18 \ \mu M \ Mn^{2+}$		$1.8 \ \mu M \ Fe^{3+}$, $0.18 \ \mu M \ Mn^{2+}$	
	$k \times 10^3$ $[hr^{-1}]$	$t_{\frac{1}{2}}$ $[hr]$	$k \times 10^3$ $[hr^{-1}]$	$t_{\frac{1}{2}}$ $[hr]$	$k \times 10^3$ $[hr^{-1}]$	$t_{\frac{1}{2}}$ $[hr]$	$k \times 10^3$ $[hr^{-1}]$	$t_{\frac{1}{2}}$ $[hr]$
3	0.425	1630	2600	0.27	311	2.23	5840	0.12
4	0.620	1120	3310	0.21	336	2.06	10400	0.067
5	3.31	209	615	1.13	479	1.45	6830	0.10
6	5.88	118	124	5.58	83.5	8.30	598	1.16

Temp.:   25°C

S(IV):   12.5 μM

In urban areas like Yokohama, Japan, the concentrations of ferric and manganous ions in rain water are generally in the range of 0.2-2.0 μM and 0.02-0.2 μM respectively, and the pH value of rain water is between 4 and 5. Therefore, a high S(IV) oxidation rate in rain water is expected from the data in Table II. A half life of several minutes to an hour is predicted. Furthermore, S(IV) in rain water is oxidized during sampling, making the measurement of S(IV) in rain water difficult. This fast oxidation rate must be one of the reasons why few reports are found on the measurement of S(IV) in rain water.

In order to determine S(IV) in rain water, it is necessary to prevent the oxidation of S(IV) between sampling and analysis. The suppressive effect on the oxidation of S(IV) was investigated by the addition of EDTA (Ethylenediaminetetraacetate) or TEA (Triethanolamine) as masking reagents for Fe^{3+} and Mn^{2+}. Table III shows the suppressive effect of EDTA or TEA at various pH values. The suppressive effect was not observed between pH 3 and 5, because neither EDTA nor TEA chelate with Fe^{3+} and Mn^{2+} at these pH values. EDTA and TEA were found to be very effective for the suppression of the oxidation of S(IV) in solutions having neutral and basic pH values.

Figure 1 shows ion chromatrogram of the test solution added with EDTA or TEA. It was difficult to determine SO_4^{2-} due to the overlapping peaks of EDTA and SO_4^{2-}. However, TEA was found to be suitable for determination of anions present in rain water by ion chromatography.

Table III. Suppressive Effect of EDTA and TEA on the Oxidation of S(IV) at Various pH at 25°C

pH of sol'n	(1) EDTA 1.0 mM		(2) TEA 0.25 mM		(3) Fe^{3+}, Mn^{2+}	
	$k \times 10^3$ [hr^{-1}]	$t_{\frac{1}{2}}$ [hr]	$k \times 10^3$ [hr^{-1}]	$t_{\frac{1}{2}}$ [hr]	$k \times 10^3$ [hr^{-1}]	$t_{\frac{1}{2}}$ [hr]
3	39.6	17.5	----	----	5840	0.12
4	16.6	41.7	5730	0.12	10400	0.067
5	9.04	76.7	1420	0.49	6830	0.10
6	4.26	163	5.24	132	598	1.16
7	0.96	722	----	----	----	----
9.3	----	----	1.23	564	----	----

(1)   18 μM, Fe^{3+}; 1.8 μM, Mn^{2+}; 125 μM, S(IV)

(2)   1.8 μM, Fe^{3+}; 0.18 μM, Mn^{2+}; 12.5 μM, S(IV)

(3)   18 μM, Fe^{3+}; 1.8 μM, Mn^{2+}; 12.5 μM, S(IV)

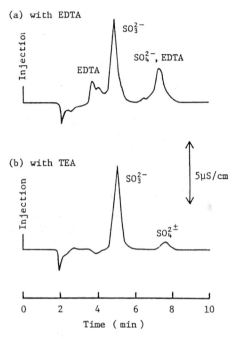

Figure 1.   Ion chromatogram of SO_3^{2-} and SO_4^{2-} in the test
             solution added with EDTA(ethylenediaminetetraacetic
             acid), and with TEA(triethanolamine)
             SO_3^{2-} conc.; 125μM, Temp.; 25°C
             (a) EDTA conc.; 1.0mM
             (b) TEA conc.; 2.5mM

An anion chromatogram of the rain water sample is shown in Figure 2. The upper ion chromatogram represents a sample where TEA was added to the rain collector before sampling. In the sample to which TEA was added, S(IV) was determined to be 2.3 μM. On the other hand, only traces of S(IV) were detected in the sample without TEA because of the rapid S(IV) oxidation. Therefore, the addition of TEA to sample enables the determination of S(IV) in rain water. A 10 mL mixture that was 250 mM TEA and 250 mM Na_2CO_3 was added to stabilize and buffer the solution. Less than 1 liter rain water was collected so that the concentration of TEA would remain effective.

Rain water samples were collected on the roof of the Faculty of Engineering Building at Keio University, Hiyoshi, Yokohama, from May to November, 1985. Hiyoshi, Yokohama is located at 5 km to the south of Kawasaki, and is affected by air pollution from the Tokyo-Yokohama Industrial Zone.

Analytical results of rain water collected at Hiyoshi, Yokohama, from May to November, 1985 are shown in Table IV. All samples were filtrated with a membrane filter (Millipore Type HA), and then the concentration of each ion and the pH values were measured. Rain water was sampled 16 times in 13 distinct rain events totaling 273 mm of precipitation. The pH value ranged between 3.7 and 4.8 with an average of 4.4. Concentrations of S(IV) and S(VI) were determined to be 0.8-23.5 μM and 6.8-84.4 μM, respectively. The average concentrations were 5.7 μM for S(IV) and 30.7 μM for S(VI). The detection limit of S(IV) by ion chromatography was estimated to be 0.3 μM at the injection of 100 μl sample solution.

Oxidation of S(IV) to S(VI) decreases the pH value of rain water. On the basis of the S(IV) concentration, the influence of the S(IV) oxidation on lowering pH values is shown in Table V. The calculation was made by subtracting the hydrogen ion concentration resulting from carbon dioxide equilibrium in the air from the measured hydrogen ion concentration in the rain samples, to obtain the hydrogen concentration caused by other acids. Then, the potential hydrogen concentration caused by the oxidation of S(IV) in rain water was calculated. The ratio between this potential hydrogen concentration and that caused by other acids excluding carbon dioxide was calculated. The results given in Table V show that the contributions of S(IV) to the decrease of pH in rain water are in the range of 6-67%.

Figure 3 shows the decay in the concentration of S(IV) for rain water collected at Hiyoshi, Yokohama. Five mL of 2.5 mM (S(IV)) solution was added to 195 mL of rain water, and the initial concentration of S(IV) was adjusted to 62.5 μM. The decay of S(IV) concentration was linear as seen in Figure 3. This is consistent with a first order reaction with respect to S(IV). A difference of oxidation rate between filtrated and non-filtrated samples was observed. The high oxidation rates in the non-filtrated rain water is assumed to be due to the presence of suspended particulate matter.

Table VI shows the rates of S(IV) oxidation measured in rain water collected in Yokohama, 1985. The rate constants of the S(IV)

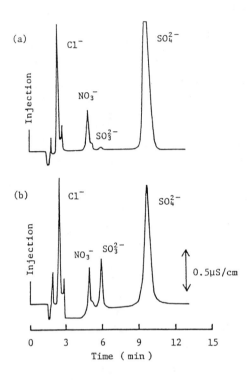

Figure 2.   Ion chromatogram of anion in rain water
            a) without TEA(triethanolamine)
            b) added with TEA(triethanolamine)
            Rain water was collected on May 20, 1985.

Table IV. Analytical Results of Rain Water
by Ion Chromatography, Yokohama, 1985

| Sample* | | Rain Fall | | | Concentration (μM) | | |
Date	Time	(mm)	pH	S(IV)	S(VI)	Cl⁻	NO₃⁻
May 20-21	1745-1100	53	4.8	2.3	21.5	11.6	7.1
May 24	1200-1645	10.2	4.5	2.1	22.8	8.4	9.8
24-25	1700-1800	15.4	4.6	2.2	18.7	33.5	14.0
May 28-29	1850-1150	4.1	4.5	9.1	49.0	16.6	26.0
	1200-1700	6.1	4.5	2.8	17.7	15.8	18.6
June 8	830-1300	7.4	4.2	2.0	11.1	30.1	52.3
June 11-12		3.4	3.8	5.4	84.4	191	151
June 12-13	2300-1615	20.4	4.4	2.5	19.3	26.8	28.6
June 18	1100-1840	5.7	4.2	4.1	51.2	94.9	45.3
18-19	1900-1230	27.5	4.8	0.8	6.8	12.1	10.2
Sept. 24-25	830-1015	2.3	3.7	11.9	62.7	278	55.8
Sept. 28-30	1500-900	34	4.5	2.0	15.9	42.5	15.2
Oct. 5-6		65	4.7	1.1	14.5	25.6	9.7
Oct. 29-30	1300-	4.8	4.1	23.5	39.5	110	26.8
Nov. 1	1040-1800	4.4	4.1	14.6	39.0	42.5	33.2
Nov. 6	1030-1500	8.9	4.5	4.4	16.7	73.0	16.3
min.		-	3.7	0.8	6.8	8.4	7.1
max.		-	4.8	23.5	84.4	278	151
Av.		-	4.4	5.7	30.7	63.3	32.5

* Samples were filtrated by Millipore membrane filter (pore size: 0.45 μm).

Table V. Contribution of S(IV) Oxidation on Lowering pH of Rain Water

Sample				Concentration (μM)			
Date	Time	pH	H$^+$	H$^+$*	S(IV)	H$^+$**	H$^+$**/H$^+$*
May 20-21	1745-1100	4.8	14.8	12.3	2.3	4.6	0.37
May 24-25	1200-1645	4.5	30.9	28.4	2.1	4.3	0.15
24-25	1700-1800	4.6	24.5	22.0	2.2	4.5	0.20
May 28-29	1850-1150	4.5	35.5	33.0	9.1	18.2	0.56
29	1200-1700	4.5	35.5	33.0	2.8	5.5	0.17
June 8	830-1300	4.2	70.8	68.3	2.0	4.0	0.06
June 11-12		3.8	174	171	5.4	10.7	0.06
June 12-13	2300-1615	4.4	37.2	34.6	2.5	5.1	0.15
June 18	1100-1840	4.2	67.6	65.1	4.1	8.2	0.13
18-19	1900-1230	4.8	17.0	14.5	0.8	1.6	0.11
Sept. 24-25	830-1015	3.7	194	191	11.9	23.8	0.12
Sept. 28-30	1500-900	4.5	34.5	32.9	2.0	4.0	0.12
Oct. 5-6		4.7	21.3	18.8	1.1	2.2	0.11
Oct. 29-30	1300-	4.1	72.4	69.9	23.5	47.0	0.67
Nov. 1	1040-1800	4.1	83.1	80.6	14.6	29.2	0.36
Nov. 6	1030-1500	4.5	34.7	32.2	4.4	8.7	0.27
min.		3.7	14.8	12.3	0.8	1.6	0.06
max.		4.8	194	191	23.5	47.0	0.67
Av.		4.4	59.2	56.7	5.7	11.4	0.23

H$^+$*:   The hydrogen ion concentration corrected for 2.5 μM carbon dioxide concentration.

H$^+$**: Nominal hydrogen ion concentration generated by oxidation of S(IV).

Table VI. Oxidation Rate and Half Life of S(IV) in Rain Water, Yokohama, 1985

Sample* Date	Time	pH	S(IV) conc. (μM)	Metal Conc. (μM) Mn	Fe	Rate Const. k (hr^{-1})	Half Life t$_{\frac{1}{2}}$ (hr)
May 20-21	1745-1100	4.8	2.3	0.025	0.084	0.12	5.8
May 24-25	1200-1800	4.6	2.2	0.051	0.337	0.66	1.1
June 11-12		3.8	5.4	0.498	2.04	3.31	0.21
Sept. 28-30	1500-900	4.5	2.0	0.016	0.215	0.28	2.5
Oct. 5-6		4.7	1.1	0.022	0.120	0.26	2.7
Oct. 29-30	1300-	4.1	23.5	0.063	0.625	1.22	0.57
Nov. 1	1040-1800	4.1	14.6	0.057	0.623	0.82	0.85
Nov. 6	1030-1500	4.5	4.4	0.020	0.166	0.22	3.2
min.		3.8	1.1	0.016	0.084	0.12	0.21
max.		4.8	23.5	0.498	2.04	3.31	5.8
Av.		4.4	6.9	0.094	0.526	0.86	2.1

Temp.; 25°C

* Samples were filtrated by Millipore membrane filter (pore size; 0.45 μm)

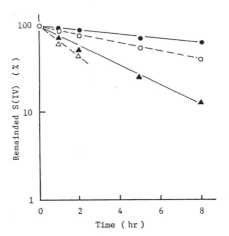

Figure 3.   Variation of S(IV) concentration in rain water with
             time by an addition of S(IV)
             Initial S(IV) concentration; 62.5μM
             Rain water was collected on May 20–21, 1985.
             ●; Filtrated by Millipore membrane filter
                 (pore size 0.45μm)
             ○; Not filtrated
             Rain water was collected on May 24–25, 1985
             ▲; Filtrated by Millipore membrane filter
                 (pore size 0.45μm)
             △; Not filtrated

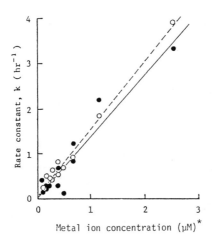

Figure 4.   Rate constant of oxidation of S(IV) and metallic
             Ion concentration in rain water
             ●; Filtrated by Millipore membrane filter
                 (pore size 0.45μm)
             ○; Not filtrated
             * Total Concentration of Fe and Mn

oxidation, k, are 0.12-3.3 hr^{-1}, which are similar to the oxidation rates in the test solutions in Table II. A large variation of the measured oxidation rates was observed in the rain water samples. It is assumed that the oxidation rate depends on the Fe^{3+} and Mn^{2+} concentration.

Figure 4 shows the relationship between the oxidation rate of S(IV) and the metallic concentration of Fe^{3+} and Mn^{2+} in rain water. The concentrations of iron and manganese in the rain water were analyzed by atomic absorption spectrometry. The increase of the oxidation rate with the increase of the metal ion concentration is shown in Figure 4. Therefore, a strong catalytic effect of Fe^{3+} and Mn^{2+} on the oxidation of S(IV) in rain water was observed.

Summary

The oxidation reaction of S(IV) in both test solutions and rain water was found to be a first order reaction. Metallic ions such as ferric and manganous ions strongly catalyze the oxidation of S(IV) in rain water. A correlation was found between the concentration of metallic ions and the rate of S(IV) oxidation. The rate constant for the oxidation of S(IV) was found to be 0.12-3.3 hr^{-1} (half life: 0.21-5.8 hr) in rain water samples collected at Yokohama, Japan, 1985. Hydrogen ions produced by the oxidation of S(IV) in rain water contribute substantially to acidity.

Literature Cited

1.   Likens, G.E, Wright, R.F., Galloway, J.N., and Butler, T.J., Scientific American, 1978, 241, 29-47.

2.   Beilke, S. and Gravenhorst, G., Atoms. Environ., 1978, 12, 231-239.

3.   Hegg, D.A. and Hobbs, P.V., Atmos. Environ., 1978, 12, 241-253.

4.   Junge, C.E. and Ryan, T.G., Q.J.R. met. Soc., 1958, 84, 46.

5.   Moller, D., Atmos. Environ., 1980, 14, 1067-1076.

6.   Huss, A., Jr., Lim, P.K., and Eckert, C.A., J. Phys. Chem., 1982, 86, 4224-4228, 4229-4233, 4233-4237.

7.   Ibusuki, T., Atmos. Environ., 1984, 18, 145-151.

8.   Altwicker, E.R. and Nass, K.K., Atmos. Environ., 1983, 17, 187-190.

9.   Butler, J.N. "Ionic Equilibrium", Addison-Wesley, Massachusetts, 1964.

RECEIVED June 12, 1987

Chapter 14

Spectroscopic Identification of Products Formed in the Gas-Phase Reaction of OH with Atmospheric Sulfur Compounds

S. C. Bhatia[1] and J. H. Hall, Jr.[1,2]

[1]Dolphus E. Milligan Science Research Institute, Atlanta University Center, 440 Westview Drive, SW, Atlanta, GA 30310
[2]School of Geophysical Sciences, Georgia Institute of Technology, Atlanta, GA 30332

The matrix-isolation infrared study of the reactions OH + R(R = CH_3SH, CH_3SSCH_3, SO_2) indicate that the products observed for CH_3SH + OH reaction are the proposed intermediate CH_3SHOH and SO_2 while CH_3SH, CH_3SHOH and SO_2 are formed in CH_3SSCH_3 + OH reaction. The reaction of hydroxyl radical with sulfur dioxide yields $HOSO_2 \cdot H_2O$ complex as the final product. The vibrational assignments for the observed products are reported.

The mechanism for the conversion of naturally occurring atmospheric sulfur compounds to sulfur dioxide is not yet established ($\underline{1}$). The sulfur dioxide produced during degradation of sulfur compounds can undergo further chemical and/or physical interactions to form sulfuric acid ($\underline{2}$), which is one of the components of acid rain. A number of sulfur compounds ($\underline{3}$) have been detected in the atmosphere; COS (carbonyl sulfide), CS_2 (carbon disulfide), H_2S (hydrogen sulfide), CH_3SH (methyl mercaptan), CH_3SCH_3 (dimethyl sulfide), and CH_3SSCH_3 (dimethyl disulfide). It is generally believed that the biological reduction of sulfur compounds is a major natural source for these atmospheric sulfur compounds. The chemical degradation of sulfur compounds of the type X-S-Y (X = H or CH_3, Y = H, CH_3 or SCH_3) is proposed to be initiated by their reactions with OH radicals. Cox and Sheppard ($\underline{5}$) by gas chromotgraphic techniques have identified sulfur dioxide as the final product for the reaction.

$$X\text{-}S\text{-}Y + OH \longrightarrow Intermediates \longrightarrow SO_2$$

The proposed mechanisms ($\underline{1}$) for the CH_3SH and CH_3SSCH_3 used in this study are: 1) the OH radical forms a weak complex with CH_3SH which further reacts with O_2 before decomposing to form sulfur dioxide. 2) an adduct is formed between CH_3SSCH_3 and OH radical which decomposes to yield CH_3S and CH_3SOH. These mechanisms have been proposed to account for the pressure-dependence and temperature-dependence of the observed reaction rates. The mercaptyl radical thus formed

0097–6156/87/0349–0170$06.00/0

could undergo further chemical reactions. To date only few studies
(6,7) have been performed to identify the intermediates or products
formed for the hydroxyl radical initiated oxidation of CH_3SH (6),
CH_3SCH_3 (6b,7), and CH_3SSCH_3.

The initial reaction of SO_2 with OH is proposed to form HSO_3
(8).   The $HOSO_2(HSO_3)$ has recently been identified and characterized
by matrix-isolation infrared spectroscopy (9). Various mechanisms
(10) have been proposed to account for the conversion of HSO_3 to
final product H_2SO_4.

This study was undertaken to isolate and spectroscopically
identify the proposed or other intermediates. The technique employed in this work is that of "Matrix-Isolation" where the reactants are allowed to react in a gas-phase kinetic cell and the
products are subsequently isolated by an inert gas. The isolated
products are then trapped at a cold window (10K) to record the
infrared spectra. This technique is well suited to study the
reactions in which intermediates or the final products are either
unstable or could undergo further chemical reactions.

Experimental

The methyl mercaptan (Matheson) and diamethyl disulfide (Kodak)
were purified by trap to trap distillation. Sulfur dioxide (AIRCO)
was used without further purification. The infrared spectra of
CH_3SH/Ar (1:50), CH_3SSCH_3/Ar (1:50) did not indicate the presence of
any impurity. The infrared spectra of SO_2/Ar (1:100) indicate the
presence of matrix-isolated water.

The hydroxyl radicals were produced by microwave discharge of
H_2O/Ar (1:50) mixture using a Kiva Corp. microwave discharger
operating at 50 watt power. The reflected voltage was always
adjusted to zero to ensure the same amount of incident power on the
quartz tube. This method of producing OH radicals have HO_2, 0 and H
atoms as byproducts (11).   We observe a weak absorption due to HO_2
(1385.7 cm^{-1}) in agreement with published data (12).   In each experiment, NO was observed at 1876.9 cm^{-1}. This is due to the
presence of $N_2(<5$ ppm) as impurity in the UHP argon gas.

Gas mixtures were prepared by standard manometeric technique.
The reaction was carried out in a gas-phase kinetic cell (13).   The
CH_3SH/Ar (1:50) or CH_3SSCH_3/Ar (1:50) or SO_2/Ar (1:00) mixtures were
introduced through inlet A, while the discharged H_2O/Ar (1:50)
mixture was introduced through port 3 (gas-phase path length ~28
cm). In each experiment, ~2.3 mmoles of the sulfur compounds (CH_3SH
or CH_3SSCH_3 or SO_2)/Ar mixture and 1.2 mmoles of microwave discharged
H_2O/Ar mixture were codeposited. The deposition times ranged from 1
hour to 1.5 hours. The products of the gas phase reactions were
matrix-isolated on the CsI window at 10K (for details of the
experimental set up, see reference 13).

The infrared spectra were recorded using a Beckman IR-4250
spectrometer with a resolution better than 1 cm^{-1} in the area of
interest. The spectrometer was interfaced with a MINC 11 micro-
computer, with all spectra digitally recorded and analyzed using our
software.

Results and Discussion

CH$_3$SH + OH Reaction. The observed absorptions for CH$_3$SH/Ar (1:50) are in agreement with the published data (14). The observed absorption due to S-H stretch is at 2941.9 cm^{-1}, while in the gas-phase this stretch is observed at 2947.1 cm^{-1}. The difference between the matrix and gas-phase vibrational frequencies is within the expected range for S-H stretch and other modes of vibrations (15). The observed infrared spectra for the CH$_3$SH + OH reaction is shown in Figure 1A. The absorptions which are not observed in CH$_3$SH/Ar, but are observed in CH$_3$SH + OH reaction must arise from the products or intermediates formed in this reaction. These absorptions are listed in Table I.

Table I: Observed Vibrational Frequencies for Products
of the CH$_3$SH + OH Reaction

Absorbing Species	Frequency[a] (cm^{-1})	Assignment
-----	2879.4	-----
-----	2551.3	-----
CH$_3$SNO	1527.9	S-NO stretch
SO$_2$	1360.0	S-O stretch
SO$_2$	1357.6	S-O stretch
SO$_2$	1350.0	S-O stretch
SO$_2$ · H$_2$O	1340.4	S-O stretch
-----	1285.7	-----
SO$_2$	1154.4	S-O stretch
SO$_2$	1149.7	S-O stretch
CH$_3$SHOH	1038.8	S--O stretch
CH$_3$SHOH	1007.6	S--O stretch
-----	707.6	-----
SO$_2$	513.8	S-O bending

[a]The infrared absorption frequencies were calibrated by using the standard CO$_2$ absorption frequencies.

Hatakeyama and Akimoto (6) have observed SO$_2$, NO, NO$_2$, HCHO, RCHO, RCH$_2$OH, and CH$_3$SO$_3$H as products in photoxidation of CH$_3$SH-RCH$_2$ONO - (NO)$_x$ - air system. The absence of RCH$_2$ONO as a reactant in our experiments precludes RCHO, RCH$_2$OH, NO, NO$_2$ as products in our study. Thus, based on previous experimental studies (6), we should expect SO$_2$, CH$_3$SO$_3$H as the final products in our study. The matrix-isolated SO$_2$ has absorptions at 1350.72, 1149.96, and 516.9 cm^{-1} (16). The gas-phase spectra of CH$_3$SO$_3$H has absorptions at 3611, 1404, and 1204 cm^{-1} (17).
The observed absorptions (Table I) at 1360.0, 1357.6, 1350.0, 1340.4, 1154.4, 1149.7, and 513.8 cm^{-1} are assigned to SO$_2$ molecule. The absorption at 1527.9 cm^{-1} is assigned to CH$_3$SNO molecule even

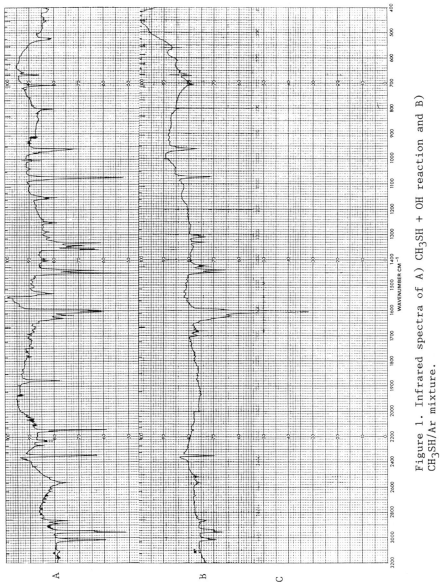

Figure 1. Infrared spectra of A) CH₃SH + OH reaction and B) CH₃SH/Ar mixture.

though the other absorptions (1304.4 and 648.4 cm^{-1}) are too weak to observe (6). The presence of CH$_3$SNO as a product suggests that CH$_3$S is an intermediate in the CH$_3$SH + OH reaction which subsequently reacts with NO to form CH$_3$SNO. The nitrogen oxide in our experimental set up is formed by the microwave discharge of N$_2$ and O$_2$ which are present as impurities in UHP argon gas. The remaining observed absorptions are at 2879.4, 2551.3, 1285.7, 1251.3, 1038.8, 1007.7, and 707.6 cm^{-1}. One of the likely molecule could be CH$_3$SHOH. This molecule has been suggested as the first inter- mediate in CH$_3$SH + OH reaction (1). The absorptions unique to this molecule will be due to S-O stretch, HSO and HOS bending. The observed vibrational absorptions due to S-O stretch occur in the 777-1083.4 cm^{-1} range in different type of molecules (18). For the HSOH molecule the S-O stretch is observed at 1083.4 and 747.4 cm^{-1} (19). The substitution of CH$_3$ group for H should lower this frequency. Thus, we assign the absorptions at 1038.8 and/or 1007.6 cm^{-1} to S-O stretch. The S-OH stretch in methane sulfonic acid (CH$_3$SO$_3$H), is observed at 980 cm^{-1}. We observe a very weak absorption at 976.3 cm^{-1}. Thus, we tentatively assign the absorp- tion at 1038.8 and 1007.6 cm^{-1} to S-O stretch in CH$_3$SHOH, since these peaks could not arise from S-OH stretch in CH$_3$SO$_3$H. The vibrational absorption due to the HOS bending mode has been observed in the 1122-1177 cm^{-1} region (18). We do observe absorptions in this region, but SO$_2$ also has absorptions at 1154.4 and 1149.7 cm^{-1}. The intensity considerations have led us to assign these vibrational frequencies to SO$_2$. It is possible that at higher resolution and sensitivity, we may be able to observe the contribution of CH$_3$SHOH complex to this absorption. The absorptions at 2879.4 and 2551.3 are unassigned.

CH$_3$SSCH$_3$ + OH Reaction. The initial step for the OH + DMDS reaction is thought to be the addition of OH radical to S-S bond (1). In that case, the initial products formed can be CH$_3$S and CH$_3$SOH. The CH$_3$S formed can undergo reaction with NO to form CH$_3$SNO as in the case of CH$_3$SH + OH reaction. We observe an absorption at 1526.3 cm^{-1} (Table II), which is assigned to the molecule CH$_3$SNO. The absorption at 1526.3 cm^{-1} has a weak shoulder at 1523.2 cm^{-1}.

As noted earlier, CH$_3$SOH, if formed would have unique absorptions due to S-OH stretch, S-O stretch and HOS bending modes. The S-OH stretch in CH$_3$SO$_3$H is observed at 827.7 cm^{-1}. We observe three absorptions in the region 800-850 cm^{-1} (Figure 2A) but the absorptions due to the fundamentals of CH$_3$SO$_3$H (1405.1 and 1203.5 cm^{-1}) are not observed. Thus, we feel that the absorptions in 800- 850 cm^{-1} region maybe due to S-OH stretch of CH$_3$SOH species. The other remaining absorptions at 1173.2, 1166.9, 1070.1, 1031.0, 1001.3 cm^{-1}, are also assigned to CH$_3$SOH molecule.

The presence of H atoms in the microwave discharge of H$_2$O (11) leads to the possibility that methyl mercaptan (CH$_3$SH) may be formed by the reaction CH$_3$S + H. The absorptions (Table II) at 3010.7 (C-H str.), 2951.3 (S-H str.), 1466.6 (C-H str.), 1326.3 (C-H str.), 1063.8 (C-H str.), 799.7 (S-H str.), and 707.6 cm^{-1} are assigned to CH$_3$SH (14). The presence of CH$_3$SH as a product further confirms the presence of CH$_3$S radical formed through the initial attack of OH radical at S-S bond.

Table II: Observed Vibrational Frequencies for Products
of the DMDS + OH Reaction

Absorbing Species	Frequency[a] (cm^{-1})	Assignment
CH_3SH	3010.7	C-H stretch
CH_3SH	2951.3	S-H stretch
-----	2870.1	-----
-----	2801.3	-----
-----	1743.5	-----
CH_3SNO	1526.3	SN-O stretch
CH_3SNO	1523.2	SN-O stretch
-----	1498.2	-----
CH_3SH	1466.6	-----
SO_2	1356.6	S-O stretch
-----	1351.3	-----
-----	1345.1	-----
SO_2	1338.8	S-O stretch
CH_3SH	1326.3	-----
-----	1248.2	-----
-----	1179.4	-----
CH_3SOH	1173.2	S--O stretch
CH_3SOH	1166.9	S--O stretch
SO_2	1155.0	S-O stretch
SO_2	1151.3	S-O stretch
SO_2	1146.6	S-O stretch
-----	1105.0	-----
CH_3SOH	1071.1	S--O stretch
CH_3SH	1063.8	-----
-----	1040.3	-----
CH_3SOH	1031.0	-----
-----	1023.2	-----
CH_3SOH	1001.2	S-O stretch
-----	999.7	-----
-----	988.8	-----
-----	974.7	-----
-----	835.7	-----
CH_3SOH	821.6	S-OH stretch
-----	801.3	-----
CH_3SH	799.7	S-H bend
CH_3SH	707.6	C-S stretch
SO_2	523.2	S-O bend

[a]The infrared absorption frequencies were calibrated by using
standard CO_2 absorption frequencies.

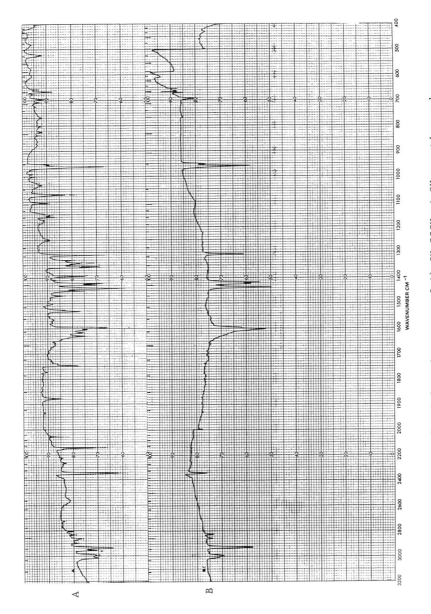

Figure 2. Infrared spectra of A) CH_3SSCH_3 + OH reaction and
B) CH_3SSCH_3/Ar mixture.

<u>SO$_2$ + OH</u>. The observed absorptions due to the products formed in SO$_2$ + OH reaction are listed in Table III.

Table III: Observed Vibrational Frequencies for Products
of the SO$_2$ + OH Reaction

Absorbing Species	Frequency[a] (cm^{-1})	Assignment
HSO$_3$ · H$_2$O	1557.6	H-O-H bend
SO$_2$ · H$_2$O	1403.1	S-O stretch
SO$_2$ · H$_2$O	1391.9	S-O stretch
SO$_2$ · H$_2$O	1348.2	S-O stretch
HSO$_3$ · H$_2$O	1338.8	S(=O)$_2$ stretch
HSO$_3$ · H$_2$O	1329.4	S(=O)$_2$ stretch
-----	1279.4	-----
-----	1141.9	-----
-----	1138.8	-----
HSO$_3$ · H$_2$O	1098.2	S(=O)$_2$ stretch
-----	1035.7	-----
-----	1029.4	-----

[a]The infrared absorption frequencies were calibrated by using the standard CO$_2$ absorption frequencies.

Comparing Figures 3A, 3C, and based on the reported spectrum of SO$_2$ ([16]), we assign the absorptions at 1348.2, 1345.1, 1338.8, 1329.4, 1148.2 and 516.9 cm^{-1} to matrix-isolated SO$_2$. The presence of H$_2$O as a reactant in our experiments could lead to the formation of clathrate complex with SO$_2$. The reported absorptions ([20]) due to SO$_2$· H$_2$O in the solid state at 78K are 780, 1140, 1155, 1340, 1350, 1640, 2410, 3230, and 3380 cm^{-1}. In order to determine the absorptions arising from the SO$_2$ · H$_2$O complex, we codeposited SO$_2$/Ar (1:100) and H$_2$O/Ar (1:50). The observed spectra (Figure 3B) has new absorptions at 1585.8, 1401.3, 1391.9, 1348.2, and 1323.2 cm^{-1}. The absorption at 516.9 cm^{-1} is due to SO$_2$ and has shifted to 513.8 cm^{-1}. The absorption at 1585.8 cm^{-1} is close to the observed HOH bend for matrix-isolated water ([21]). Thus, we assign this absorption (1585.8 cm^{-1}) to HOH bending for the SO$_2$ · H$_2$O complex. The other observed

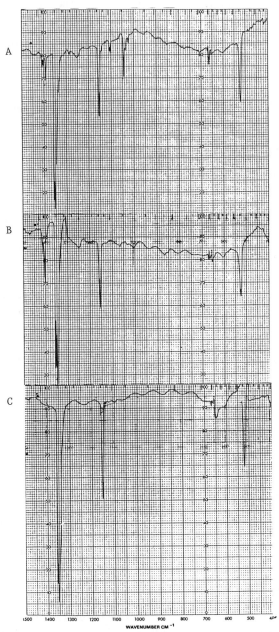

Figure 3. Infrared spectra of A) SO_2 + OH reaction, B) SO_2/Ar (1:100) + H_2O/Ar (1:50), and C) SO_2/Ar (1:100).

absorptions are close to the observed absorptions due to SO_2 molecule
(<u>16</u>). Thus, we assign the absorptions at 1401.3, 1391.9, 1348.2, and
1323.2 cm^{-1} to $SO_2 \cdot H_2O$ complex. A similar behavior is observed for
matrix-isolated $SO_3 \cdot H_2O$ complex (<u>22</u>), where the absorption peaks due
to this complex are very close to those observed for matrix-isolated
SO_3 and H_2O. The shift in vibrational frequencies of SO_2 and
closeness of the new observed absorptions to that of SO_2 suggest that
complex is weak and could have the structure.

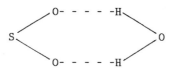

    The remaining absorptions observed in SO_2 + OH reaction are at
1557.6, 1326.3, 1279.4, 1141.9, 1138.8, 1101.3, 1098.2, 1035.7, and
1029.4 cm^{-1}. Hashimoto et al. (<u>9</u>) have assigned the absorptions at
3539.9, 1309.2, 1097.3, and 759.5 cm^{-1} to $HOSO_2$ molecule, but their
absorptions at 1286.8 and 1285.4 cm^{-1} are not assigned. Thus, we
assign the absorptions at 1326.3, 1098.2 cm^{-1} to a molecule having
$S(=O)_2$ stretch. The possible molecules with $S(=O)_2$ are $HOSO_2$, $HOSO_2 \cdot$
H_2O complex, H_2SO_4 (the final product of the hydroxyl radical
initiated oxidation of SO_2), $H_2SO_4 \cdot H_2O$ complex. We do not observe
any absorptions near the gas-phase or the matrix-isolated absorp-
tions due to H_2SO_4 (<u>23,24</u>), and the $H_2SO_4 \cdot H_2O$ complex (<u>22</u>). This
only leaves the possibility that we may be observing different
isomers of HSO_3 molecule and/or $HSO_3 \cdot H_2O$ complex.
    The four possible geometric isomers of HSO_3 are shown below.

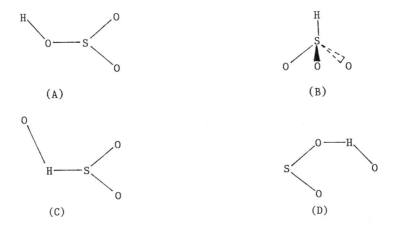

Ab-initio SCF calculations ($\underline{25}$) for the ionic forms of structure A ($HOSO_2^-$) and structure B (HSO_3^-) predict structure A to be slightly more stable (~4 kcal/mole), and to our knowledge no theoretical calculations have been reported for the structures C and D.

The vibrational assignments for structure A has been discussed by Hashimoto et al. ($\underline{9}$). Structure B and C should have unique absorptions due to S-H stretch. The S-H stretch in different molecules is observed in the 2500-2600 cm^{-1} region. However, we did not observe any absorptions in this region. Thus, it rules out the possibility of HSO_3 with structures B and C. The structure D will have a unique absorptions due to OHO and HOS bending modes, but we do not observe any absorptions which can be attributed to OHO and HOS bending. This rules out the possibility of structure D for the HSO_3 molecule.

Our observed vibrations (1326.3 and 1098.2 cm^{-1}) are too close to the reported values ($\underline{9}$) for $HOSO_2$ (structure A). Thus, we feel that the absorptions at 1557.6 (H-O-H bend), 1326.3, 1101.3, and 1098.2 cm^{-1} could arise from a $HOSO_2 \cdot H_2O$ complex. The absence of uncomplexed $HOSO_2$ in our experiments (gas-phase path length ~28 cm) in contrast to the results of Hashimoto et al. ($\underline{9}$) (gas-phase path length ~1 cm) can be attributed to the increase path length.

In all of the SO_2 + OH experiments when the matrix sample was allowed to warm to room temperature (298K), the residual spectra had broad absorptions centered at 1245, 1170, 1030, 860, 595, and 570 cm^{-1}. A comparison of the residual spectra and reported absorptions of $CsHSO_3$ ($\underline{26,27}$) indicate that the product formed on CsI window by the reaction of the product ($HOSO_2 \cdot H_2O$) does not have same structure as observed by Johansson et al. ($\underline{27}$). Based on the reported ($\underline{28}$) Raman vibrational frequencies, we assign the absorptions at 1245 and 1030 cm^{-1} to ν_{as} S-O str. and ν_s S-O stretch respectively. The absorptions at 1170, 595, and 570 cm^{-1} are assigned to δ_s O-H, δ_{as} S-O, and δ_s S-O respectively, but the absorption at 860 cm^{-1} is unassigned. The absence of the residual spectra in SO_2 + H_2O experiments rules out the possibility that the observed residual spectra is due to the product (H_2SO_3) formed by the reaction of unreacted SO_2 and H_2O (ΔH = -1.73 kcal/mole) with the CsI window. This observation provides us with an indirect evidence that we are observing $HOSO_2 \cdot H_2O$ as the product for the gas-phase reaction SO_2 + OH, which at high temperature (T > 45K) reacts with CsI window to form $CsHOSO_2$.

Conclusions

Our results indicate that the OH initiated oxidation of CH_3SH and CH_3SSCH_3 proceed by the mechanisms suggested by Wine et al. ($\underline{1}$) and that SO_2 is a major product in these reactions. The sulfur dioxide formed in these reactions as well as from anthropogenic sources can react with OH to form $HOSO_2$. Our observations lead us to postulate that most of tropospheric $HOSO_2$ formed due to SO_2 + OH reaction will be complexed with H_2O. The experiments with O_2 and NO_x as additional reactants are underway to determine whether the $HOSO_2$ and H_2O complex formation can compete with the proposed reaction of $HOSO_2$ with O_2. Howard et al. ($\underline{30}$) have recently determined the rate of

$HOSO_2 + O_2$ reaction to be 4.4×10^{-13} and show that SO_3 and HO_2 are the reaction products.

Acknowledgment

We wish to thank Dary Engram for performing the experiments and ALCOA Corp. for financial support. One of us (JHH) acknowledges the support from NSF grant ATM 8009560.

Literature Cited

1. a) Wine, P. H.; Kreutter, N. M.; Gump, C. A.; Ravishankara, A. R., J. Phys. Chem. 1981, 85, 2660 and references therein.
   b) Wine, P. H.; Thompson, R. J.; Semmes, D. H., Int. J. Chem. Kinet. 1984, 16, 1623.
2. Calvert, J. G.; Mohnen, V., Acid Deposition Atmospheric Process in Eastern North America, N.A.S. Report (National Academy Press, Washington, 1983) app. A, p. 155; Leu, M. T., J. Phys. Chem. 1982, 86, 4558.
3. Gradel, T. E., Rev. Geophys. Space Phys. 1977, 15, 421.
4. Sze, N. D.; Ko, M. K. W., Atmos. Environ. 1980, 14, 1223.
5. Cox, R. A.; Sheppard, D., Nature (London), 1980, 284, 330.
6. a) Hatakeyma, S.; Akimoto, H., J. Phys. Chem. 1983, 87, 2387.
   b) Grosjean, D., Environ. Sci. Technol. 1984, 18, 460.
7. Niki, H.; Maker, P. D.; Savage, C. M.; Breitenbach, L. P., Int. J. Chem. Kinet. 1983, 15, 647.
8. Calvert, J. G.; Stockwell, W. R., In acid precipitation: SO2, NO and NO2 oxidations mechanisms; Atmospheric Considerations (Ann Arbor Science, Ann Arbor, 1983, ch. 1, and references therein).
9. Hashimoto, S.; Love, G.; Akimoto, H., Chem. Phys. Letts. 1984, 107, 198.
10. Niki, H.; Maker, P. D.; Savage, C. M.; Breitenbach, L. P., J. Phys. Chem. 1984, 84, 14 references therein; Davis, D. D.; Ravishankara, A. R.; Fischer, S., Geophys. Res. Lett. 1979, 6, 113.
11. Wilson Jr., E., J. Phys. Chem. Ref. Data. 1972, 1, 539.
12. Milligan, D. E.; Jacox, M. E., J. Chem. Phys. 1963, 33, 2627.
13. Bhatia, S. C.; George-Taylor, M.; Merideth, C. W.; Hall Jr., J. H., J. Phys. Chem. 1983, 87, 1091.
14. Trotter, I. F.; Thompson, H. W., J. Chem. Soc. 1946, 481.
15. Hallam, H. E. (editor), Vibrational spectroscopy of trapped species, 1973, John Wiley and Sons, N. Y.
16. Allavena, M.; Rysnk, R.; White, D.; Calder, V.; Mann, D. E., J. Chem. Phys. 1969, 50, 3299.
17. Chackalackal, S. M.; Stafford, F. E., J. Am. Chem. Soc. 1966, 88, 4815.
18. Bellamy, L. J., The infrared spectra of complex molecules. Metheun and Co., LTD (London) 1964.
19. Pinchas, S.; Laulicht, I., Infrared spectra of labelled compounds (Academic Press, N. Y., 1971).
20. Harvey, K. B.; McCourt, F. R.; Shurvell, H. F., Can. J. of Chem. 1964, 42, 960.

21. Barnes, A. J.; Szczepaniak, K.; Orville-Thomas, W. J., J. Mol. Str. 1980, 59, 39.
22. Bondybey, V. E.; English, J. H., J. Mol. Spectrosc. 1985, 109, 221.
23. Holland, P. M.; Casteman, A. W., Chem. Phys. Lett. 1978, 56, 511.
24. Chackalackal, S. M.; Staford, F. E., J. Am. Chem. Soc. 1966, 88, 723.
25. Stromberg, A.; Gropen, O.; Wahlgren, U.; Lindquist, O., Inorg. Chem. 1983, 22, 1129.
26. Simon, V. A.; Schmidt, W. Z., Electrochem. 1960, 64, 737.
27. Johansson, L.; Lindquist, O.; Vannerberg, N., Acta. Cryst. 1980, B36, 2523.
28. Simon, A.; Kreigsmann, H., Chem. Ber. 1956, 89, 2442.
29. Benson, S. W., Chem. Rev. 1978, 78, 23.
30. Private Communication, will appear in December, 1986 issue of J. Phys. Chem.

RECEIVED March 16, 1987

Chapter 15

Characterization of a Facility To Simulate In-Cloud Chemical Transformations

A. W. Gertler, N. F. Robinson, and D. F. Miller

Energy and Environmental Engineering Center, Desert Research Institute, University of Nevada System, P.O. Box 60220, Reno, NV 89506

Laboratory simulations of aqueous-phase chemical systems are necessary to 1) verify reaction mechanisms and 2) assign a value and an uncertainty to transformation rates. A dynamic cloud chemistry simulation chamber has been characterized to obtain these rates and their uncertainties. Initial experimental results exhibited large uncertainties, with a 26% variability in cloud liquid water as the major contributor to measurement uncertainty. Uncertainties in transformation rates were as high as factor of ten. Standard operating procedures and computer control of the simulation chamber decreased the variability in the observed liquid water content, experiment duration and final temperature from ± 0.65 to ± 0.10 g m^{-3}, ± 180 to ± 5.3 s and ± 1.73 to ± 0.27°C respectively. The consequences of this improved control over the experimental variables with respect to cloud chemistry were tested for the aqueous transformation of SO_2 using a cloud-physics and chemistry model of this system. These results were compared to measurements made prior to the institution of standard operating procedures and computer control to quantify the reduction in reaction rate uncertainty resulting from those controls.

In-cloud chemical processes transform soluble trace gases into various ionic products. In the case of acid precursors, such as SO_2 and NO_2, definitions of the significant chemical reactions in aqueous cloud droplets are necessary for the mathematical description of acid deposition. These significant reactions can be inferred from measurements in the real atmosphere (1,2), and they can be identified in controlled laboratory experiments (3,4). Since measurements in the real atmosphere may be characterized by large uncertainties (1), laboratory simulation of aqueous phase chemical systems supplement

0097–6156/87/0349–0183$06.00/0

these measurements by 1) verifying the end products of reaction mechanisms and 2) assigning a value and an uncertainty to transformation rates.

Quantification of the uncertainty in the measured transformation rates is crucial if the data are to be used as inputs to models for risk assessment. Without knowledge of the accuracy, precision, and validity of these measured values it is impossible to develop realistic abatement strategies.

This paper will:

● Describe a cloud chemistry simulation facility to emulate atmospheric aqueous phase interactions among gases, particles, and liquid water droplets.

● Identify the most significant physical variables controlling these interactions.

● Quantify the uncertainty of gas to solute transformation rates resulting from uncertainty in the control of the cloud-physical parameters.

System Overview

The cloud chemistry simulation chamber (5,6) provides a controlled environment to simulate the ascent of a humid parcel of polluted air in the atmosphere. The cloud forms as the pressure and temperature of the moist air decreases. By controlling the physical conditions influencing cloud growth (i.e. initial temperature, relative humidity, cooling rate), and the size, composition, and concentration of suspended particles, chemical transformation rates of gases and particles to dissolved ions in the cloud water can be measured. These rates can be compared with those derived from physical/chemical models (7,9) which involve variables such as liquid water content, solute concentration, the gas/liquid interface, mass transfer, chemical equilibrium, temperature, and pressure.

A functional representation of the cloud chemistry simulated chamber is shown in Figure 1. The chamber is constructed of a cylindrical aluminum inner shell 1.8 m in diameter, 2.5 m in height with dome-shaped ends that provide a total volume of 6.6 m³. The walls are jacketed and a steel outer skin, providing temperature uniformity within 0.2°C. Access ports serve for evacuation, pressurization, recirculation, and sampling.

A high-capacity water-seal vacuum pump downstream of an automatically controlled valve provides for chamber evacuation and pressure regulation. The maximum cooling rate is approximately 5°C min⁻¹. The minimum practical pressure is 140 mbar and the minimum temperature is approximately -40°C. Maximum cloud lifetime on the order of 20 min can be realized, limited by nonadiabatic wall conditions and the finite fall speeds of the cloud droplets.

Cloud liquid water content (LWC) is measured by a CO_2 laser transmissometer (λ = 10.6 µm) which linearly relates observed extinction to LWC (10,11).

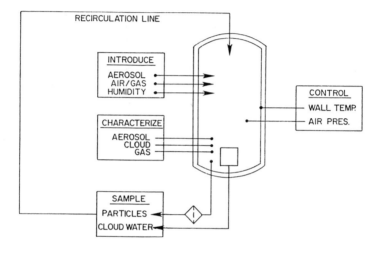

Figure 1.   Cloud chamber schematic.

The experimentally verified theoretical relationship for the extinction coefficient σ_e is given by

$$\sigma_e = \frac{3 \pi c(\lambda)}{2 \lambda \rho} \cdot LWC \tag{1}$$

where ρ is the density of water, $c(\lambda)$ is the wavelength dependent slope of the linearized fit to the Mie scattering function when plotted against particle size, and LWC is the cloud liquid water content. The approximation is valid for droplet diameter less then 28 µm (11).

A cloud water collector that separates unactivated (interstitial) particles from cloud droplets by jet impaction of these droplets on inert surfaces (12) provides a sample for chemical analyses.

The operational procedures of the chamber have recently been upgraded from manual to automatic with the installation of a dedicated computer system (Kinetic Systems Inc., CAMAC with DEC LSI 11/23 microprocessor). This allows precise and reproducible control which was impossible under manual operation. Computer assisted operation was achieved through the development of an algorithm which controls the chamber wall temperature and cooling rate while maintaining a specified differential between air and wall temperature ($\Delta T = 0.0 \pm 0.2°C$). The differential is maintained by adiabatic cooling of the air caused by variation of the rate of evacuation.

Standard operating procedures were instituted along with the computer control. These consisted of procedure check lists to ensure protocols were followed. Conditions prior to commencement of an experimental run were as follows:

Initial air temperature, T_i	24.0 ± 0.5 °C
Initial dew point temperature, T_d	21.0 ± 0.2 °C
Initial pressure (ambient), P	$860. \pm 15$ mb
Aerosol concentration, n_p	$7500. \pm 200$ cm^{-3}
Run-mean cooling rate, dT/dt	-1.5 ± 0.05 °C min^{-1}
Air-wall temperature difference, ΔT	0.0 ± 0.2 °C
Reaction interval, Δt_r	10.0 ± 0.1 min

A run was not performed until these conditions were met.

The system has been characterized with respect to background impurities in the chamber air and in the collected cloud water (Table I). Ammonia is a significant impurity. In the absence of intentionally added reagents, it balances the major anions in the cloud water which are carbonate and formate. The anion/cation balance of background (i.e., blank) cloud water is typically within 10% of unity.

Background non-methane hydrocarbon levels are generally less than 20 ppbC. A typical sample (Table I) indicates that the major components are ethane, propane and acetylene. Because only picomolar amounts of these hydrocarbons would exist in the cloud water, the effects of these background levels on aqueous-phase chemistry are expected to be negligible. The effect of the organic acids is not expected to be significant unless sources of OH exist. Formaldehyde is known to inhibit aqueous SO_2 oxidation, but its concentration here is insignificant compared to the concentrations of SO_2 intentionally

Table I. Trace Background Impurities in the System

	Species	Concentration
Air	NH_3	<2 ppb
	Total nonmethane hydrocarbon	<20 ppbC
	ethane	9.8 ppbC
	propane	3.3 ppbC
	acetylene	3.8 ppbC
	ethylene	0.5 ppbC
Cloud Water	NH_4+	40 μM
	Total organic acids and carbonyls	18 μM
	formate	11.5 μM
	acetate	5.3 μM
	formaldehyde	0.3 μM

added to the cloud chamber. SO_2 experiments are typically conducted with aqueous $S(IV)$ concentrations ranging between 20 and 2000 μM. Thus in this type of experiment, the SO_2 concentration and the conversion to sulfate dominate the pH of the cloud water.

Sources of Variability

The cloud chemistry simulation chamber is a complicated measurement system which cannot be totally controlled, and it is necessary to identify and quantify the sources of variability in the observed chemical and physical parameters. This examination provides the basis for estimating the accuracy, precision, and validity of transformation rates as well as their values.

In order to understand the sources of experimental variability it is important to define terms such as precision, accuracy and validity which are used to describe the results. The precision of an observable is estimated from periodic performance tests and replicate analyses. When separate measurements are combined to obtain data, then the precisions of each separate measurement must be appropriately combined to obtain the overall precision of the results. Accuracy is estimated via comparison of a measurement value with an independent standard. The difference between an observed value and the "true" value as determined by comparison with a standard quantifies the accuracy. Within this context, an observable can be precisely measured and yet be inaccurate. Validity is determined by defining standard operating procedures and identifying deviations from them, and describes the degree to which assumptions of the measurement method have been met. Values are either removed or flagged when deviations take place. The overall measurement process which leads to the reported result is then defined as the procedures, standards, performance tests, audits and validation criteria which produce a measurement with known value, precision, accuracy and validity. Within this framework, the sources of variability in the system can be examined to determine the validity of the experimental results and to quantify the precision associated with those results.

The main question when assessing uncertainties in the cloud chemistry simulation results is: What system parameters have the greatest influence on the observed chemistry? Uncertainties in previously observed transformation rates of SO_2 to sulfate with this facility are as large as a factor of ten (5). If we assume the first order rate of transformation of SO_2 to SO_4, R_{SO_2}, to be

$$R_{SO_2} = \frac{R \ T \ LWC \ \Delta C_{SO_4}}{\rho \ \Delta t_r P_{SO_2}} \tag{2}$$

where R is the gas law constant, T is the average temperature, ΔC_{SO_4} is the sulfate concentration in the cloud water, ρ is the density of water, Δt_r is the cloud lifetime, and P_{SO_2} is the initial gas phase SO_2 concentration. A change in transformation rate, σR_{SO_2}, is related to changes in each parameter by

$$\sigma R_{SO_2} = R_{SO_2} \left[\left(\frac{\sigma T}{T} \right)^2 + \left(\frac{\sigma LWC}{LWC} \right)^2 + \left(\frac{\sigma \Delta C_{SO_4}}{\Delta C_{SO_4}} \right)^2 + \left(\frac{\sigma \Delta t_r}{\Delta t_r} \right)^2 + \left(\frac{\sigma P_{SO_2}}{P_{SO_2}} \right)^2 \right]^{1/2} \quad (3)$$

The non-negligible terms in Equation 3 are temperature, liquid water content, and cloud lifetime.

An analysis of data acquired in numerous experiments confirms the influence of variability in these parameters on measured SO_2 oxidation rates. LWC was found to be the most important physical variable. The variability in LWC, particle concentration, n_p, intial temperature, T_i, final temperature, T_f, dew point, T_d and reaction time Δt_r for the total data set and four subsets composed of different experimental matrices is listed in Table II. Total set is composed of the mean values for all experimental runs performed in the chamber while the four other sets refer to specific subsets of the total as defined by added trace gases (SO_2, NO_2, O_3 and O_3/SO_2) and CCN size (0.1 μm diameter, 0.08 μm diameter or a polydisperse distribution). The variability in liquid water is seen to be between 11 and 27% for these sets. In order to reduce the variability in these parameters, a set of standard operating procedures was instituted along with a dedicated computer for system control.

Results

Replicate experiments were performed in the absence of added trace gases to quantify the reproducibility of the physical parameters both with and without computer control. The results of these experiments are compared with previous results (5) in Table III. Standard operating procedures and computer controls have decreased the variability in the observed liquid water content, experiment duration, and final temperature from ± 0.65 to ± 0.10 g m^{-3}, ± 180 to ± 5.35 s and ± 1.73 to ± 0.27°C, respectively.

For the results of Steele et al. (5), using Equation 3, we find

$$\frac{\sigma R_{SO_2}}{R_{SO_2}} = 63.7\%$$

while the computer control case yields

$$\frac{\sigma R_{SO_2}}{R_{SO_2}} = 14.5\%.$$

This represents an improvement of a factor of 4.4 in reaction rate uncertainty.

An example of the LWC reproducibility using computer control is shown in Figure 2 for a set of un-normalized traces. This represents much improvement over earlier results where manual controls were used. The improvement in LWC variability can be compared with that expected from the theoretically derived uncertainty using a model of

Table II. Mean Values and Standard Deviations for Cloud Runs

	$(10^3 n_p \text{ cm}^{-3})$	T_i (°C)	T_f (°C)	T_d (°C)	Δt_r (s)	LWC (g m^{-3})
Total Set	7.44/1.37	23.3/1.27	9.18/2.85	21.2/.934	446/114.4	2.24/.575
SO_2 Small CCN	7.82/.252	20.8/.387	11.3/1.64	20.6/.326	566/141.5	1.52/.405
NO_2 Small CCN	9.06/3.05	24.0/.605	9.80/2.48	21.2/.736	341/58.1	1.86/.477
O_3	7.58/.195	23.7/.610	9.96/.691	21.7/.646	441/40.7	2.29/.241
O_3/SO_2	7.54/.294	24.1/.621	10.2/1.19	21.7/.424	451/24.6	2.26/.348

Table III. Mean Values and Standard Deviations For Selected Cloud Runs (M/σ)

Series	n_p (10^3 cm^{-3})	T_i (°C)	T_f (°C)	T_d (°C)	Δt_r (s)	Sample Vol (ml)	LWC (g m^{-3})
Control Runs	7.53/0.17	24.06/0.19	3.71/0.27	21.11/0.17	598.1/5.3	4.50/0.69	3.24/0.10
Steele et al., (5)	7.86/0.81	21.22/0.58	1.13/1.73	21.16/0.60	520.0/180	---	1.70/0.44

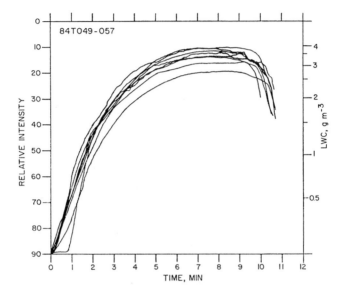

Figure 2. Uncorrected traces of IR intensity from CO_2 transmissometer and the inferred liquid water content LWC for several test runs.

the cloud simulation chamber system (9).   It can be shown that the uncertainty in LWC, σLWC, is

$$(\sigma LWC)^2 = \left(\frac{M_w L}{R}\right)^2 \left[\frac{P_{W_D}^2}{T_D^2}(\sigma T_D)^2 + \frac{P_{W_f}^2}{T_f^2}(\sigma T_2)^2\right] \quad (4)$$

where P_{W_D} and P_{W_f} are the water vapor condensed out between the dewpoint T_d and final temperature T_f, M_w is the molecular weight of water, R is the ideal gas constant and L a constant of the system. For the experimental value of 3.24 g m^{-3} this yields a standard error of 0.083 g m^{-3} in close agreement with the observed value of 0.10 g m^{-3}.

Summary

The characterization of the factors which control the accuracy, precision, and validity of measurements made in a simulation facility for studying in-cloud chemical processes was described.   An analysis of a large number of experimental data collected under widely varying conditions was performed.   Cloud liquid water content, an observable principally dependent on cooling rate and reaction time, was found to be the most influential of the physical factors controlling the resultant chemistry.   In order to precisely control and reproduce the physical conditions in the simulation facility, standard operating procedures and computer control were instituted.   This method reduced the uncertainty of the SO_2 to sulfate transformation rate by a factor of 4.4.

Application of these procedures to future work will yield transformation rate data of known precision.   Additional audits and protocols are necessary to derive data accuracy and validity.   One of the shortcomings of previous experiments is they provide only a value of the observable while neglecting these three attributes.   The institution of this methodology to chemical transformation data obtained with this system would yield results with known uncertainty for use in models of atmospheric chemistry and physics.   Application of the general methodology which comprises the overall measurement process is important not only in the context of measured transformation rates but also in all experiments and programs where the collection of quality data is desired.

Acknowledgments

This work has been supported in part by the Electric Power Research Institute under projects RP1343-1 and RP1434-3 and the Coordinating Research Council, Atlanta, Georgia, under project CAPA-21-80.   We would also like to acknowledge L. Piehl for technical assistance.

Literature Cited

(1)   Hegg, D.A. and P.V. Hobbs, Atmos. Environ., 16, 1633, (1982).

(2)   Dittenhoefer, A.C. and R.G. dePena, J. Geophys. Res., 85, 4499, (1980).

(3)   Lee, Y.-N. and S.E. Schwartz, J. Phys. Chem., 85, 840, (1981).

(4)   Martin, L.R. and D.E. Damschen, Atmos. Environ., 15, 1615, (1981).

(5)   Steele, R.L., A.W. Gertler, U. Katz, D. Lamb and D.F. Miller, Atmos. Environ., 15, 2341, (1981).

(6)   Gertler, A.W., D.F. Miller, D. Lamb and U. Katz in Chemistry of Particles, Fogs and Rain. J.L. Durham, ed., Ann Arbor Science, Ann Arbor, MI, Vol. 2, 131, (1984).

(7)   Scott, B.C., Atmos. Environ., 16, 1735, (1982).

(8)   Hales, J., Atmos. Environ., 16, 1775 (1982).

(9)   Robinson, N. and M.R. Whitbeck, J. Air Poll. Control Assoc., 35, 746, (1985).

(10) Gertler, A.W. and R.L. Steele, J. Appl. Meteor., 19, 1314, (1980).

(11) Chylek, P., J. Atmos. Sci., 35, 286, (1978).

(12) Katz, U., Communications a la VIIIeme, Conference International sur la Physique des Nuages. Clermont-Ferrand, France, 697, (1980).

(13) Richards, L.W., J.A. Andersen, D.L. Blumenthal, J.A. McDonald, G.L. Kok and A.L. Lazrus, Atmos. Environ., 17, 911, (1983).

RECEIVED May 15, 1987

WET AND DRY DEPOSITION

Chapter 16

Comparisons of Wet and Dry Deposition: The First Year of Trial Dry Deposition Monitoring

B. B. Hicks, R. P. Hosker, Jr., and J. D. Womack[1]

National Oceanic and Atmospheric Administration, Atmospheric Turbulence and Diffusion Division, Post Office Box 2456, Oak Ridge, TN 37831

A trial program has been initiated to test inferential methods for measuring dry deposition. Although present capabilities are very limited, preliminary results for sulfur deposition at a few selected locations confirm expectations that submicron particle deposition contributes far less sulfur than does sulfur dioxide gas exchange at the surface. Overall, average total deposition of sulfur by dry mechanisms appears to be much the same as by wet deposition in the northeast, although the short-term difference can be large (in either direction) at any particular location.

There is no simple device which enables the measurement of dry deposition in a manner as convenient as for wet deposition. Instead, comparatively less direct methods must be used, none of which is fully proven as yet. For particle exchange, leaf-washing and through-fall techniques (1) can provide measurements of the accumulated deposit on natural surfaces. Likewise, accumulation on snow surfaces can be sampled, and subjected to subsequent chemical analysis. It is evident, however, that such methods only apply in certain circumstances. Budget techniques are sometimes advocated, such as in the case of calibrated watersheds, but these have rarely delivered unequivocal results. The difficulty that arises is that the dry deposition must necessarily be computed as the difference between poorly determined in-flow and out-flow measurements. These, and a wide variety of other experimental methods, have been reviewed elsewhere (2).

Few such techniques are applicable in the case of trace gas exchange; instead, micrometeorological methods have risen in popularity. In concept, such methods evaluate the flux across a plane above the surface rather than the deposition at the surface itself. Considerable care is necessary to ensure that the flux evaluated above the surface is the same as that at the surface. This constraint is the reason for the widely acknowledged micrometeorological requirements for uniform conditions, surface homogeneity, and terrain simplicity. The most common micrometeorological methods are eddy-correlation and the interpretation of gradients (2). Of these

[1]On assignment from Oak Ridge Associated Universities

two, eddy-correlation is preferred because it provides a direct measurement of the turbulent flux, whereas gradient methods rely on the availability of an eddy diffusivity in order to yield the desired answers. This eddy diffusivity is frequently difficult to derive.

In general, the turbulent exchange of trace gas and aerosol particles cannot always be assumed to be downwards. For many trace gases, the surface constitutes both a source and a sink, leading to wide temporal variations in both the direction and the magnitude of the net exchange. For some chemical species, however, the surface can be assumed to be a continuing sink. Such species include several chemical compounds of current importance, such as sulfur dioxide, nitric acid vapor, and ozone. In such instances, dry deposition fluxes to natural surfaces can be inferred from air concentration data, provided accurate evaluations are available of the efficiency with which the surface scavenges pollutants from the air to which it is exposed. This simple approach is the foundation for the so-called concentration monitoring or inferential method for assessing dry deposition.

The inferential method relies upon the availability of accurate concentration data and corresponding deposition velocities. However, knowledge of these properties alone does not permit the desired deposition data to be computed. As an extension of dry deposition research programs, a trial network has been set up to test the inferential method. Here, the scientific basis for the network operation will be discussed, and preliminary data will be presented.

Theoretical Foundations

Figure 1 presents an example of eddy flux data from a recent intensive field program. The diurnal cycle which is characteristic of most deposition phenomena is clearly evident. If the goal is to derive weekly averaged values of dry deposition, so as to parallel the weekly averaged wet deposition data produced by the National Trends Network, then two options are available. Either concentrations and deposition velocities must be derived with sufficient time resolution to resolve the diurnal cycle, leading to an assessment of the weekly average as an integral of the time varying product, or both properties must be averaged over a sufficiently long time that the average values have statistical uncertainty small in comparison to the diurnal cycle. Because of the cost of chemical analysis, the second alternative is preferred, if it can be applied without great loss of precision. It is partly for this reason that a nested network operation has been initiated.

Figure 2 shows the trial network as it is presently configured, including the supporting sub-network of more intensive measurements intended to provide benchmark data for testing the inferential methods. At stations of this special sub-network (the "CORE" network), data are recorded with finer time resolution, and deposition fluxes are measured using more direct measurement techniques whenever possible.

Measurement of Deposition Velocity

Estimation of appropriate deposition velocities requires balanced consideration of all of the factors controlling the transfer of the

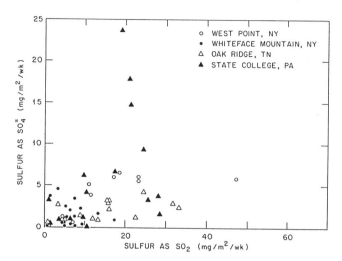

Figure 1. An example of a time sequence of eddy flux measurements of submicron sulfate particles, obtained during a recent study over a deciduous forest at Oak Ridge, TN. Note that negative values indicate fluxes directed towards the ground, i.e., deposition.

Figure 2. The NOAA dry deposition trial network. Additional stations with similar goals but with expanded emphasis on air chemistry are presently being set up by the Environmental Protection Agency, with an initial concentration of effort in the northeast.

material of interest. For some chemical species that are captured efficiently upon contact with any natural surface (such as nitric acid vapor), these factors are largely aerodynamic. Most discussion of the subject identifies two major atmospheric resistance components influencing trace gas and submicron particle transfer: an aerodynamic resistance which is controlled by wind speed, surface roughness, and atmospheric stability, and a quasi-laminar boundary layer resistance which is determined by surface friction and the molecular diffusivity of the substance in question.

Biological resistances are important in the case of gases like sulfur dioxide, which enter plant biomass through stomata. Sulfur dioxide is known to be transferred to mesophyllic tissue in much the same way as carbon dioxide (3). The photosynthetically-mediated exchange properties of plants are therefore critically important. Field experiments have shown that nitrogen dioxide and ozone are transferred similarly, although questions concerning the solubility of these species and the corresponding difficulties with which they enter moist mesophyllic tissue remain to be answered.

All of the many biological transfer processes combine to determine a net surface resistance to transfer. Empirical relationships can be used to infer stomatal resistance from data on photosynthetically active radiation, water stress, temperature, atmospheric humidity and carbon dioxide levels. The resulting net surface resistance has been coupled with mathematical descriptions of aerodynamic and boundary-layer resistances in a "big leaf" model derived on the basis of agricultural and forest meteorology literature (4). At present, the big-leaf model is relatively coarse, permitting application only to areas dominated by maize, soybeans, grass, deciduous trees, and conifers.

In practice, this big-leaf surface resistance model is an engineering tool designed for routine application. A considerably more sophisticated, multilevel canopy model has been developed for comparison purposes and to guide the future development of the big-leaf component. Details of both the engineering big-leaf model and the subcanopy model are presented elsewhere (4, 5).

Measurement of Concentration

Accurate measurement of air quality is a demanding but relatively straightforward chemical task. In the present context, the measurement program is complicated by the need to obtain data in remote locations where concentrations are low. Concentrations must be measured with an accuracy similar to the derivation of deposition velocities (i.e., probably of the order of $\pm$ 30%). There are, of course, other uses for the chemical data for which greater accuracy is certainly warranted. As a convenient goal to guide the chemical measurement program, an accuracy of $\pm$ 10% has been targeted.

Several integral measurement methods were evaluated in the early stages of this program. The wet-chemistry bubbler system deployed in Europe for remote measurement purposes cannot distinguish different chemical species. Since the deposition velocity is very species dependent, clear distinction among different chemical species is required to derive dry deposition rates. Filterpack methods have limitations as well. At the 1982 Technical Committee meeting of the National Atmospheric Deposition Program, conducted in St. Louis, a

filterpack method was recommended, provided modifications could be
made to resolve several perceived difficulties. The desired
filterpack system would permit simple measurement of submicron
aerosol particles using a Teflon filter, detection of nitric acid
vapor using a subsequent nylon filter, and measurement of sulfur
dioxide using a final filter doped with potassium carbonate (or
alternatively, potassium bicarbonate, sodium carbonate, or sodium
bicarbonate). It was recommended that large particles be excluded
from the sampling system, since their deposition cannot be well
addressed using the inferential methods as they are now employed. A
horizontal intake tube is presently being used to permit large
particles to settle before the first filter of the filterpack is
encountered. A heating element along this tube raises the
temperature of the air passing through the tube, so as to maintain a
near-constant temperature at the filter faces (typically about 25 C).
This has essentially eliminated occasions of filter liquefaction.
      It is acknowledged that heating the incoming air stream will
have adverse consequences in the case of some chemical species. In
particular, it is feared that apparent nitric acid concentrations
will be affected by the consequences of volatilization of ammonium
nitrate particles, should such particles exist in the air being
sampled. As yet, there are insufficient data to address this
question directly. The self-regulating heater applies the greatest
temperature increment during the coldest conditions, so that the
thermal diurnal cycle to which the filters are exposed is
substantially reduced. In the context of nitric acid vapor
measurement, it is not yet clear whether the heater is a net positive
or negative influence. From the viewpoint of the validity of the
sulfur dioxide concentrations that are obtained, there is no such
doubt; the heater is an advantage.

Site Operations

The chemical sampler described above is operated at each of the sites
in Figure 2, along with a set of meteorological and surface sampling
devices selected to provide data from which deposition velocities can
be derived. The methods by which these data are analyzed and details
of the measurements being made are given elsewhere (4). In
particular, sensors have been deployed to detect when dewfall, rain,
etc. cause the foliage to be moistened. When the canopy is wet, it
is known to be an improved sink for sulfur dioxide. However, the
magnitude of the effect on deposition velocity is not yet well known.
      Field site operators are required to service the equipment once
every week, at the same time as required by wet deposition networks.
At the time of this writing, discussions are taking place concerning
possible modifications to both the instrumentation and sampling
protocols used in the initial stages of this trial network operation.

Results

Figures 3, 4, and 5 illustrate month by month comparisons between wet
and dry deposition of sulfur, as derived from the dry deposition
operation described here and from the published records of the MAP3S
precipitation chemistry network. For the dry deposition, inferred
values of the deposition of sulfur as sulfur dioxide have been added

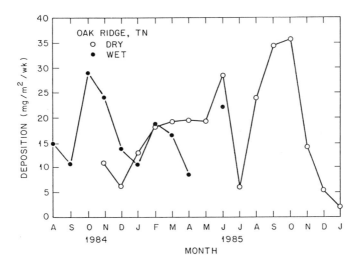

Figure 3. A comparison between dry and wet deposition rates of sulfur, as computed from the trial dry deposition data reported here and from records of MAP3S precipitation chemistry network, for Oak Ridge, Tennessee. Data are reported as average weekly values, computed for each month.

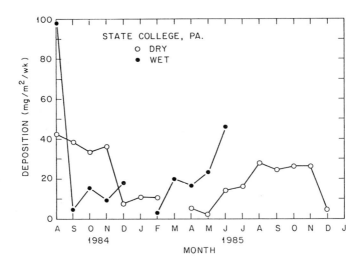

Figure 4. As in Figure 3, but for State College, Pennsylvania.

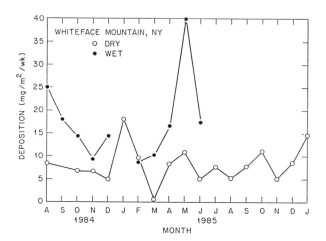

Figure 5. As in Figure 3, but for Whiteface Mountain, New York.

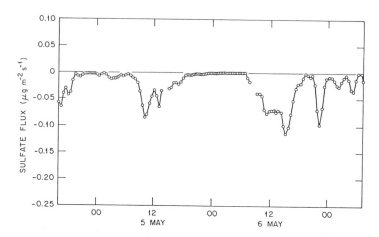

Figure 6. A comparison between weekly sulfur deposition associated with submicron particles and the corresponding deposition resulting from sulfur dioxide uptake at the surface.

onto the values deduced for the deposition of sulfur as submicron sulfate. For the wet deposition, the total sulfur content of the precipitation samples is used. Values are reported as the average weekly deposition for each month.

As yet, the data do not permit a clear picture of the comparison between wet and dry deposition of sulfur. For some periods, it is evident that dry deposition greatly exceeds wet, but for other periods the opposite is true. At this time, generalization is not possible, nor are the dry deposition values computed with enough confidence to warrant extended discussion. In particular, the derivation of dry deposition assumes, for the moment, that surfaces when wetted behave as if they were wetted by rainfall (typically containing dissolved SO_2 as a consequence of their fall through the lower atmosphere and hence a poor receptor for depositing SO_2 molecules), whereas in reality wetting by dewfall will cause an increase in the sulfur dioxide deposition rates. For this reason, the dry deposition values plotted in Figures 3, 4, and 5 are viewed as underestimates, likely to be increased somewhat as the result of research presently under way.

Figure 6 is a plot of particulate sulfur deposition versus the gaseous component. It is often claimed that the deposition of sulfur as submicron particles is small in comparison to the deposition as gaseous sulfur dioxide. Inspection of the diagram reveals that the present data and analysis are in support of this common contention.

Conclusions

In the absence of some general technique suitable for monitoring dry deposition, inferential methods provide a solution. The trial network presently in place appears to be operating as expected. Weekly data produced by this network already reveal the expected importance of dry deposition as a major contributor to the net input of atmospheric sulfur to terrestrial ecosystems, and show the expected dominance of gaseous input over submicron particle deposition.

Acknowledgments

This work was supported by the National Oceanic and Atmospheric Administration as a contribution to the National Acid Precipitation Assessment Program.

Literature Cited

1. Lindberg, S. L., and R. C. Harriss, *Water, Air and Soil Pollut.* 16, 13 (1981).
2. Hicks, B. B., M. L. Wesely, and J. L. Durham, Critique of Methods to Measure Dry Deposition, EPA Workshop Summary, NTIS PB81-126443 (1980).
3. Chamberlain, A. C., Chapter 22 of "Atmospheric Sulfur Deposition," Ann Arbor Science, Ann Arbor, Michigan (1980).
4. Hicks, B. B., D. D. Baldocchi, R. P. Hosker Jr., B. A. Hutchison, R. T. McMillen, and L. C. Satterfield, NOAA Technical Memorandum, ERL/ARL-241 (1985).
5. Baldocchi, D. D., B. B. Hicks, and P. Camara, ATDL 85/7, *Atmos. Environ.*, in press (1986).

RECEIVED May 13, 1987

Chapter 17

Rainwater Chemistry near an Isolated SO₂ Emission Source

Richard J. Vong[1], Timothy V. Larson[1], William H. Zoller[3], David S. Covert[2],
Robert J. Charlson[4], Ian Sweet[1], Richard Peterson[3], Theresa Miller[3],
John F. O'Loughlin[3], and Margaret N. Stevenson[3]

[1]Department of Civil Engineering, University of Washington FX-10, Seattle, WA 98195
[2]Department of Environmental Health, University of Washington FX-10,
Seattle, WA 98195
[3]Department of Chemistry, University of Washington FX-10, Seattle, WA 98195
[4]Department of Atmospheric Sciences, University of Washington FX-10,
Seattle, WA 98195

A network of 38 rainwater collection sites was
established in the Seattle-Tacoma area of
Washington State both upwind and downwind of the
dominant regional SO_2 emission source, a copper
smelter. Rainwater samples were chemically
analyzed for pH, major ions and trace metals (via
INAA). Results are presented for a precipitation
event sampled by the network on February 14-15,
1985. Two collectors were operated at each site
with these paired results statistically screened
for potential contamination based on indpendently
measured experimental uncertainties. Geographical
mapping of rainwater concentrations demonstrated a
clear enhancement of H^+, excess $SO_4^=$, and
trace metals downwind of the smelter. Principal
component analysis revealed the influence of
seasalt, crustal material, and a component
interpreted to represent smelter SO_2 and trace
metal emissions.

It is important to improve our understanding of the complex
relationships between emissions and subsequent deposition
of atmospheric sulfur compounds. These relationships are
difficult to examine in the northeastern United States and
in central Europe because the relative contributions of
local and distant emissions vary. In the Puget Sound area
of Washington State clean background air (1) moves inland
from the Pacific Ocean past a relatively small number of
emission sources. Most precipitation falls as rain and is
associated with cyclonic frontal systems which result in
steady southwesterly air flow aloft. The combination of a
clean background, very few sulfur sources, and consistent
meteorology suggests that rainwater source-receptor
relationships may be simpler in the Puget Sound area than
elsewhere.

0097–6156/87/0349–0204$06.00/0
© 1987 American Chemical Society

The two major SO_2 emission sources in Western
Washington are a copper smelter located in Tacoma, WA.
(4 kg/sec SO_2) and a coal fired power plant located near
Centralia,WA. (1.7 kg/sec SO_2). Additional SO_2 sources
in the Seattle-Tacoma area total about 50 percent of the
smelter's SO_2 emissions.

The approach taken to observe the impact of the
copper smelter on mesoscale variations rainwater
composition was to determine the spatial, temporal, and
experimental components of the variability of a number of
appropriate chemical species in the rainwater. This paper
presents results for 1985, during smelter operation, and
includes: (1) estimates of the experimental variability in
chemical composition, (2) an approach for a two step
chemical and statistical screening of the data set, (3) the
spatial variation in rainwater composition for a storm
collected on February 14-15, and (4) a principal component
analysis of the rainwater concentrations to help identify
source factors influencing our samples.

Experimental

A network of 38 rainwater sampling sites was established
upwind and downwind of the copper smelter in the
Seattle-Tacoma area of Washington State. Figure 1 shows
the location of the rainwater sampling sites, the copper
smelter, and urban areas of Western Washington State.
Storms sampled by this network were pre-selected based on
synoptic meteorological information in an attempt to sample
cyclonic frontal rain that was fairly uniform over the 80
km. extent of our network. The sampling protocol required
that a period of good atmospheric ventilation preceed rain
sampling. Dry deposition was not evaluated but is expected
to be small compared to wet deposition due to low ambient
pollutant concentrations during rainy weather.

Surface wind speed and direction from six sites were
available at four hour intervals during the 24 hour sample
collection. These data indicate that surface winds in the
Tacoma-Seattle area were consistently southwesterly at 10
knots on February 14-15. A rawindsonde confirmed
southwesterly flow aloft. Frontal precipitation as rain
occurred with the mean rainfall accumulation across the
network of 0.5 cm. in a 3 hour period.

Hydrogen ion was computed from measurements of pH on
the unfiltered rainwater samples. The samples were then
filtered and chemically analyzed by inductively coupled
argon plasma emission spectroscopy (ICP) for the soluble
fraction of Na, Mg, Ca, K, Fe, and Zn, by ion
chromatography (IC) for NO_3^-, Cl^-, SO_4^-, Na^+,
and NH_4^+, by flameless atomic absorption spectroscopy
(AAS) for Pb, and by instrumental neutron activation
analysis (INAA) for the soluble fraction of Na, Al, Ti, Ca,
Cu, V, Mn, In, Br, Sb, As, and Au. 50 ml of the filtered

rainwater was frozen, freeze-dried to residue, re-dissolved in Ultrex HNO_3 and deionized H_2O, transfered to polyethylene bags, and again freeze-dried to residue for INAA. Irradiation with thermal neutrons was performed at the Los Alamos Omega West reactor. The first irradiation (shorts) was for 5 minutes with a flux of $6 * 10^{12}$ $n/cm^2/sec$. Later there was a second irradiation (longs) for 4 hours with a flux of $9.7 * 10^{12}$ $n/cm^2/sec$. Shorts were counted on a Ge(Li) detector for 5 minutes after a 5 min. decay and for 19 min. after a 20 min. decay. Longs were counted on a Ge detector for 4 hours after a 3-5 day decay and 8 hours after a 30 day decay. The filters used to remove particulate matter from the rainwater samples also were analyzed by INAA to determine the insoluble fraction of trace metal species.

Two pre-washed (HNO_3, then repeated distilled, deionizied H_2O rinses until conductivity was less than 1 uS/cm) funnel and bottle collectors were deployed at each site in response to a weather forecast. The sites were operated by community college students, Seattle Water Department personnel, high school teachers and students, and University of Washington personnel. At one 'control' site which we operated ourselves at a representative but particularly ideal location (behind a locked gate on a large grassy field which was well removed from traffic and combustion sources), ten co-located samples were collected to determine the 'uncontaminated' experimental uncertainties. These measurements quantify the overall experimental uncertainties due to the rain sampler preparation, handling, and transport to the field site, rainwater collection, sample filtration and storage, and the analytical procedures. Table 1 presents these uncertainties for the 10 co-located samplers. For rain amount, H^+, $SO_4^=$, As, Sb, Mg, Cl^-, and NO_3^- the measured field collection and chemical analysis combined uncertainties represented 4-13 percent of the measured concentrations. For Na^+, Pb, and Ca^{++} the measured uncertainties represented 22-26 percent of the measured concentrations.

Data Screening

The paired samples which were collected at each site were compared to the results of the 10 sampler experiment to detect samples of poor quality. This procedure was utilized to insure than experimental uncertainties did not contribute to the observed variation in composition. The variance for each species listed in Table 1 from the control site was statistically compared to the variance for the paired samples at all sites with an F-test. One of the paired measurements at a site was rejected if their variance was significantly (p <0.005) greater than measured at the control site and one of the pair had a significantly (p <0.005) poorer charge balance (sum of

Table I
Experimental Uncertainty from 10 Co-located Samplers
Collected at one 'Control' Site for Two Rain Events
(Expressed as the average of two storms in stated units)

Analyte	Mean[a]	Units	Std.Dev.[b]	(100* b/a)
Cl	31.1	ueq/L	3.9	13 %
NO3	5.8	ueq/L	0.3	5 %
H+	13.1	ueq/L	0.54	4 %
rain	0.5	cm	0.03	6 %
SO4	16.7	ueq/L	0.83	5 %
As	8.5	ppb	0.88	10 %
Sb	0.83	ppb	0.098	12 %
Pb	4.	ppb	1.	25 %
Na	23.4	ueq/L	5.2	22 %
Mg	6.6	ueq/L	0.5	8 %
Ca	10.6	ueq/L	2.8	26 %
NH4 *	3.3	ueq/L	2.3 *	70 % *

a Average for two storms except As, Sb, NH_4 which are
  one storm.
b Standard deviation as the mean of the two standard
  deviation(s).
* Below detection limit samples reduce confidence in
  the NH_4^+ result. NH_4^+ precision is not well
  determined.

cations/anions either less than 0.88 or greater than 1.2)
than the 'control' site samples. Remaining pairs were
averaged before further analysis. Five percent of the
measurements were rejected based on this statistical and
charge balance criteria (2).

Results

The rainwater chemical concentrations were examined to
determine the spatial variations of several species over
the mesoscale extent of the sampling network. Geographical
mapping of rainwater concentrations demonstrated an
enhancement of H^+, $SO_4^=$, As, Pb, Cu, In, and Sb
downwind of the smelter (to the northeast), consistent with
the hypothesis that the smelter was an important source of
these species.
    Figure 2 depicts the variation in excess, non-seasalt,
$SO_4^=$ ($SO_4^=$ xs, calculated as $SO_4^=$ minus 0.25 *
Na^+ on a mass basis), H^+ from pH, total As (sum of
soluble and insoluble), and soluble Pb over the network for
a storm sampled on February 14-15, 1985. For this storm,
the insoluble fraction of As was 20 percent of the
concentrations in the soluble phase and was very similiar
to soluble As in geographical distribution. Except for Pb,
the plotted concentrations are highest just to the
northeast of the smelter. Pb and NO_3^- are generally
highest in the Seattle area and further northeast although
Pb was also elevated near the copper smelter for other
storms collected by our network. This is consistent with a
possible automotive source of Pb and NO_3^- in the
Seattle area.
    Other species of interest include Sb, Ca, Na^+,
and V. Soluble and insoluble Sb had very similiar
geographical distributions to that of As. The mass ratio of
As/Sb in rainwater was 8:1, similiar to their ratio in
aircraft samples collected in February 15, 1986 in smelter
plume (3) and to the As/Sb ratio in fine and total
particles collected at two ground level sites in the middle
of our network, during the same precipitation event. Ca and
V are highest north of the city of Seattle, consistent
with a possible influence by a cement plant and fuel
burning sources which are located in the industrial area
just upwind (to the southwest). V was present in the
soluble and insoluble fractions of the rain. Na^+ is
largely present in the soluble fraction and is highest in
the Olympia and Tacoma areas south of the smelter,
consistent with the location of those sites generally
closer to the Puget Sound.
    We have analyzed the rainwater chemical data with
multivariate data analysis techniques to identify sources
influencing the area covered by our sampling network. Two
events were included in the principal component analysis
(PCA): the February 15 storm presented here and another
storm collected during smelter operation on March 20, 1985

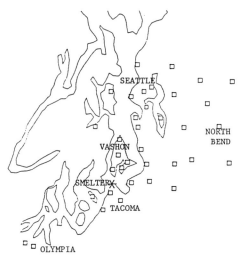

Figure 1: Map of Western Washington State, USA with rainwater sampling sites indicated along with the location of the copper smelter and urban population centers.

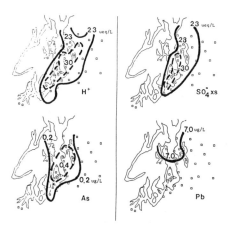

Figure 2: Spatial variation of rainwater H^+, $SO_4^=$xs, As, and Pb concentrations for a storm collected February 14-15, 1985. Solid and dashed lines define constant concentrations (units indicated on map).

and reported elsewhere (2). The calculations were performed
using the ARTHUR software (4). Since the concentrations of
each species over the network were more nearly log-normal
than normal, the data were natural-log transformed before
further analysis. The data were also preprocessed
('autoscaled') to give each variable equal weight in the
PCA (4,5). The number of significant components in the
rainwater data was determined to be 3-5 based on the
Malinowski indicator function criteria or cross-validation
which determine the number of components that minimize the
residual variance not described by the model (6,7). These
components were examined for the loadings of each species
(how well a species correlates with the component). The
chemical composition of each factor or component was
interpreted to be the chemical species with factor loadings
of at least 0.25 (2,5). The composition of the three
significant components is:

(a) Mn, Al, Ca, Ti, V (insoluble), NO_3^- (soluble),
(b) As, Sb, Pb, Cu, Fe, H^+, $SO_4^=$ xs (both soluble and
    insoluble fractions of the metals),
(c) Na^+, Cl^-, Mg^{++} (soluble).

These three components describe 62 percent of the
variance in the original data set (2). Component (a) is
interpreted to represent a low level influence of crustal
material on our samples. Component (c) is interpreted to
represent the influence of seasalt due to the proximity of
our sampling area to saltwater in the Puget Sound.
Component (b) may represent the influence of the Tacoma
copper smelter emissions. It could result from production
of $SO_4^=$ from atmospheric oxidation of SO_2 in the gas
or liquid phases. The chemical composition of component (b)
also corresponds to the trace metal fingerprint of the
Tacoma copper smelter as identified in several studies
(5)(8)(9)(10). The values of factor scores for component
(b) can be thought of as the relative degree of influence
of the smelter's emissions at a given site in our rain
sampling network. As expected, the lowest factor scores for
component (b) correspond to the meteorologically upwind
area of our network (south of the smelter) and the highest
factor scores occur immediately downwind of the smelter (to
the northeast) (2). In other words, the data correlations
for this principal component have a similiar spatial
variation as the single species which are mapped in
Figure 2.

Discussion

Examination of the spatial variation in the concentrations
of excess $SO_4^=$, As, and H^+ reveals an area of
influence of some source of sulfur and arsenic on rainwater
composition immediately to the northeast (downwind) of
Tacoma,WA. Since the Tacoma smelter is the major emission

source of As and SO_2 in the region, it is very probable that the smelter is the source of those same species in downwind rain and also the cause of the depression in rainwater pH.

Principal component analysis has identified at least three factors which contribute to the composition of rainwater near the copper smelter. Seasalt and crustal material are two important contributors to the soluble and insoluble fractions, respectively, of our rain samples. The remaining component has been interpreted to result from the gaseous and particulate emissions from the copper smelter. Smelter emissions can potentially produce at least two separate components, considering that the rainwater excess $SO_4^=$ is most likely produced by gas or liquid phase oxidation of gaseous SO_2 emissions from the smelter (or other smaller SO_2 sources), the trace metals in component (b) are emitted by the smelter as particles, and the large number of resulting pathways for incorporation of the two types of smelter emissions into cloud and rain drops. However, for the two events examined in this analysis, the trace metal and H^+ /$SO_4^=$ xs component concentrations were best described by a single principal component.

Conclusions

Measurement of the experimental uncertainties in our rain sampling procedures and the application of these uncertainties in a screening procedure to eliminate questionable samples from the data set increases the confidence in the interpretation of spatial variations in rainwater composition and of the principal component analysis. Results presented here for a storm collected during smelter operation suggest that it was the major source of the downwind excess $SO_4^=$ elevation above background and the pH depression below the background value of 5.

Acknowledgments

This work was supported by USEPA and Battelle PNL as part of the National Acid Precipitation Assessment program but has not been reviewed by them and the findings are those of the authors and not the USEPA.   The authors are grateful to the Seattle Water Department, Evergreen State College, Green River and Highline Community Colleges, Vashon Island, Tacoma, Olympia, King County, and Mt. Vernon School Districts for providing sampling sites and for sample collection.

Literature Cited

(1) Vong,R.J., 'Simultaneous Observations of Rainwater and Aerosol Chemistry at a Remote Mid-latitude Site', PhD Dissertation, University of Washington, Seattle,WA., 1985.

(2) Vong,R.J., Larson,T.V., and Zoller,W.H., 'A
     Multivariate Chemical Classification of Rainwater
     Samples', accepted for publication in Chemometrics
     and Intelligent Laboratory Systems, 1986.

(5) Alkezweeny,A.J., Peterson,R.E. and Laulainen,N.S.,
     unpublished data, Battelle PNL, Richland,WA, 1986.

(4) Duewer,D.L., Harper,A.M., Koskinen,J.R., Fasching,J.L.,
     and Kowalski,B.R., ARTHUR multivariate software,
     version 3-7-77, Infometrics,Inc., Seattle,WA., 1977.

(5) Vong,R.J., Frank,I.E., Charlson,R.J., and Kowalski,
     B.R., 'Exploratory Data Analysis of Rainwater
     Composition', in Environmental Applications of
     Chemometrics, ACS Symposium Series 292, (ed. J.J.
     Breen and P.E.Robinson), 34-52, American Chemical
     Society, Washington, D.C., 1985.

(6) Malinowski,E.R., 'Abstract factor Analysis- a Theory of
     Error and its Application to Analytical Chemistry', in
     Chemometrics, Theory and Application, (ed. B.R.
     Kowalski), ACS Symposium Series 52, American Chemical
     Society, Washington, D.C., 1977.

(7) Wold,S., Technometrics, 20,, 397, 1978.

(8) Knudson,E.J., Duewer,D.L., Christian,G.D., and
     Larson,T.V., 'Application of Factor Analysis to Rain
     Chemistry in the Puget Sound Region', in Chemometrics
     Theory and Application, (ed. B.R.Kowalski), ACS
     Symposium Series 52, American Chemical Society,
     Washington, D.C., 1977.

(9) Larson,T.V., Charlson,R.J., Knudson,E.J.,
     Christian,G.D., and Harrison,H., Water, Air, and
     Soil Pollution, 4, 319, 1974.

(10) Vong,R.J., Larson,T.V., Covert,D.S. and Waggoner,A.P.,
     Water, Air, and Soil Pollution, 26, 71-84, 1985.

RECEIVED July 17, 1987

Chapter 18

Sulfur, Halogens, and Heavy Metals in Urban Summer Rainfall

S. Landsberger[1,3], S. J. Vermette[2], and J. J. Drake[2]

[1]Nuclear Reactor, McMaster University, Hamilton, Ontario L8S 4K1, Canada
[2]Department of Geography, McMaster University, Hamilton,
Ontario L8S 4K1, Canada

We have employed two multi-elemental techniques
(INAA and ICP-AES) to determine sulphur, halogens
and 14 other trace elements in urban summer rainfall. Quality control was assured using NBS
reference materials. The overall accuracy and
precision of these two methods makes possible the
routine analysis of many environmentally important
trace elements in acid rain related investigations.
Enrichment factor calculations showed that several
elements including S, Cu, Zn and Cr were abnormally
enriched in the urban atmosphere. A comparison of
three separate sites showed a strong gradient of
metal deposition from the industrial to the out-
laying areas.

The study of pollutant deposition in an urban environment is often
reported from bulk rain samples (1) without due consideration being
given to the individual contributions of wet and dry deposition.
The interpretation and utility of elemental concentrations derived
from bulk samples is restrictive and of limited use due to their
dependence on time of exposure to dry deposition, varying volumes
of collected rainwater and wind direction, all of which are often
not reported.

The intent of this paper is to report wet-period elemental
concentrations for 18 targeted trace elements in the summer rains
of the very heavy industrialized city of Hamilton, Ontario. Samples
were collected from three rain events in the summer of 1985 and
although the sampling period represents a small fraction of total
summer rains, useful environmental interpretations can be made.

[3]Current address: Department of Nuclear Engineering, University of Illinois,
214 Nuclear Engineering Laboratory, 103 South Goodwin Ave., Urbana, IL 61801

In particular, we demonstrate the usefulness and compatibility
of two multi-element methods of analysis: instrumental neutron
activation analysis (INNA) and inductively coupled plasma-atomic
emission spectroscopy (ICP).

The results and interpretations reported here are preliminary
and part of an on-going study of pollutants in urban precipitation.

Rain Sampling

Wet-period rainwater samples (washout and rainout) were collected
from three sites in the Hamilton area: near the industrial area
(beach strip), in the city centre and at the rural Hamilton Airport
(Figure 1).

The wet-period collectors employed were modified Canadian
Atmospheric Environment Service standard raingauges. All components
of the gauge are made of plastic and consist of a funnel with an
orifice of 100 cm^2, a graduated collection tube and the housing unit.
The entire gauge stands about 36 cm in height. The modification
includes a spring loaded plastic lid which keeps the orifice of the
gauge covered during dry periods. The onset of rain wets and thus
weakens a degradable tissue which normally holds the lid closed.
The force of the spring tears the tissue and opens the lid thus
exposing the collector orifice to the rain. The amount of rain
required to wet the tissue enough to open the collector is 0.1 mm.
A more detailed description of the gauge and its operation has been
reported elsewhere (2). Samples were collected immediately after
each rain event.

The funnel and collector tubes were thoroughly washed with
deionized distilled water and ultra pure nitric acid prior to each
installation. One mL of nictric acid was then added to the collector
tubes to prevent absorption. After collection the samples were
refrigerated prior to analysis. Precautions were taken to maintain
clean laboratory conditions.

Chemical Analysis

Instrumental Neutron Activation Analysis (INAA)

The collected rain samples were analysed by INAA at the McMaster
Nuclear Reactor. Ten elements (AL, Br, Ca, Cl, Cu, I, Mg, Mn. Na
and V) were determined.

An aliquot of 5 mL of rainwater was placed into an acid washed
polyethylene vial and transported via a 'rabbit' carrier to the
reactor core which has a nominal neutron flux of 5×10^{12}n cm^{-2} sec^{-1}.
The samples were irradiated for five minutes. The irradiated vials
were then transferred to inert vials which were placed at the snout
of a 22% efficient APTEC detector coupled to a Caneberra Series 90
multichannel analyser and a pile up rejector unit. The resolution
of the system was 2.1 KeV at the 1332 KeV cobalt peak. Typical
dead times were 10% or less. The samples had an average delay time
of 100 seconds and were counted for a period of 10 minutes.

Synthetic standards were used to calibrate the system, and NBS
standards were analysed together with the samples to ensure quality
control: results are shown in Table I.

TABLE I. Results for NBS 1643b Certified Water Standard

Element	INAA[1] (ppb)	ICP-AES[1] (ppb)	NBS Value[2] (ppb)
Al	18 +- 3	---	---
B	---	96 +- 1	(94)
Ba	---	43 +- 1	---
Br	<4	---	---
Ca	35500 +- 2600	38103 +- 1000	(35000)
Cl	4985 +- 220	---	---
Co	---	28 +- 1	26 +- 1
Cr	---	19 +- 2	18.6 +- 0.4
Cu	26 +- 5	25 +- 3	21.9 +- 0.4
Fe	---	102 +- 1	99 +- 8
I	<2	---	---
Mg	7633 +- 667	8133 +- 200	(15000)
Mn	31 +- 1	26 +- 1	28 +- 2
Na	8620 +- 385	---	(8000)
Ni	---	52 +- 4	49 +- 3
S	---	390 +- 14	---
V	43 +- 1	49 +- 1	45.2 +- 0.4
Zn	---	65 +- 1	66 +- 2

[1] All results represent an average value of 4 replicates and standard deviations.

[2] All NBS values certified except those in parenthesis. Several other elements have no provided values.

Inductively-Coupled Plasma Mass Spectroscopy (ICP-AES)

The remainder of the samples were analysed by ICP at the University of Toronto's Institute of Environmental Studies. Concentrations of eight elements (B, Ba, Co, Cr, Fe, Ni, S and Zn) were determined. A complete description of the instrumentation and methodology has been reported elsewhere (3).

Results and Discussion

Elemental Concentrations

The results for the three summer rain events are presented in Table II. As can be seen, there is a wide range of determined concentrations. Our preliminary analysis has shown that the highest concentrations of all elements occurred downwind of the industrial area. The elemental concentrations, particularly for Cu, Mn, Fe, V, and Zn, were substantially lower for sites upwind of the industrial area. Of particular significance was the high concentration of sulphur determined at all three sites. Concentration levels varied from 1180 to 4960 ppb, which are significantly above background levels normally found in rain. Sulphur concentrations varied by only a

TABLE II.   Results for Three Summer Rain Events

Ranges of Concentrations (ppb)

Element	Beach Strip	City Core	Airport
Al	227-2410	53-397	44-758
B	<14	<14	<14
Ba	3-34	2-8	2-12
Br	<1-10	3-13	6-9
Ca	2760-30600	236-3350	196-4540
Cl	429-1070	85-368	90-419
Cr	<7-30	<7	<7
Co	<10	<10	<10
Cu	10-40	<5-23	<7-18
Fe	494-868	24-210	18-200
I	1-10	2-4	4-5
Mg	540-5300	340-920	<120-1870
Mn	148-1497	3-57	3-41
Na	173-2050	84-319	74-577
Ni	<10-30	<10	<10
S	2086-4957	1189-3061	1162-2801
V	3-28	0.2-1	0.1-1
Zn	42-214	36-122	<12-158

factor of five for all rain events and at all three locations.   This
is contrast to the heavy metals (e.g. Zn, Fe, Mn) which ranged in
concentration from 20 to 50 to 500 times, respectively.   This
suggests that a large portion of the sulphur is derived from sources
other than those within the urban area.   The deposition of heavy
metals is confined to the industrial core with a strong gradient
from the industrial to the outlying areas (Figure 1).   Unfortunately
several key elements, such as B, Co, and Ni, could not be determined
by ICP due to high detection limits.

Enrichment Factors

Enrichment factors (EF) were computed using aluminum and sodium as
reference eelements for the earth's crust (4) and seawater (5),
respectively.   Enrichments were calculated by

$$EF = \frac{X/C \text{ Rainwater}}{X/C \text{ Reference Material}}$$

where X is the concentration of the element of interest and C is
the concentration of the reference element.   This procedure is used
to evaluate anthropogenic and natural (e.g. crustal and oceanic)
contributions to elemental loadings.   All elemental enrichment
factors, with the exception of I, Br, and Cl, were determined using
crustal aluminum.   A thorough discussion of EF calculations is given
elsewhere (6).

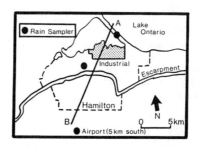

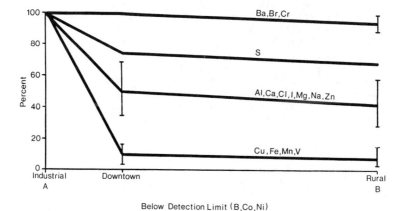

Below Detection Limit (B,Co,Ni)

Figure 1. Location of rain samplers and urban cross-section of average elemental concentrations in rainwater.

The largest EF values were exhibited by sulphur (870-3700).
High EF values were also noted for Cu (<90-400), Zn (<120-830), and
Mn (1-500), with the lower ranges reported for the rural airport
site. Iron showed relatively low EF values (< 1 to 30). Vanadium
exhibited EF values generally from 1 to 10 with the exception of one
event where the value was 68. Concentrations from chromium never
exceeded 30 ppb with EF values ranging from 25 to 100. Halogen EF
values, when compared to sodium concentrations in the ocean, were
generally less than 10 with the exception of iodine. The iodine
enrichment is believed not to be anthropogenic but to arise from
preferential enrichment from the oceans (7).

Conclusions

Eighteen targeted elements have been determined in urban summer
rainfall. We have demonstrated that INAA and ICP offer a unique
combination in determining many environmentally important elements
in a totally non-destructive fashion. Unfortunately, the main disadvantage of both techniques is that neither Pb, Cd, Co, B, and to
a certain extent Cr, cannot be reliably determined in precipitation.
        The work reported here represents one aspect of an on-going
study into the intra-urban distribution and sources of pollutants
in urban precipitation. A dense network of bulk, wet-period and
sequential rain samplers, along with intensity rain gauges are
operating within the Hamilton area.

Literature Cited

1.   Galloway, J.N.; Thornton, J.D.; Norton, S.A.; Volchok, H.L.;
     McClean, R.A.N. Atmospheric Environment 1982, 16, 1677.
2.   Vermette, S.J.; Drake, J.J. Atmospheric Environment 1986, in
     press.
3.   Landsberger, S.; Jervis, R.E.; Balicki, A. International
     Journal of Environmental Analytical Chemistry 1985, 19, 219.
4.   Wedepohl, K.H. "Geochemistry"; Holt, Rinehart and Winston
     Inc: New York, 1971; 91 pp.
5.   Bowen, H.J.M. "Trace Elements in Biochemistry"; Academic Press:
     London, 1966, 241 pp.
6.   Rahn, K.A. "The Chemical Composition of the Atmosphere
     Aerosol"; Technical Report, Graduate School of Oceanography,
     University of Rhode Island, 1976, 264 pp.
7.   Cicerone, R.J. Reviews of Geophysics and Space Physics 1981, 19,
     123.

RECEIVED May 15, 1987

Chapter 19

Introduction of Formate and Acetate Ions into Precipitation: Assessment of Possible Pathways

E. G. Chapman and D. S. Sklarew

Pacific Northwest Laboratory, P.O. Box 999, Richland, WA 99352

Statistical analysis of data from three sites in the eastern United States suggests that little or no correlation exists between low molecular weight organic and inorganic ion concentrations in precipitation, whereas organic ions such as formate and acetate are highly correlated and are probably introduced into precipitation by the same pathway. Based on agreement between observed and calculated potential clear air concentrations of formic and acetic acids, the most plausible pathway involves the scavenging of gas-phase-produced precursors. Further assessment of atmospheric hydrocarbon reactions is needed to better identify specific mechanisms and precursors in this pathway.

The role of low molecular weight organic compounds in precipitation chemistry is of increasing interest to atmospheric scientists. Formate ($HCOO^-$) and acetate (CH_3COO^-) ions have been detected in significant concentrations in precipitation collected throughout the world; typical concentrations observed in remote, rural, and urban areas ([1-4]) are indicated in Table I. Acid forms of these ions are suspected as the parent compounds, although organic salts or compounds such as peroxyacetylnitrate (PAN), which produces acetate and nitrate ions upon dissolution in acidic aqueous solutions ([5]), are also potential sources. Assuming that acid forms are indeed the parent compounds, contributions of the organic acids to free acidity levels as high as 65% have been reported ([6]).

Table I. Observed Organic Anion Concentrations in Precipitation

Location	Range (μM)		Reference
	Formate	Acetate	
Amsterdam Island	2.5-12.	0-2.0	(1)
Round Lake, WI	<0.4-42.	<0.8-24.	(2)
Geneva Lake, WI	1.2-18.	<0.8-8.0	(2)
Charlottesville, VA	0.9-47.	0.7-21.	(3)
Los Angeles, CA	2.3-10.2	2.7-87.6	(4)

0097–6156/87/0349–0219$06.00/0

The mechanisms and pathways that can lead to the presence of low molecular weight organic compounds in precipitation are not well understood. Potential pathways can be classified into three main categories: scavenging of aerosol particles containing organic salts and acids, aqueous-phase oxidation of aldehydes and other acid precursors, and homogeneous gas-phase production with subsequent scavenging. Determining the dominant pathway is important for assessing the potential impact of organic compounds on overall precipitation chemistry, and in particular, for assessing inter-actions with inorganic compounds. For example, preliminary modeling studies suggest that aqueous-phase organic acid formation via oxidation of aldehydes by free radicals may inhibit sulfate production in cloud droplets (7). The degree of inhibition, other organic-inorganic interactions, and the complexity of the dominant reaction mechanism may have important implications for developing large-scale regional acid deposition models.

To better assess potential inorganic-organic ion relationships and the plausibility of various pathways that could lead to the presence of low molecular weight organic ions in precipitation, statistical analyses and equilibrium scavenging calculations were performed on organic and inorganic precipitation chemistry data obtained at three sites in the eastern United States. The results of these analyses were compared to theoretical expectations based on the various pathways.

Methodology

Previously published data from two sites on the Wisconsin Acid Deposition Monitoring Network (2) and the University of Virginia site of the MAP3S Precipitation Chemistry Network (PCN) (3, 8) were used in the current study. The Wisconsin data were obtained for samples collected during the spring of 1984, and the Virginia data were related to selected samples analyzed during the summer of 1983. All three sites operated under similar protocols; precipitation was collected on a daily basis using wet/dry Aerochem Metric samplers, and organic acid aliquots were preserved with a biocidal agent to prevent degradation before analysis. All inorganic analyses were conducted at Pacific Northwest Laboratory (PNL). Organic ion analyses of the Wisconsin samples were also conducted at PNL using ion exclusion chromatography (ICE). Organic ion analyses of the Virginia samples were performed on site at the university, also using ICE. Similar ranges and volume-weighted mean concentrations of the organic ions were observed at the three sites. Details of field collection protocols, analytical procedures and individual sample results are available elsewhere (2, 3, 9, 10).

Organic-inorganic ion relationships were investigated by performing a correlation analysis on the data sets generated by the two studies. All statistical analyses were conducted using MINITAB, a commercially available statistical package (11), with data segregated according to site.

Information obtained during the statistical analyses was used in evaluating aerosol scavenging and aqueous-phase oxidation as the dominant pathways for introducing formate and acetate ions into precipitation. The plausibility of homogeneous gas-phase production

of the organic acids with subsequent scavenging was evaluated via
equilibrium scavenging calculations. These calculations involved
determining the gas-phase concentrations of formic and acetic acids
in equilibrium with the aqueous-phase concentrations measured in
the precipitation samples, as given by the equation

$$G = C_1 [H^+] M / \{K_H (K_1 + [H^+])\} \tag{1}$$

where

$\qquad$ G = equilibrium gas-phase concentration ($\mu g/m^3$)
$\qquad$ C_1 = conversion factor to $\mu g/m^3$
$\qquad$ $[H^+]$ = hydrogen ion concentration ($\underline{M}$)
$\qquad$ M = total aqueous-phase organic ion and undissociated
$\qquad\qquad$ acid concentration measured by ICE ($\underline{M}$)
$\qquad$ K_H = Henry's Law coefficient ($\underline{M}$/atm)
$\qquad$ K_1 = acid dissociation constant ($\underline{M}$)

Potential gas-phase organic acid concentrations [P ($\mu g/m^3$)]
were then calculated for two assumed values of cloud liquid water
content (L, g H_2O/m^3 air) using the equation

$$P = G + \{C_2 (ML)\} \tag{2}$$

where C_2 is again a conversion factor to $\mu g/m^3$. Equation 1 is
derived from mass balance and dissociation equilibrium considerations, and includes the assumption that only formic and acetic
acids contributed to measured organic ion concentrations. Equation 2 is based on a mass balance and yields the clear air organic
acid concentration that would result if liquid water in a cloud
evaporated rather than precipitated. Values used for the various
parameters were based on a total pressure of 1 atm and an assumed
temperature of 10°C (see Table II). K_H and K_1 values were
obtained from Weast (12).

Table II. Values Used in Calculating Equilibrium and Potential
$\qquad\qquad$ Gas-Phase Organic Acid Concentrations

Parameter	Formic Acid	Acetic Acid
K_H ($\underline{M}$/atm)	1.02×10^4	2.85×10^4
K_1 ($\underline{M}$)	1.77×10^{-4}	1.76×10^{-5}
C_1	1.98×10^9	2.58×10^9
C_2	4.6×10^4	6.0×10^4

Results and Discussion

Organic-Inorganic Ion Relationships. Figures 1 and 2 summarize the
Pearson product moments calculated for various formate-inorganic ion
and acetate-inorganic ion pairings, respectively. The correlation
coefficients were generally low (r values usually < 0.6) and

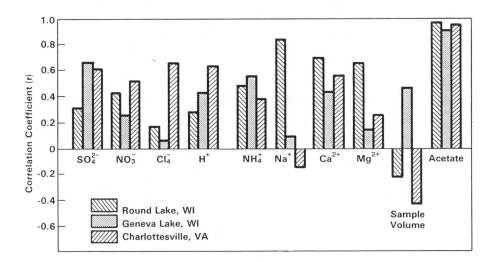

Figure 1.   Correlation Coefficients for Formate-Inorganic Ion Pairings

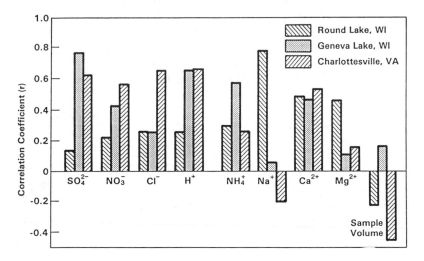

Figure 2.   Correlation Coefficients for Acetate-Inorganic Ion Pairings

relatively nonuniform among the sites for a given pairing. Ammonium and calcium ions demonstrated the most uniform correlations, although considerable intersite variability still exists. Ammonium ion emerged as the primary predictor at two of the three sites in a stepwise regression analysis to statistically identify the variable with the strongest linear relationship with formate and acetate. However, values for the estimated standard deviation about the regression line indicate that the selection of ammonium ion may have been fortuitous rather than from an actual relationship. Correlations with sulfate varied substantially for both formate and acetate, with r values ranging from 0.14 to 0.76. Sulfate was not selected as a predictor in any stepwise regression analysis. The results of this analysis suggest that no strong relationship exists between organic and inorganic ions in the precipitation samples included in this study.

In contrast, the statistical analysis revealed that formate and acetate concentrations were highly correlated at all three sites (r > 0.89). Regression analysis based on the equation $[HCOO^-] = m \times [CH_3COO^-] + b$ yielded values of m ranging from 1.8 to 2.4. The intercepts (b values) were not statistically different from zero. The high correlation coefficients and uniform slope values suggest that the same pathway introduces both formate and acetate into precipitation.

Assessment of the Aerosol Scavenging Pathway. If surface reactions on aerosols and subsequent aerosol scavenging were the primary pathways introducing formate and acetate into precipitation, a substantial and consistent correlation between the organic anions and major aerosol components would be expected. Note that ammonium, a major component of fine particles, and calcium, a major component of coarse particles, demonstrate the most uniform (albeit still relatively low) correlations with formate and acetate. However, other factors, such as similar sources (e.g., biological) or similar seasonal concentration variations can influence the degree of correlation observed for various ions. The magnitude of the correlation coefficients, the intersite variability, and the stepwise regression results suggest that these other factors cannot be ignored in discussing potential organic-ammonium and organic-calcium relationships. Based on the current analysis, the scavenging of aerosols cannot be eliminated as a viable pathway for the introduction of low molecular weight organic compounds into precipitation. However, the ambiguity of the statistical analysis results suggests that aerosol scavenging is probably not the dominant pathway.

Assessment of Aqueous-Phase Oxidation Pathway. The results of two modeling studies (7, 13) employing chemical reaction schemes that included aqueous-phase formic acid formation are summarized in Table III. The reaction mechanism used by Adewuyi et al. (7) included the aqueous-phase oxidation of formaldehyde by hydrogen peroxide and hydroxy radicals; the mechanism of Chameides (13) included only oxidation by hydroxy radicals. Neither model included reactions for the formation of acetic acid. By comparing Table III with Table I, it can be seen that the concentrations of formic acid

predicted by the models are at the very low end of the concentration
range typically observed in precipitation. Potential gas-phase
formic acid concentrations predicted by the models for clouds
evaporating after 1 h are also substantially lower than observed
clear formic acid concentrations given in Table IV. There are
several possible explanations for the disagreement between observations and model predictions. For example, other reactions not
included in the models may be important for aqueous production of
formic acid, or the atmospheric time scale for production may be
greater than that simulated in the models. Initial conditions or
assumed values of certain parameters used in the models may not be
realistic for the atmospheric conditions that actually lead to
formic acid formation, although the rather extensive sensitivity
analysis and wide range of initial conditions examined by Adewuyi
et al. (7) make this unlikely. Alternatively, aqueous-phase production may not be the dominant pathway leading to the presence of
organic ions in precipitation.

Table III. Model Calculations: Aqueous-Phase
Oxidation of Formaldehyde

Predicted [HCOO$^-$] (μM)	Predicted Potential Gas Phase [HCOOH] (μg/m^3)	Reference
0.2-1	0.01-0.3	(7)
1.5-4	0.07-0.12	(13)

Table IV. Clear Air Observations of Formic and Acetic Acids

Location	Observed Concentrations (μg/m^3)		Reference
	Formic Acid	Acetic Acid	
Riverside, CA	3.0-14.5	-	(16)
Riverside, CA	4.9-35.	-	(17)
Los Angeles, CA	2.0-20.	-	(18)
Tucson, AZ	3.0-4.9	2.6-10.	(19)
Saguaro National Monument, AZ	1.0-2.8	0.5-2.3	(19)
Sells, AZ	1.0-2.2	1.0-2.3	(19)
Upper Troposphere Over Alamogordo, NM (Balloon Flight)	0.8-1.2	-	(20)

This possibility takes on greater credence upon re-examination
of the approximately 2:1 ratio of formate to acetate concentrations
consistently observed in the Wisconsin and Virginia precipitation
samples. As derived from thermodynamic data (12, 14), the effective
K_H for formaldehyde is approximately 7000 M/atm at 25°C; the
effective K_H for acetaldehyde is on the order of 11 M/atm. Assuming
that aqueous-phase oxidation of the two aldehydes occurs at
approximately the same rate, typical gas-phase concentrations of
acetaldehyde would have to be about 300 times greater than corresponding formaldehyde concentrations to account for the observed

formate-to-acetate ratio. Such large variations in atmospheric aldehyde concentrations have not been observed; measurements at Upton, New York, (15) indicated formaldehyde/acetaldehyde ratios in the range of 2 to 4.

The current analysis cannot be used to eliminate aqueous-phase oxidation as a potential pathway for introducing low molecular weight organic ions into precipitation; however, the analysis does suggest that it is not the dominant pathway.

Assessment of Homogeneous Gas-Phase Production. Equilibrium and potential gas-phase organic acid concentrations calculated from formate and acetate concentrations in the Wisconsin and Virginia precipitation samples are summarized in Table V. Calculated potential gas-phase levels of 0.02 to 5 $\mu g/m^3$ formic acid are lower than measured urban concentrations (16-18) given in Table IV, but agree surprisingly well with clear air observations of 1.0 to 4.9 $\mu g/m^3$ in the rural southwest (19). Calculated potential acetic acid concentrations of 0.02 to 3.1 $\mu g/m^3$ also agree well with rural observations of 0.5 to 10 $\mu g/m^3$. Obvious uncertainties exist in comparing values calculated from precipitation collected in one part of the country with measurements taken in another region, but the degree of agreement suggests that equilibrium scavenging of gas-phase-produced organic compounds is a plausible pathway for introducing formate and acetate into precipitation.

The major gas-phase reactions involved in this pathway are not definitively known. However, reactions of ozone with olefins to form Criegee intermediates (e.g., CH_2OO and CH_3CHOO), which subsequently react with water vapor to form carboxylic acids, have been proposed (21-23). Such reactions have been included in a homogeneous gas-phase reaction model (22), but predicted formic acid concentrations were substantially lower than the observed values given in Table IV. Acetic acid formation was not reported. However, the model was designed to focus on the gas-phase generation of tropospheric inorganic acids and, because of computational constraints, employed a simplified hydrocarbon reaction mechanism involving CH_4, one "typical" alkane and one "typical" alkene. In light of the simplified hydrocarbon chemistry, pathways involving Criegee intermediates may in reality be important in introducing low molecular weight organic ions into precipitation. Further study of the gas-phase reactions is needed to explore this possibility.

Conclusions

Statistical analysis of precipitation chemistry data collected at three sites in the United States indicates that the inorganic and organic analytes show little or no correlation. In contrast, formate and acetate concentrations are highly correlated ($r > 0.89$) and consistently produce a formate/acetate ratio of approximately 2. An assessment of the plausibility of various pathways that could introduce the organic compounds into precipitation suggests aqueous-phase oxidation of aldehydes is probably not a major contributor because of the large atmospheric acetaldehyde concentration that must be postulated to produce the observed formate/acetate ratio. Alternatively, potential gas-phase formic and acetic acid

Table V. Equilibrium and Potential Gas-Phase Concentrations of Organic Acids Calculated From Wisconsin and Virginia Precipitation Measurements

Calculated Gas-Phase Values

Site	HCOOH ($\mu g/m^3$)						CH$_3$COOH ($\mu g/m^3$)					
	Equilibrium[a]		Potential[b] L = 0.25		Potential[b] L = 1.0		Equilibrium[a]		Potential[b] L = 0.25		Potential[b] L = 1.0	
	Range	Mean[c]	Range	Mean[c]	Range	Mean[c]	Range	Mean[c]	Range	Mean[c]	Range	Mean[c]
Round Lake, WI	<0.02-1.9	0.41	<0.02-2.4	0.55	0.02-3.9	0.59	<0.02-1.6	0.28	<0.02-2.0	0.36	0.02-3.1	0.41
Geneva Lake, WI	0.02-1.2	0.38	0.02-1.4	0.48	0.08-2.0	0.75	0.03-0.59	0.26	0.03-0.72	0.31	0.05-1.1	0.49
Charlottesville, VA	<0.02-3.2	1.5	0.02-3.6	1.70	0.06-5.0	2.4	0.05-1.6	0.59	0.05-1.9	0.70	0.08-2.8	1.1

[a] Calculated from Equation 1
[b] Calculated from Equation 2
[c] Arithmetic mean

concentrations calculated from the precipitation chemistry data agree surprisingly well with rural clear air measurements. The agreement suggests that homogeneous gas-phase reaction and scavenging are a likely pathway for introducing organic acids into precipitation.

Acknowledgments

The authors gratefully acknowledge the technical comments of R. C. Easter and the help of N. C. Van Houten in preparing the final manuscript. Although the research described in this article has been funded wholly or in part by the United States Environmental Protection Agency through a Related Services Agreement with the U.S. Department of Energy Contract DE-AC06-76RLO 1830 to Pacific Northwest Laboratory, it has not been subjected to Agency review and therefore does not necessarily reflect the views of the Agency, and no official endorsement should be inferred.

Literature Cited

1.   Galloway, J. N.; Gaudry, A.   Atmos. Environ. 1984, 18, 2649-2656.
2.   Chapman, E. G.; Sklarew, D. S.; Flickinger, J. S.   Atmos. Environ. 1986, 20, 1717-1725.
3.   Keene, W. C.; Galloway, J. N.   Atmos. Environ. 1984, 18, 2491-2497.
4.   Kawamura, K.; Kaplan. I. R.   Anal. Chem. 1984, 56, 1616-1620.
5.   Holdren, M. W.; Spicer, C. W.; Hales, J. M.   Atmos. Environ. 1984, 18, 1171-1173.
6.   Galloway, J. N.; Likens, G. E.; Keene, W. C.; Miller, J. M. J. Geophys. Res. 1982, 87, 8771-8786.
7.   Adewuyi, Y. G.; Cho, S. Y.; Tsay, R. P.; Carmichael, G. R. Atmos. Environ. 1984, 18, 2413-2420.
8.   Rothert, J. E.; Dana. M. T.   The MAP3S Precipitation Chemistry Network: Seventh Periodic Summary Report (1983), PNL-5298, Pacific Northwest Laboratory: Richland, WA, 1984.
9.   Dana, M. T.   The MAP3S/RAINE Precipitation Chemistry Network: Quality Control, PNL-36122, Pacific Northwest Laboratory: Richland, WA, 1980.
10. Chapman, E. G.   Central Analysis Laboratory Procedures for the Wisconsin Acid Deposition Monitoring Network, 2311204999, Report to Wisconsin Power & Light Company: Madison, WI, 1983.
11. Ryan, T. A.; Joiner, B. L.; Ryan, B. F.   MINITAB Reference Manual, Pennsylvania State University: University Park, PA, 1982.
12. Weast, R. C. Ed.   CRC Handbook of Chemistry and Physics; CRC Press: Boca Raton, FL, 1984.
13. Chameides, W. L.; Davis, D. D.   Nature 1983, 304, 427-429.
14. Kurtz, J.   J. Am. Chem. Soc. 1967, 89, 3524-3528.
15. Tanner, R. L.; Meng, Z.   Environ. Sci. Technol. 1984, 18, 723-726.
16. Tuazon, E.; Graham, R.; Winer, A.; Easton, R.; Pitts, J.; Hanst F. P.   Atmos. Environ. 1978, 12, 865-875.

17. Hanst, P.; Wilson. W.; Patterson, R.; Gay, B. W.; Chaney, L.; Burton, C. S. A Spectroscopic Study of California Smog. EPA 650/4-75-006, Research Triangle Park, NC, 1975.
18. Hanst, P.; Wong, N.; Bragin, J. Atmos. Environ. 1982, 16, 969-981.
19. Dawson, G.; Farmer, J.; Moyers, J. Geophys. Res. Let. 1980, 7, 725-729.
20. Goldman, A.; Murcray, F.; Murcray, D.; Rinsland, C. Geophys. Res. Let. 1984, 11, 307-311.
21. Atkinson, R.; Lloyd, A. C. J. Phys. Chem. Ref. Data 1984, 13, 315-444.
22. Calvert, J. G.; Stockwell, W. R. Environ. Sci. Technol. 1983, 17, 428A-443A.
23. Niki, H.; Maker, P. D.; Savage, C. M.; Breitenbach, L. P. Environ. Sci. Technol. 1983, 17, 312A-322A.

RECEIVED January 12, 1987

Chapter 20

Comparison of Weekly and Daily Wet Deposition Sampling Results

L. E. Topol[1], M. Lev-On[1], and A. K. Pollack[2]

[1]Environmental Monitoring and Services, 4765 Calle Quetzal, Camarillo, CA 93010
[2]Systems Applications, 101 Lucas Valley Road, San Rafael, CA 94903

An initial analysis of data from a one-year field study
comparing the concentrations of weekly measured samples
and weekly values derived from daily samples indicated
that the weekly measured ion concentrations were generally larger. Although the mean relative bias values
ranged from 0 to 34%, most values were less than 10%.
In addition, the greatest differences were found in the
fall season with biases greater than 10% occurring for
ammonium, chloride, sodium, potassium, calcium and
magnesium. Samples were collected at three sites in
Georgia, Kansas and Vermont to represent the southeastern, central (west of the Mississippi River) and northeastern regions of the United States. The measurements
included precipitation weight, pH, sulfate, nitrate,
chloride, ammonium, potassium, sodium, calcium and magnesium. Other than the two different sampling intervals, all field and laboratory procedures were identical.

Precipitation sampling networks in the United States generally
collect either daily (UAPSP, MAP3S) or weekly (NADP, NTN) samples.
In the case of the weekly schedule, samples can remain in the
collector under ambient conditions for up to seven days, possibly
resulting in chemical changes. The occurrence and magnitude of such
changes are potentially important in determining the use of weekly
composition data for studying wet deposition effects and long-term
trends.

In order to determine the importance of chemical changes
introduced by the longer sampling period, a collocated sampling
study was implemented from October 1983 to October 1984 at three
sites of the Utility Acid Precipitation Study Program (UAPSP) network. The sites were selected to represent the southeastern,
central (west of the Mississippi River) and northeastern regions of
the United States.

The objective of the study was to compare the concentrations
obtained from weekly samples with those derived from the daily
samples. A comparison of precision of weekly and daily measurements

0097–6156/87/0349–0229$06.00/0
© 1987 American Chemical Society

will be reported separately. For this study a daily sample is the
total occurrence of precipitation greater than 0.51 mm (0.02 inch)
in a 24-hour period (starting at about 9:00 a.m. local time); a weekly sample is the precipitation occurring in the period from 9:00 a.m.
of the sample pick-up day, generally Monday, to the same time and day
of the following week. The results were calculated for all sites on
an annual and seasonal basis. Analyses of the data using both parametric and nonparametric statistical tests were performed to detect
significant differences in compared values.

Four weekly versus daily (or event) sampling studies using the
same type of samplers as in the present study have been reported. A
Florida study (1) used three samplers monitoring on a daily, weekly
and biweekly schedule for twelve months. All analyses were performed
at the University of Central Florida within ten days of collection.
No statistically significant differences in precipitation composition
with sampling interval were found. At Pennsylvania State University
(2) a comparison of the ion concentrations for weekly and daily
samples indicated that the weekly samples yielded lower concentrations and deposition values for all the ions analyzed. A study at
North Carolina State University (3) involved four daily and six
weekly collectors. The data indicated that gross changes in pH and
specific conductance did not occur with collection periods of one
week, but since no other analyses were performed, the data do not
eliminate the possibility that selected chemical changes may have
occurred. At Argonne National Laboratory (4) two samplers, activated
by a single sensor, were used for approximately two years. This
approach assured simultaneous opening and closing of both collectors
in contrast to the other studies. The weekly samples were analyzed
by the Illinois State Water Survey whereas the event samples were
analyzed by Argonne. Weekly samples were found to have significantly less NH_4^+ and H^+ in all seasons and more $SO_4^=$ in every season but
summer. The weekly samples had significantly more Ca^{+2} and Mg^{+2}
during seasons with little precipitation No significant differences
between weekly and event NO_3^- were evident.

The present study is unique in several ways: (a) three regular
UAPSP monitoring sites were utilized, and each of the sites was
equipped with four identical precipitation samplers, two collecting
daily samples and two weekly samples; this allows for duplicate data
as well as the calculation of precision for both sampling schedules;
(b) all analyses were performed in the same laboratory; (c) except
for the sampling schedule, all procedures were identical.

Procedures

For this study three sites from the UAPSP network that typified
different regions and climates of the eastern United States were
selected. These sites were Uvalda, GA, in the Southeast, Lancaster,
KS, west of the Mississippi River, and Underhill, VT, in the Northeast. Criteria used for site selection for precipitation monitoring
are outlined in the U.S. EPA Quality Assurance Manual for Precipitation Measurement Systems (5).

Collocated sampling was performed at the three sites for approximately one year, from October 9, 1983 for Georgia and Vermont and
October 12, 1983 for Kansas to August 15, October 10, and October 17,
1984 for Georgia, Vermont and Kansas, respectively.

Field Operations. Each site had four automatic precipitation collectors (Aerochem Metrics) and a Universal Recording Weighing Bucket Rain Gauge (Belfort) with an eight-day spring powered clock and strip chart recorder. An event pen marker was interfaced with the samplers and noted the sampler lid open and close times on the rain gauge strip chart.

All operators were trained in the site operations based on the U.S. EPA "Operation and Maintenance Manual for Precipitation Measurement Systems" (6) and the UAPSP "Field Operator Instruction Manual" (7). Daily site visits were generally made at about 9:00 a.m. local time to check the equipment and to remove any precipitation collected by the daily samplers. Weekly samples were removed on Monday from the Georgia and Vermont sites and on Tuesday at the Kansas site. If no event occurred for a week, the buckets were rinsed with deionized water to remove any dust that may have deposited and they were then reused. Analysis of the rinse water served as a dynamic blank.

For the samples greater than 0.51 mm, a maximal volume of 500-ml was transferred to a clean, labeled, plastic bottle and sealed; the rest of the sample was discarded. If less than 0.51 mm, the sample was also discarded and was lost from the weekly composite of daily results. This will produce some errors in the comparisons with the weekly samples. The daily sample was stored in a refrigerator at about 4°C to minimize degradation. The same procedure was followed for the weekly samples except that these were shipped the same day that they were collected and were not refrigerated.

For shipping to the laboratory, the daily samples were packed directly from the refrigerator into an insulated Styrofoam box with four frozen gel packs. Weekly samples were packed together with the corresponding daily samples and the carton was shipped by air freight each week.

Quality control procedures (5-7) in the field included semi-annual audit visits. These procedures were employed to maximize capture of uncontaminated samples, to identify and document them, to preserve their integrity until their arrival at the laboratory, to obtain dynamic blanks and to determine each site's precision and accuracy of pH and conductivity measurement. (The field measurements were used as a quality control to determine if precipitation samples had degraded between the field and laboratory measurements.)

Laboratory Operations. If sufficient sample was present, the following order of analysis was taken to minimize chance of degradation: pH, NH_4^+, $SO_4^=$, NO_3^-, Cl^-, Ca^{+2}, Mg^{+2}, Na^+, and K^+. The pH was measured electrometrically, NH_4^+ by automated colorimetry, the anions by ion chromatography, and the metallic cations by flame atomic absorption. If insufficient sample was available for complete analysis, the anions were measured before ammonium. All samples were analyzed without filtration. However, the samples were decanted to eliminate sedimented particles.

All analytical instruments were calibrated at least once a day. In addition, reagent blanks, spikes and split samples were run daily. A full description of the quality control program implemented for UAPSP by EMSI is provided elsewhere (8-9).

Data Management. Data were invalidated for the following reasons: obvious physical contamination of a sample, instrument malfunction, evidence of erroneous data entry, and outlying observations.

Laboratory chemists manually checked approximately 5% of all data, concentrating on extreme observations of concentrations and ion balance data, thus verifying instrument calibration and integrity of the analytical process. Based on these checks some samples were designated for reanalysis followed by reentry of results into the data base. No extreme observations were deleted from the main data base if they passed all the checks described here. Below-detection-level values were set equal to zero.

The distribution of collocated differences for the daily and weekly measurements were used to detect outliers. The distributions for the three precipitation types at each site were symmetrical with long tails. In this study, the tails were truncated at $\pm 3\sigma$ from the mean for each observable, and pairs of samples with the extreme (i.e. minimum and maximum) differences were rejected from parametric statistical analyses according to the following criteria:

(a)   one of the four major ion differences (H^+, $SO_4^=$, NO_3^- and NH_4^+) of that sample pair was outside the 3σ acceptance limits.

(b)   at least three of the minor ion differences of that sample pair were outside the 3σ acceptance limits, or

(c)   one of the minor ion differences of that sample pair was outside the 3σ acceptance limits and three out of the four primary ion differences for the same sample pair were at either extreme of the collocated pair distribution.

The screening steps outlined above reduced the number of daily samples from 67, 86 and 142 to 63, 72 and 133, and the corresponding weekly samples from 35, 38 and 52 to 33, 37 and 47 for the Georgia, Kansas and Vermont sites, respectively. These screened data represent 94%, 84% and 94% of the total daily samples and 94%, 97% and 91% of the total weekly samples from the three respective sites.

The small fraction of data in the tails are probably due to contamination and their elimination removes their disproportionately large influence on hypothesis testing by parametric methods. Non-parametric techniques are relatively insensitive to the data in the tails of the distribution, and unscreened data were used for these analyses.

The collocation data were used to determine concentration means and medians of daily and weekly sampling and to obtain the bias between the measured weekly and the derived weekly values, composited from the corresponding daily results. All derived weekly concentrations were calculated separately for each collector as the precipitation-weighted mean, $C = \sum_i C_i P_i / \sum_i P_i$, where C_i and P_i are the daily concentration and sample weight. For derived weekly precipitation, the sum of the daily volumes for the week was taken for each precipitation collector.

The data were classified by sampling site, and by meteorological season (spring = March - May, summer = June - August, fall = September - November, and winter = December - February).

Only events greater than 0.51 mm (0.02 inch) rain gauge depth
were included in this study to ensure that sufficient sample was
available for analysis. Thus if a week had only small daily events,
no corresponding daily and derived weekly data were available; however, events greater than 0.51 mm allowed partial analysis and were
included.

When an observable value was missing, no collocated difference
was obtained for that observable. However, to calculate a mean
value if one of the observables was missing, the valid collocated
measurement was taken as the mean. For a week which contained one
or more missing daily samples the derived weekly and the corresponding measured weekly samples were discarded from the comparison only
if the precipitation of the missing daily sample(s) accounted for
more than 20% of the week's total. This was done to maximize the
number of data points and the power of the statistical tests.

Statistical Testing. Preliminary evaluation of the data for collocated concentration differences for each of the observables showed
that the distributions were symmetrical but not Gaussian. Similar
distributions were obtained for measurement bias (weekly derived
minus weekly measured concentrations) as shown in the Results
section below. Therefore, both a robust parametric test (paired
t-test (10)) and a nonparametric test (Wilcoxon signed rank test
(11) were performed to determine the statistical significance of
the differences. The advantages of the Wilcoxon test are that it
applies under more general conditions than the t-test and it is
affected only minimally by extreme values; the disadvantage is that
the test compares relative ranks of the data and not the actual
data values. Although the statistical significance of parametric
test results are sensitive to the outlier rejection scheme chosen,
the parametric tests require fewer data points to detect population
differences at the same significance level.

To test the differences among sites and among seasons, analysis
of variance (ANOVA) techniques were utilized. For the one-way ANOVA
the standard F-test was augmented by the Welch and Browne-Forsythe
tests (12), in order to account for the unequal variances of the
compared groups (sites or seasons). Throughout this study a significance level of 0.05 was utilized. All the tests were performed
with the BMDP statistical routines (13).

Results and Discussion

A calendar of weekly events showing the number of samples for each
week after outlier rejection is presented for each site in Figure 1.
The greatest number of both daily and weekly events occurred in
Vermont and the smallest number in Georgia. The largest number of
events per month occurred in July for Georgia, and in May and June
for Kansas and Vermont.

Site Method Bias. Method bias, defined as derived weekly minus
measured weekly values, and relative mean bias, the bias per mean
derived weekly value, were calculated for each site. The average
of the collocated pair results for each daily and weekly sample
was used. Figure 2 shows the distribution of the method bias for
hydrogen ion and sulfate for each site. The median, mean, and

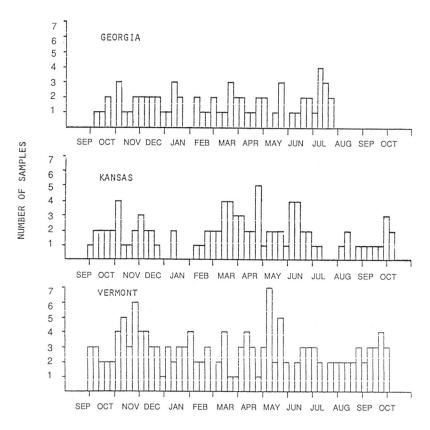

Figure 1. Number of samples per week for the Georgia, Kansas and Vermont sites for 1983–1984.

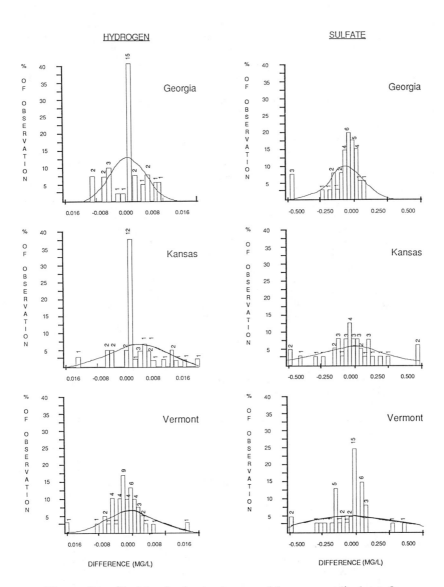

Figure 2. (Weekly derived minus weekly measured) data for hydrogen ion and sulfate at the Georgia, Kansas and Vermont sites. (The number of data points included in each bar is listed above the bar, and all extreme values are included in the extreme bars. The curve represents the Gaussian distribution calculated from the mean and standard deviation of the data.)

relative mean values of the resulting bias for all observables for
all the precipitation types combined are listed for the three sites
in Table I. The median and mean biases that tested to be significant by the Wilcoxon and paired t-tests, respectively, are noted in
the table. Differences in the significant results between the two
tests may be due to the slightly different distributions used because of outlier deletion. The choice of outliers will effect the
t-test results, which depend on the mean and standard deviation, but
will not affect the Wilcoxon test results which do not depend on the
spread of the distribution.

Most of the bias values are negative, indicating that the weekly measured concentrations are larger than the weekly derived values.
For the Georgia site, the weekly measured values are larger than, or
equal to, the ones derived from the daily data for all the observables except potassium. The Georgia site also shows the largest
number of analytes with statistically significant bias between the
two collection methods. The larger precipitation amounts, as well
as ion concentrations, for the weekly collected samples indicate
that evaporation is not the cause of the larger observed concentrations. Possible explanations are: (a) small precipitation samples
(<0.5 mm), which generally are more concentrated than larger event
samples, are not included in the derived weekly values but are
included in the measured weekly amounts if other events occurred
during the week, and (b) the weekly samplers open sooner than the
daily samplers, catching more of the initial rainfall which generally
contains more washout of constituents. The Kansas site has the
least number of significant method differences even though its bias
data for Ca^{+2} and Mg^{+2} are larger than the significant biases for
these two parameters at the other two sites; this is because the
Kansas measurements vary more than the Georgia and Vermont measurements.

The Georgia site, although having the most significant bias
results, has relative mean bias values under 8% for all the observables except Ca^{+2} for which the bias is 11.5%. For Kansas, the
relative mean bias values are 10% or less, except for H^+, K^+ and
Mg^{+2}. For Vermont, the values of the relative bias are less than
11%, except for K^+. The relative weekly bias for hydrogen ion and
sulfate are compared for the three sites in Figure 3. All extreme
points are truncated at the 50% difference level. It is evident
that most of the data lie within the ±10% range.

A one-way ANOVA detected significant differences in the mean
bias for only H^+ and Na^+ among the sites, as indicated in Table I.
The small differences in the weekly bias results among the three
sites for all the other observables were not declared statistically
significant since they are small relative to the random fluctuations
in the measurements at each site. For the observables other than
H^+ and Na^+, the method bias is expected to be similar at the three
sites. Except for K^+, the differences between the relative mean
bias for weekly and daily composited samples are generally under
12%; for the major ions, NH_4^+, $SO_4^=$ and NO_3^-, the method bias is
typically much smaller (<8%).

The results of this study are in general agreement with those of
Schroder et al. (3) and Sisterson et al. (4), but disagree with
de Pena et al. (2). The present results indicate that weekly sampling

Table I. WEEKLY (DERIVED - MEASURED) SITE CONCENTRATION BIAS (mg/l)

Observable	Georgia			Kansas			Vermont		
	Median Bias	Mean Bias	Relative Bias (%)[a]	Median Bias	Mean Bias	Relative Bias (%)	Median Bias	Mean Bias	Relative Bias (%)
Precip(g)	-34.6	-19.2	-0.8	0.2	-37.4	-2.5	17.4[W]	22.2	1.4
H^+ (*)	-0.0003[W]	-0.0004	-1.7	0.0007	0.0027[t]	16.0	0.0022	0.0014	2.7
$SO_4^=$	-0.037[W]	-0.053[t]	-4.2	-0.041	-0.030	-1.7	0.002	-0.036	-1.8
NO_3^-	-0.043[W]	-0.055[t]	-7.1	-0.020	-0.044	-2.9	0.006	0.006	0.3
NH_4^+	-0.011[W]	-0.008	-4.5	0.0056	-0.0004	-0.1	0.004	-0.007	-2.4
Cl^-	-0.009[W]	-0.014	-3.5	0.003	0.002	1.6	0.003	-0.001	-0.7
Na^+ (*)	-0.001[W]	-0.018[t]	-8.1	0.0003	-0.0003	-0.5	0.001	-0.001	-3.0
K^+	-0.000	0.002	7.2	-0.001	-0.009	-20.4	-0.002[W]	-0.005	-33.8
Ca^{+2}	-0.006[W]	-0.011	-11.5	-0.009	-0.048	-10.3	-0.006[W]	-0.008	-7.8
Mg^{+2}	-0.0008	-0.0016[t]	-5.1	-0.0014	-0.0045	-12.1	-0.0009[W]	-0.0016[t]	-10.6

a. Relative Bias = Mean Method Bias/Mean Derived Weekly Concentration.

(*) Significant differences among site means based on one-way ANOVA.

W - Significant differences between weekly and derived concentrations, based on Wilcoxon signed-ranks test.

t - Significant differences between weekly and derived concentrations, based on paired t-test.

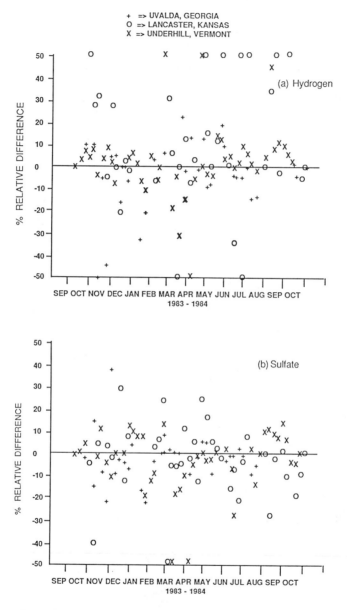

Figure 3. Variation of percent relative bias (weekly derived – measured/weekly derived) with time for hydrogen ion and sulfate at the Georgia, Kansas and Vermont sites.

generally yields higher annual mean concentrations than daily sampling, but the differences are small, are assumed to be due to method and not site to site difference, and are not considered practically significant. However, a network that changes its sampling schedule will see the bias effect and, although small, it can interfere with trend analysis.

Effect of Season on Method Bias. The effect of season on the concentration bias was also examined. For the fall quarter, the 1983 and 1984 data were combined. The median, mean and relative mean biases for the weekly derived minus weekly measured concentrations (for all sites grouped together) and the respective Wilcoxon and paired t-test results are presented in Table II. Significant bias is seen from either the Wilcoxon or t-test for nitrate and calcium in the spring, and for hydrogen in the summer. However, the fall season reveals significant bias by both tests for H^+, $SO_4^=$, Cl^-, Na^+, Ca^{+2} and Mg^{+2} and for K^+ by the Wilcoxon test only. The measured weekly concentrations are larger than the derived ones in all these significant bias cases except for H^+. Higher Ca^{+2} and Mg^{+2} concentrations, which generally are from basic soil dust, are expected to yield lower acidity (H^+) in all samples. A one-way ANOVA detected significant differences in bias among the seasons for NO_3^-, Cl^- and Mg^{+2} only, as shown in Table II. The results indicate that a majority of the analytes show significant bias in the fall, and the largest relative bias for all observables also occurs in the fall. The significant fall season biases are difficult to explain. For the four major ions, the relative biases are under 13%. The large bias for potassium indicates that there are sampling problems, possibly due to adsorption-desorption from the plastic bucket. These results indicate that the bias in concentration between weekly and daily samples is similar for most of the constituents in all seasons but the fall.

Summary and Conclusions

The results of this study indicate that

* Concentrations of weekly collected samples are generally higher than those of the derived weekly samples.
* No correspondence occurs between concentration bias for the major ions and the bias in precipitation volume collected. Therefore, the observed biases cannot be attributed to evaporation.
* Although many ionic concentration biases between the weekly measured and derived samples are statistically significant, their magnitude is generally ≤10% of the mean concentration, and therefore are not considered practically significant.
* An analysis of bias by season indicates that the largest number of significant method bias values occur for most of the ions in the fall (September - November).

From these results it is concluded that a network that changes its sampling schedule will see a small bias effect which can interfere with trend analysis. In addition, the seasonal differences in concentration strongly favor monitoring and data analysis for a whole year and preferably for complete seasons.

Table II. WEEKLY (DERIVED - MEASURED) CONCENTRATION BIAS (mg/l) BY SEASON

Observable	Winter			Spring			Summer			Fall[a]		
	Median Bias	Mean Bias	Relative Bias (%)[b]	Median Bias	Mean Bias	Relative Bias (%)	Median Bias	Mean Bias	Relative Bias (%)	Median Bias	Mean Bias	Relative Bias (%)
Precip(g)	-4.8	-14.7	-0.9	-1.5	-11.0	-0.5	10.3	4.1	2.0	10.4	25.2	1.3
H^+	0.0000	-0.0011	-3.1	0.0003	0.0000	0.4	0.0004	-0.0019^t	-3.7	0.0021^W	0.0014^t	3.6
$SO_4^=$	-0.022	-0.000	0.0	-0.023	-0.116	-7.0	-0.035	-0.059	-1.9	-0.036^W	0.022^t	1.0
NO_3^- (*)	-0.003	0.050	-2.5	-0.041^W	-0.072	-6.7	-0.021	-0.074	-3.8	-0.027	-0.124	-9.0
NH_4^+	0.006	0.010	4.4	-0.010	-0.004	-1.1	-0.011	-0.035	-7.0	-0.004	-0.040	-12.4
Cl^- (*)	0.004	0.005	2.1	-0.003	-0.004	-2.3	-0.002	-0.003	-1.1	-0.010^W	-0.037^t	-17.3
Na^+	0.000	-0.004	-3.3	0.000	-0.006	-5.9	0.001	-0.001	-1.2	-0.002^W	-0.023^t	-19.6
K^+	-0.002	-0.003	-12.4	-0.001	0.000	-1.5	0.001	0.072	62.2	-0.005^W	-0.028	-119.0
Ca^{+2}	-0.003	-0.006	-3.7	-0.009^W	-0.021	-8.5	-0.003	0.068	16.0	-0.013^W	-0.066^t	-38.4
Mg^{+2} (*)	-0.0003	-0.0007	-2.8	-0.001	-0.002	-8.3	-0.001	0.013	21.7	-0.003^W	-0.008^t	-31.2

a. The fall data combine 1983 and 1984 measurements.

b. Relative Bias (%) = 100 x Mean Bias/Derived Weekly Concentration.

(*) Significant differences among seasons based on one-way ANOVA (all sites combined).

W - Significant differences between weekly and derived concentrations, based on Wilcoxon signed-ranks test.

t - Significant differences between weekly and derived concentrations, based on paired t-test.

Acknowledgments

This study was funded by the Utility Acid Precipitation Study Program (UAPSP), Washington, DC, under Contract RP U101-1 and the U.S. Environmental Protection Agency, Research Triangle Park, NC, under Contract 68-02-3767. The guidance by Drs. Peter K. Mueller of the Electric Power Research Institute and William J. Mitchell of the USEPA throughout this study was very helpful. The authors thank Drs. R.J. Schwall and R. Vijayakumar of the Environmental Monitoring and Services, Inc. for their help in the statistical analysis.

Literature Cited

1. Madsen, B.C. Atmos. Environ. 1982, 16, 251-19.
2. de Pena, R.G.; Walker, K.C.; Lebowitz, L.; Micka, J.G. Atmos. Environ. 1985, 19, 151-6.
3. Schroder, L.J.; Linthurst, R.A.; Ellson, J.E.; Vozzo, S.F. Water, Air, Soil Poll. 1984, 20, 1-11.
4. Sisterson, D.L.; Wurfel, B.E.; Lesht, B.M. Atmos. Environ. 1985, 19, 1453-69.
5. "Quality Assurance Handbook for Air Pollution Measurement Systems. Vol. V. Manual for Precipitation Measurement Systems, Part I. Quality Assurance Manual"; U.S. Environmental Protection Agency, EPA-600/4-82-042a, March 1982.
6. "Quality Assurance Handbook for Air Pollution Measurement Systems. Vol. V. Manual for Precipitation Measurement Systems, Part II. Operation and Maintenance Manual"; U.S. Environmental Protection Agency, EPA-600/4-82-042b, January 1981.
7. Topol, L.E. "Field Operator Instruction Manual for Utility Acid Precipitation Study Program (UAPSP). UAPSP 104"; Utility Acid Precipitation Study Program: Washington, D.C., 1983.
8. Topol, L.E. "Plan for Controlling the Quality of Measurements and Data Base in the Utility Acid Precipitation Study Program (UAPSP)"; Environmental Monitoring & Services, Inc., January 1982.
9. Carlin, L.M.; Long, T.; Ozdemir, S. "UAPSP Laboratory Standard Operating Procedures. UAPSP 102"; Utility Acid Precipitation Study Program: Washington, D.C., 1982.
10. Box, G.E.P.; Hunter, W.G.; Hunter, J.S. "Statistics for Experimenters"; John Wiley & Sons: New York, 1978; chapter 5.
11. Conover, W.J. "Practical Nonparametric Statistics"; 2nd ed. John Wiley & Sons: New York, 1980; chapter 5.
12. Brown, M.B.; Forsythe, A.B. Technometrics 1974, 166, 129-32.
13. "BMDP Statistical Software"; University of California Press, Los Angeles, CA, 1983.

RECEIVED March 4, 1987

Chapter 21

Chemistry of Wintertime Wet Deposition

Jean Muhlbaier Dasch

Environmental Science Department, General Motors Research Laboratory, Warren, MI 48090

Four years of winter precipitation data from southeastern Michigan were examined to help understand the
higher NO_3^-, but lower SO_4^{--}, concentrations in snow
than in winter rain. The higher NO_3^- levels in snow
could be attributed to the lower precipitation depths
associated with snow events than with rain events.
Conversely, SO_4^{--} was far higher in winter rain than
in snow. The SO_4^{--} concentrations were highly correlated with the temperatures of the cloud layers. The
data suggests that SO_2 is incorporated and oxidized to
SO_4^{--} in clouds most efficiently when the hydrometeors
are present as liquid droplets. The fact that NO_3^-
does not show the same relationship suggests that
incorporation of nitrogen species into cloud water
followed by oxidation is not as important a process
for nitrogen as for sulfur.

The SO_4^{--}/NO_3^{--} ratio of winter precipitation is lower than that of
summer precipitation in the northeastern United States and eastern
Canada (1,2). Part of this difference can be attributed to differences between rain and snow, since snow has a lower SO_4^{--}/NO_3^- ratio
than summer rain, or even winter rain (2,3). Several studies (3,4)
have shown SO_4^{--} to be lower in snow than in winter rain in the
northeastern United States. NO_3^-, on the other hand, frequently
shows the reverse trend with higher concentrations in snow than in
winter rain (4,5). The higher NO_3^- concentrations in snow than in
rain could not be attributed to air temperatures, synoptic patterns,
precipitation rate, wind direction or wind speed in an analysis by
Raynor and Hayes (5). They suggested that since both winter rain
and snow originate from sub-freezing clouds, the higher NO_3^- concentrations found in snow than rain must be due to more efficient
below-cloud scavenging of nitrogen species in the air by snowflakes
than by raindrops. Modeling studies by Chang also suggest that
snowflakes should scavenge gas-phase HNO_3 more efficiently than
raindrops (6).

In this paper, four years of winter precipitation data will be
examined to provide insights into the mechanisms by which sulfur and

nitrogen species are incorporated into precipitation. Concentrations of SO_4^{--} and NO_3^- in winter rain and snow will be considered in terms of precipitation depth, ambient concentrations, wind direction and cloud temperatures.

Experimental

Wet deposition was collected during four winters at a site in Warren, MI, a suburb north of Detroit. The samples were collected from late December to early April for four winters starting with the 1981/82 winter. The water equivalent of the wintertime precipitation during the four winters was 24, 12, 15 and 33 cm, respectively. The snowfall during the four winters was 147, 34, 86 and 124 cm. Annual precipitation data will also be referred to in this paper, which is based on sampling at this site from summer, 1981 to summer, 1983.

Wet deposition was collected on an event basis in polyethylene buckets in Aerochem Metric collectors set to open only during precipitation periods. The precipitation time was determined from a Belfort recording rain·gauge. The precipitation depth (as water equivalent) was determined as the volume of precipitation in the bucket divided by the area of the bucket opening (638 cm²). The precipitation was filtered through 0.4 μm pore Nuclepore filters to remove particles and was then refrigerated until time for analysis. The ions, NO_3^- and SO_4^{--}, were analyzed by ion chromatography.

The concentrations of particles and gases in air were measured during the last two winters to allow a comparison of precipitation composition with levels of pollutants in the air. Each sampling period lasted 3 to 5 days. Air was sampled at 10 L/min through a triple-stack filter: a 1-μm pore-size Teflon filter collected particles, a 1-μm pore-size nylon filter collected HNO_3 as well as any NO_3^- that volatilized from the first filter, and double cellulose nitrate filters impregnated with a 25% K_2CO_3, 10% glycerol solution collected SO_2. The Teflon filter was extracted in 50 mL of deionized water and the extract was analyzed for NO_3^- and SO_4^{--}. The nylon filter was extracted in 50 mL of the same bicarbonate-carbonate eluant used in the ion chromatograph and the extract was analyzed for NO_3^-. The SO_2 filters were extracted in 100 mL of a 0.2% H_2O_2 solution and the extract was analyzed for SO_4^{--}. In addition, NO_2 was collected on a cartridge containing diphenylamine and analyzed by the method of Lipari (7).

Meteorological data were obtained from Local Climatological Data collected at the Detroit Metropolitan Airport, 39 km SW of Warren. Upper air data were based on rawinsonde, constant pressure data collected twice daily at Flint, MI, 75 km NW of Warren. The meteorological data were obtained from the National Climatic Data Center in Asheville, NC.

Results

Winter precipitation was collected in Warren, MI over a four-year period. Precipitation was classified as rain, snow, or mixed rain and snow based on the Local Climatological Data from Detroit Metropolitan Airport. The volume-weighted mean concentrations are shown in Table I. The weighted standard deviations were calculated as

Table I. Concentrations of Ions in Winter Precipitation

	Rain	Mixed	Snow
No. Events	31	25	29
NO_3^- (μeq/L)	31±3.3	34±3.1	41±4.9
SO_4^{--} (μeq/L)	66±4.6	55±5.2	26±3.5
SO_4^{--}/NO_3^-	2.1	1.6	0.63

described by Topol (4). SO_4^{--} is lowest during snow events. NO_3^- is indeed higher in snow than in rain, as found in other studies (4,5). The opposite trend in SO_4^{--} and NO_3^- leads to a strong downward trend in SO_4^{--}/NO_3^- ratios from rain to snow events. The SO_4^{--}/NO_3^- ratios are similar to those measured elsewhere in the northeastern United States (4). The trends in NO_3^- and SO_4^{--} will be considered individually below.

Nitrate Concentrations. The higher concentrations of NO_3^- found in snow than in winter rains have been attributed to higher scavenging of HNO_3 in the air by snowflakes than by raindrops (4,5,6). Another possibility will be considered here: that concentration differences can be explained based on precipitation depth. Concentrations of ions such as SO_4^{--} and NO_3^- in precipitation have been shown to vary inversely with precipitation depth (8). During the winter periods considered in this paper, the average precipitation depth for winter rain events was 1.3 cm compared to 0.42 cm (as water equivalent) for snow events. The effect of this difference is shown in Table II

Table II. Precipitation Events Separated by Precipitation Depth

| | < 0.4 cm | | 0.4 - 0.8 cm | | > 0.8 cm | |
	Rain	Snow	Rain	Snow	Rain	Snow
No. Events	6	22	7	5	18	3
Volume (mL)	156	138	398	347	1179	1081
NO_3^- (μeq/L)	78	59	43	44	27	24
SO_4^{--} (μeq/L)	117	36	88	28	61	15
SO_4^{--}/NO_3^-	1.5	0.61	2.1	0.64	2.3	0.63

where events are separated by precipitation depth. Based on this division, the NO_3^- concentrations are not higher in snow events than in rain events.

A multiple regression analysis was also performed to determine the effect of precipitation depth and precipitation type (snow vs. rain) on the NO_3^- concentration. Cloud temperature was used as a measure of precipitation type and was calculated as described in the next section. Although NO_3^- concentrations were found to be inversely correlated with precipitation volume, there was no significant correlation between NO_3^- concentrations and temperature. Therefore, at this location, the lower water content of snow events

compared to rain events appears sufficient to explain the higher
NO_3^- concentrations found in snow; there is no evidence that HNO_3 in
the air is scavenged more efficiently by snow than by rain.

SO_4^{--} Concentrations. Based on Tables I and II, there can be no
doubt that SO_4^{--} levels in winter rain are far higher than in snow
at this location, despite differences in precipitation depth. Two
possible sources of the difference are the following: higher
ambient SO_2 and SO_4^{--} concentrations available for scavenging during
rain events or higher SO_2 to SO_4^{--} conversion during rain events.
These possibilities will be considered further.

Ambient concentrations of particles and gases were measured at
ground level during the 1983-84 and 1984-85 winters to determine if
higher concentrations were available for scavenging during winter
rains and snows. Since the ambient data did not correspond to particular precipitation events, they were roughly grouped into snow
periods and rain periods. The results of this grouping are seen in
Table III. Based on a Student T-test, the only statistically significant differences at the 95% confidence level is for NO_2 which is

Table III. Concentrations of Particles and Gases in Air
during Rain Periods and Snow Periods
$(\mu g/m^3)$

	Rain Periods	Snow Periods
NO_3^-	3.5±2.1	3.5±1.9
SO_4^{--}	3.5±1.3	4.2±1.9
HNO_3	1.4±0.96	1.3±0.78
SO_2	19±9.9	22±10
NO_2	17±7.9	24±10

higher during snow periods. The sulfur species are actually somewhat higher during snow periods than during rain periods. Therefore, the higher SO_4^{--} levels in rain cannot be attributed to higher
levels of ambient sulfur species available for scavenging.

The origin of the storm system could also lead to differences
in precipitation concentrations. Sulfur emissions within 480 km of
Warren are twice as high from the south or east as from the north or
west, and NO_2 emissions are almost ten times higher from the east,
south or west as from the north (3). Since more snow events than
rain events were from the cleaner north, this might explain the
lower SO_4^{--} levels in snow than in rain. To evaluate this, the
ground level wind direction was determined during each precipitation
period based on the Local Climatological Data from Detroit Metropolitan Airport. The data was divided into N, E, S, and W quadrants.
Events with a wind shift of more than 100° were excluded from the
analysis. The volume-weighted mean concentrations are shown in
Table IV. Note that the number of events is small from some directions.

The NO_3^- concentrations are lower in rain than snow from all
directions, but that can be explained based on the lower precipitation depth in snows than rains. The SO_4^{--} levels are considerably

Table IV.   Effect of Wind Direction on Precipitation Concentration
            (μeq/L)

| | -----SO_4-- ----- | | ------NO_3^- ------ | |
	Rain	Snow	Rain	Snow
North	44 (1)*	20 (5)	16 (1)	20 (5)
East	63 (9)	15 (4)	35 (9)	46 (4)
South	72 (10)	39 (7)	31 (10)	54 (7)
West	48 (3)	47 (2)	28 (3)	48 (2)

* Values in parentheses are the number of events represented by
  each mean.

higher in rain than in snow for three directions. Therefore, the
ground-level wind direction cannot explain the higher sulfate levels
in rain than snow.

It is also possible that snow scavenges particulate SO_4^{--} less
efficiently than rain, but this cannot be determined from this data
set. However, indications from the literature suggest that the
reverse is true. Knutson et al. (9) reviewed several studies showing that snow scavenged particles faster than rain. Chan and Chung
(10) also found a higher scavenging ratio for SO_4^{--} particles by
snow than rain.

The other possibility to be considered is that of greater SO_2
to SO_4^{--} conversion in cloud water during rain events than during
snow events. The conversion rate will depend on a variety of factors including the SO_2 concentration, the concentration of oxidants
such as ozone or hydrogen peroxide, and the incorporation and reaction of these species in cloud hydrometeors. The concentrations of
SO_2 and oxidants are unlikely to show large variations from December
to early April when these samples were collected. More likely, the
factor of importance is the state of the precipitation in the cloud,
whether frozen or liquid, or the relative length of time in each
state. The state of the precipitation would affect both the incorporation and reaction of sulfur species in cloud drops. First, during the freezing process, most of the dissolved SO_2 is lost from the
drop as indicated by experiments of Iribarne et al. (11). Secondly,
the oxidation of the remaining dissolved SO_2 within an ice crystal
will be retarded compared to reaction within a droplet. It has been
argued that the precipitation state is unimportant in winter storms,
because all cloud moisture would be expected to be frozen at cloud
levels, whether it appeared as rain or snow at ground level (5).
However, Scott found higher SO_4^{--} levels in rimed snowflakes where
growth occured by accretion of water droplets than in unrimed snowflakes where growth occurred by vapor deposition (12).

We investigated the effect of the temperature in the clouds for
the storms of the first two winters using the upper air data from
Flint, MI. For each precipitation event, the cloud region was
roughly defined as the altitudes with relative humidities greater
than 90%. The median temperature in this altitude range was next
determined. The temperature for the snow events ranged from $-14°$ C

to -4° C with a median of -10° C whereas the rain or mixed events ranged in temperature from -15° C to 11° C with a median of 1° C. Based on these temperatures it appears to be untrue that most cloud layers are frozen in the winter at this location, since drops can easily exist in a supercooled state at these temperatures (13).

Figure 1 shows a plot of the SO_4^{--}/NO_3^- ratio in the precipitation as a function of cloud temperature. A highly significant, positive correlation exists (r=0.75) between the SO_4^{--}/NO_3^- ratio and the temperature in the cloud. The ratio of SO_4^{--}/NO_3^- is used, rather than SO_4^{--} concentrations, to normalize for the effect of precipitation depth; SO_4^{--} in precipitation also correlated with cloud temperature but to a lesser degree (r=0.35).

It is impossible to draw a division between solid-phase and liquid-phase hydrometeors based on the cloud temperature because of supercooling and because cloud drops most likely go through solid and liquid phases as the water circulates from the low, warmer altitudes to the high, cooler altitudes. However, this graph should provide an indication of the state of the system, with hydrometeors at the low temperatures existing as ice crystals and hydrometeors at the higher temperatures existing as liquid drops and a gradation of conditions in-between. Therefore, this evidence suggests that the higher SO_4^{--} levels in rain than in snow is due to the greater dissolution and reaction of SO_2 in liquid drops than ice crystals. Conversely, the fact that NO_3^- concentrations are the same in rain and snow indicates that the dissolution of NOx into drops followed by oxidation is a less important process than for SO_2.

Discussion

Four years of winter precipitation events were analyzed in terms of SO_4^{--} and NO_3^- concentrations to provide information on the mechanisms by which these ions are incorporated into precipitation. NO_3^- was higher in snow than in winter rain, as suggested by other studies. However, in this study the difference could be attributed to the lower precipitation depths associated with snows than with winter rains. There was no evidence that snow scavenged HNO_3 more efficiently than rain at this location.

Conversely, SO_4^{--} was far higher in winter rains than in snow. This could not be explained in terms of the ambient levels of sulfur species or the scavenging of SO_4^{--} particles. However, the cloud temperatures were high enough in the case of rain to suggest that the cloud hydrometeors could have been present as liquid droplets rather than ice crystals. The SO_4^{--} concentrations of the precipitation were correlated with winter cloud layer temperatures. The data suggests that SO_2 is incorporated and oxidized to SO_4^{--} in clouds when the hydrometeors are present as liquid droplets. The fact that NO_3^- levels are the same in both rain and snow suggests that incorporation of nitrogen species into cloud water followed by oxidation is less important a process for nitrogen than for sulfur.

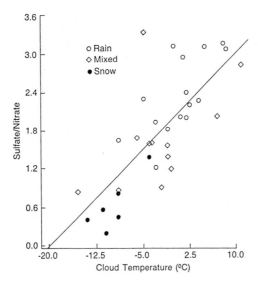

Figure 1.   The influence of cloud termperature on the
SO_4^{--}/NO_3^- ratio of winter precipitation.   (Reprinted with
permission from ref. 14.   Copyright 1987 Pergamon.)

Acknowledgments

I thank Ken Kennedy for collecting samples, Frank Lipari, William Scruggs, Pat Mulawa, and Rene Vandervennet for sample analysis and George Wolff and Sudarshan Kumar for helpful discussions.

Literature Cited

1. Bowersox, V.C.; Stensland, G.J.,"Seasonal Patterns of Sulfate and Nitrate in Precipitation in the United States," 74th Air Pollution Control Meeting, Paper 81-6.1, June 1981.
2. Summers, P.W.; Barrie, L.A., "The Spatial and Temporal Variation of Sulphate to Nitrate Ratio in Precipitation in eastern North America," presented at Muskoka Conference, September, 1985.
3. Dasch, J.M.; Cadle, S.H. Atmos. Environ. 1985, 19, 789.
4. Topol, L.E. Atmos. Environ., 1986, 20, 347.
5. Raynor, G.S.; Hayes, J.V., In Precipitation Scavenging, Dry Deposition, and Resuspension, Pruppacher, H.R., Semonin, R.G., Slinn, W.G.N., Eds., Elsevier Press, 1983, p 249.
6. Chang, T.Y. Atmos. Environ. 1984, 18, 191.
7. Lipari, F. Anal. Chem. 1984, 56, 1820.
8. Barrie, L.A. J. Geophys. Res. 1985, 90, 5789.
9. Knutson, E.O.; Sood, S.K.; Stockham, J.D. Atmos. Environ. 1976, 10, 395.
10. Chan, W.H.; Chung, D.H.S. Atmos. Environ. 1986, 20, 1397.
11. Iribarne, J.V.; Barrie, L.A.; Iribarne, A., Atmos. Environ. 1983, 17, 1047.
12. Scott, B.C. J. Applied Met. 1981, 20, 619.
13. Pruppacher, H.R., In Chemistry of the Lower Atmosphere, Rasool, Ed., Plenum Press, NY, 1973, pp 1-67.
14. Dasch, J. M. Atmos. Environ. 1987, 21, 141.

RECEIVED March 25, 1987

Chapter 22

Pollutant Deposition in Radiation Fog

Jed M. Waldman[1], Daniel J. Jacob[2], J. William Munger, and Michael R. Hoffmann

Department of Environmental Engineering Science, California Institute of Technology (138-78), Pasadena, CA 91125

A study of atmospheric pollutant behavior was conducted in the southern San Joaquin Valley of California during periods of stagnation, both with and without dense fog. Measurements were made of gas-phase and aerosol pollutant concentrations, fogwater composition, and deposition of solutes to surrogate surfaces. Deposition rates for major species were 5 to 20 times greater during fogs compared to nonfoggy periods. Sulfate-ion deposition velocities measured during fog were 0.5 to 2 cm s^{-1}. Rates measured for nitrate ion were generally 50% below those for sulfate, except for acidic fog (pH<5) conditions, because nitrate was less effectively scavenged by neutral or alkaline fogs. In radiation fogs, scavenging of ambient aerosol was observed to increase as liquid water content rose. The lifetimes for atmospheric sulfate and ammonium were short (6-12 h) during dense fog compared to the ventilation rate (>3 d) for valley air.

Deposition during fog episodes can make a significant contribution to the overall flux of pollutants in certain ecosystems. Furthermore, when atmospheric stagnation prevents normal ventilation in a region, fog deposition may become the main route of pollutant removal. Fogs can consequently exert dominant control over pollutant levels in certain environments.

The southern San Joaquin Valley (SJV) of California is a

[1]Current address: Department of Environmental & Community Medicine, UMDNJ-Robert Wood Johnson Medical School, Piscataway, NJ 08854
[2]Current address: Center for Earth & Planetary Physics, Harvard University, Cambridge, MA 02138

region prone to wintertime episodes of atmospheric stagnation. These lead to elevated pollutant concentrations and/or dense, widespread fogs. Major oil-recovery operations plus widespread agricultural and livestock feeding activites are important sources of SO_2, NO_x, and NH_3 in the valley. A multi-faceted program of field monitoring was conducted in the SJV during the winter 1984-85, focusing on aspects of pollutant scavenging and removal in the fog-ladden atmosphere. Concentrations of major species were measured in gas, dry aerosol, and fogwater phases. In addition, depositional fluxes were monitored by surrogate-surface methods. These measurements were employed to directly assess the magnitude of enhanced removal rates caused by fog.

METHODS

Field monitoring was conducted at two SJV sites, Bakersfield Airport and Buttonwillow. Fogwater was sampled by event using rotating-arm-collectors (RAC) with sampling intervals of 1 to 2 h. Liquid water content (LWC) values were averaged over the fogwater sampling intervals, calculated from the rate of RAC collection. Atmospheric concentrations of aerosol, nitric acid and ammonia were monitored using dual-filter methods. Total aerosol samples were collected on open-faced Teflon filters operated side-by-side. Nylon filters and glass-fiber filters impregnated with oxalic acid collected $HNO_3(g)$ and $NH_3(g)$, respectively. Samplers were run twice daily (0000 to 0400 and 1200 to 1600 PST), except during fog episodes, when they were run continuously for 2 to 4-h intervals. Further details of sampling methods and sites are given elsewhere (1,2).

Polystyrene petri dishes (154 cm^2) with their lip (1.2 cm) upwards were deployed to continuously monitor fog and dry particle deposition. These were changed twice per day (0800 and 1600 PST) during nonfoggy periods or, more frequently during fog, concurrent to filter sampling intervals. Petri dishes (PD) were extracted with 10 mL of distilled, de-ionized water immediately following the end of ambient exposure. Subsequent extractions indicated that complete recovery (i.e.,>90%) was achieved. Side-by-side sample comparisons were in good agreement.

The use of surrogate surfaces to measure deposition rates remains controversial due to the uncertainty in extrapolating these results to natural surfaces, especially regarding deposition of gases or submicron aerosol (3). The conditions in the SJV during the fog/aerosol study allowed us to apply simplifying assumptions regarding the dominant deposition processes. The valley is uniformly flat, and over 85% of the surface cover is open cropland or rangeland. There is minimal canopy structure, especially during wintertime. On a regional scale, the terrain is relatively sparse and rather inefficient for impaction. Furthermore, winds in the SJV under stagnant conditions are usually quite light (<2 m s^{-1}); friction velocities measured at the Airport site (1) were consistently very low (U*<20 cm s^{-1}) Therefore, it was expected that sedimentation would be the main pathway for fog droplet and coarse aerosol deposition, and an open collector would reliably monitor that rate.

RESULTS

The winter 1984-85 was characterized by restricted ventilation in the southern SJV. A cap on mixing heights was effectively maintained by a temperature inversion based at 200-800 m above ground level. As in our previous SJV studies (2,4), atmospheric aerosol as well as fogwater samples were found to be dominated by NH_4^+, NO_3^- and SO_4^{2-}. Other constituents were generally measured at concentrations far below these major species, although H^+ and S(IV) were also substantial for several fogwater samples. Overall, these ions accounted for >95% of all the measured solute equivalents. Total aqueous concentrations in fogwater were routinely measured in the 1-3 meq L^{-1} range. Total ion concentrations measured by filters (dry aerosol or fog droplets plus interstitial aerosol) were 1-2 µeq m^{-3}.

Nitric acid concentrations were routinely below detection limits (<0.005 µeq m^{-3}), with the exception of a few measurable values (<0.05 µeq m^{-3}) during daytime intervals. Substantial gaseous ammonia was measured during most intervals. During nonfoggy periods, N(-III) in the gas phase often exceeded the aerosol amount. In higher pH fogs, gaseous ammonia measured 20-50% of total N(-III), while much lower levels were found when fogwater acidities were below pH 5.

As might be expected to accompany changing ambient conditions, material fluxes to ground surfaces varied greatly during the study periods. Deposition samples was dominated by the same major ion species measured in aerosol and fogwater samples, NH_4^+, NO_3^-, and SO_4^{2-}. These deposition rates for PD surfaces are shown in Figure 1 for the important sampling intervals at the Bakersfield Airport. Fluxes measured to surrogate-surface collectors were generally small for dry periods. A sharp increase in the deposition of all ions accompanied fog in each case. For major ions in fog, the enhancement was 5 to 20 times the rates during dry intervals. This was due to the increases in particle size, triggered by aerosol activation and formation of the droplet phase.

The measured deposition rates were normalized to the ambient concentrations of total aerosol loading to calculate deposition velocities. Calculations were made using total and fogwater loadings. We use notations:

(C) = total (aerosol+gas+fogwater) loading of species C in the atmosphere,

and $(C)_f$= fogwater loading of species C, i.e. aqueous fogwater concentration x estimated LWC.

Hence, the total and fog deposition rates, respectively, can be expressed:

$$V_d = \text{measured flux}/(C)$$

and

$$V_{d,fog} = \text{measured flux}/(C)_f$$

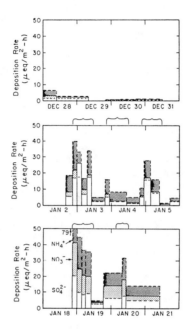

Fig. 1.   Deposition rates of major ions to petri dish collectors at
the Bakersfield Airport site.   Brackets above indicate
periods of dense fog.

   The total and fog deposition velocities for major ions are
shown in Figure 2. In this presentation, clear episodes of higher
rates can be seen for the episodes of fog. Greater fractions of
S(VI) than N(V) were scavenged by droplets during most events; this
led to higher total deposition rates (solid lines in Figure 2) for
sulfate compared to nitrate. At the same time, the fog deposition
values showed strong correlation between the two species ($r^2=0.92$,
n=21), indicating that differences in removal rates were determined
by their respective scavenging efficiencies. This also verified
that the composition in the fogwater was the principal factor
affecting the proportion of solutes removed. The median value of
$V_{d,fog}$ was approximately 2 cm s^{-1} with measurements in the range 1-5
cm s^{-1}. These rates were comparable to the terminal settling
velocity of typical fog droplets (i.e., 10-40 μm diameter).

DISCUSSION

Solutes measured in the droplet phase, $(C)_f$, is a subset of the
total (aerosol + gas + fogwater) loading, $^f(C)$, measured by the
filter methods. Ion ratios for concurrent SJV fogwater and filter
samples reflected the extent of varying conditions in the environment and showed considerable scatter. For example, the nitrate-to-
sulfate ratios in total aerosol samples were distinctly different
than found in fogwater. The average ratio in Bakersfield fogwater
was near 2 and approximately unity in Buttonwillow samples.
However, the actual proportion of N(V) to S(VI) in the atmosphere
was much greater than indicated in fogwater samples (Figure 3).
During most sampling intervals, N(V) scavenging was from 20 to 80%
less efficient than for S(VI). In acid fogs, however, N(V)
scavenging was more efficient. All the points above the 1:1 line in
Figure 3 correspond to intervals with fogwater pH<5.

   The higher atmospheric acidity is believed to have altered
N(V) partitioning prior to fog formation. Higher HNO_3(g) concentration would be present in the pre-fog air (5). Subsequently,
nitric acid would be scavenged following the formation of fog.
However, measured HNO_3(g) was not as high as the observed enhancement of N(V) scavenging. Depletion of gaseous ammonia accompanied
the period of higher atmospheric acidity and low pH fog. In the
absence of detectable NH_3(g), it is postulated that newly formed
N(V), apparently incorporated into a coarser aerosol fraction, was
more readily scavenged in fog.

   One primary determinant for atmospheric, hence fogwater,
acidity is the relative abundance of ammonia (2). In an ammonia
source region such as the SJV, there are factors which can suppress
or accelerate NH_3 release. Conditions under which fogwater acidity
was low were related to factors favoring ammonia release from
sources, such as higher soil moisture and temperatures (6).

   When widespread stagnation suppresses convective transport out
of the basin, the accumulation of pollutants may proceed. The
buildup of atmospheric constituents will be governed by: (a) primary
emissions; (b) in situ transformations (production or loss terms);
(c) intrabasin circulation; (d) ventilation; and (e) removal by

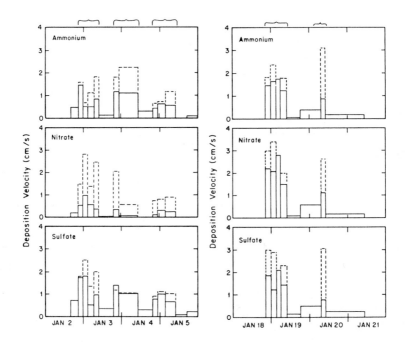

Fig. 2. Deposition velocities of major ions for two periods shown in
Figure 1. Solid lines indicate V_d; dashed lines indicate
$V_{d,fog}$. Brackets above indicate periods of dense fog.

NITRATE / SULFATE EQUIVALENT RATIO

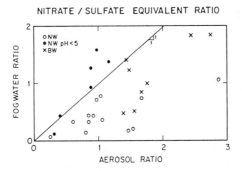

Fig. 3. Comparison of nitrate-to-sulfate equivalent ratios for
simultaneous fogwater and filter samples at Bakersfield
Airport and Buttonwillow sites.

Table I. CHARACTERISTIC REMOVAL TIMES[a]
AND PRODUCTION RATES[b] IN RADIATION FOGS:
SOUTHERN SAN JOAQUIN VALLEY SITES

Date	Duration[c] (hr)	H[d] (m AGL)	τ_d(hr)			Rate (ppb hr^{-1})		
			NH_4^+	NO_3^-	SO_4^{2-}	E_A	E_N	E_S
Bakersfield Airport								
28 Dec 84	4	200	6	15	6	1.5	0.3	0.5
2-3 Jan 85	14	240	6	10	6	1.5	0.4	0.7
3-4 Jan 85	12	210	6	42	6	0.6	0.1	0.2
4-5 Jan 85	12	230	11	27	7	0.8	0.1	0.5
14 Jan 85	3	500	12	22	7	0.7	0.2	0.4
18-19 Jan 85	14	300	6	4	5	1.5	1.1	0.5
20 Jan 85	7	350	11	9	12	0.9	0.7	0.3
Buttonwillow								
2-3 Jan 85	17	290	7	6	7	2.3	1.4	0.3
3-4 Jan 85	17	260	10	17	9	0.5	0.2	0.1
4-5 Jan 85	15	230	7	18	6	0.9	0.2	0.2

a. Characteristic time for pollutant removal:

$\tau_d = H/V_d$, where V_d = Flux/(Ambient Concentration).

b. Production or emission rate to balance deposition rates:

E_C = Deposition/(H x Duration) expressed as NH_3, NO_x and SO_2.

c. Duration of dense fog event.

d. Mixing height at site.

deposition to ground surfaces. The mixing height, H, controls the
volume in which these processes occur. During dense fog, deposition
becomes the predominant loss term for secondary aerosol species.

Flux measurements to collector surfaces demonstrated that
removal rates can be very rapid. In Table I, characteristic times
have been calculated for deposition during dense fog. These values
were determined from the total solute fluxes, mixing heights, and
average pollutant concentrations measured during the individual
events. The removal times were calculated to be 6 to 12 h for these
periods with the exception of N(V) in non-acidic fogs. Between the
occurrences of fog, aerosol deposition was substantially reduced;

deposition velocities were generally an order of magnitude below in-fog values. Fogs persisted more than 50% of the time for several periods in January. In the absence of production terms, aerosol components would be >90% depleted during protracted fog episodes. However, such a net depletion was not observed; by inference, in situ production rates must have at least equaled deposition rates.

As a lower limit, we calculated production rates necessary to balance removal rates of aerosol species measured during fog (i.e., production rate $\cong$ deposition flux/H). Essentially, this equates terms (b) and (e) as given above and neglects the rest. Production rates have been calculated in units of the primary emissions, NH_3, NO_x, and SO_2 (Table 1). Sulfur dioxide values measured at the fog-study sites were mostly <10 ppb, although spatial variability of SO_2, especially near the oil fields make the calculation of an areal average concentration questionable. Assuming 10 ppb for the gaseous concentration, the pseudo first-order $S(IV)$ oxidation rates were calculated to be 2-7% h^{-1}. Considering that advection represented a loss term for the Bakersfield area, the total sinks were likely to have been even greater than measured by deposition alone. Hence, consideration of advection would increase the estimates of $S(IV)$ oxidation rates.

ACKNOWLEDGMENTS

We are grateful to the California Air Resources Board for their financial support (CARB A4-075-32) and their assistance in the field during this project. We are also grateful for the cooperation of the personnel at the Bakersfield Airport, the National Weather Service office in Bakersfield, and the Buttonwillow Recreation Department.

LITERATURE CITED
1.   Waldman, J.M., Ph.D Thesis, California Institute of Technology, Pasadena, 1986.
2.   Jacob, D.J., Munger, J.W., Waldman, J.M., and Hoffmann, M.R., J. Geophys. Res. 1986, 91D, 1073.
3.   Dolske D.A. and Gatz D.F., J. Geophys. Res. 1985, 90D, 2076.
4   Jacob, D.J., Waldman, J.M., Munger, J.W., and Hoffmann, M.R., Tellus 1984, 36B, 272.
5.   Jacob, D.J., Waldman, J.M., Munger, J.W., and Hoffmann, M.R., J. Geophys. Res., 1985, 91D, 1089.
6.   Dawson, G. A., J. Geophys. Res. 1977, 82, 3125.

RECEIVED January 12, 1987

Chapter 23

Deposition of Chemical Components in Japan

Y. Dokiya[1,3], M. Aoyama[1], Y. Katsuragi[1], E. Yoshimura[2], and S. Toda[2]

[1]Geochemical Division, Meteorological Research Institute Nagamine 1, Yatabe,
Tsukuba, Ibaraki 305, Japan
[2]Department of Agricultural Chemistry, University of Tokyo Bunkyoku,
Tokyo, 113, Japan

In order to determine the chemical characteristics of Japanese
rain, the major chemical components were determined at eleven
stations throughout Japan for two years. The principal component analysis showed that nitrate and calcium can be used to
characterize the local factors. The deposition of sulfate is
discussed in relation to its origin. Some typical differences
were observed between the stations on the Pacific side and the
Japan Sea side of Honshu Is.

Increasing acidity of rain and snow is one of the most
important worldwide air chemistry problems. In Japan, fortunately,
the main industrial areas are located at the down wind side of
Honshu Island. In addition, the buffering capacity of the soil near
these industrial areas is fairly high owing to the high content of
organic matter, even though the chemistry of the soil itself is
rather acidic because of its volcanic origin. Thus, the characteristic symptoms caused by acid rain have not been widely reported
yet, except for some direct damage to cedar trees (1) or acute
medical symptoms on men by photo oxidants in early summer (2).

A knowledge of the chemical components in the deposition
throughout Japan is needed in order to evaluate the effect of
increasing rain acidity. Intensive studies have been done on the
chemical components in precipitation or deposition, especially at
the industrialized area of the Pacific side. However, systematic
data are lacking for the less industrialized area on the Japan Sea
side.

In this study, the authors utilized aliquots of samples that
were obtained at eleven stations throughout Japan for the purpose of
determination of radioactive fallout. The chemical components of
monthly deposition samples were obtained during 1984-1985, in order
to characterize the rain and snow in Japan.

[3]Current address: Meteorological College, Asahicho, Kashiwa, 277, Japan

0097–6156/87/0349–0258$06.00/0

Experimental

Collection of Samples

Monthly total deposition samples were collected in stainless steel samplers (0.5 m²) in the observation fields covered with lawn at twelve stations in Japan, the locations of which are summarized in Table 1 and Fig. 1 together with brief descriptions of their environmental conditions.

A known amount of distilled water was added to each sampler in the period when no rain was observed. At the end of each month, the sample solution was transferred into flexible polyethylene bottles and sent to the Meteorological Research Institute at Tsukuba Science City for analyses of the chemical components.

A comparison of stainless steel samplers and plastic samples was previously done in the observation field of Tsukuba for several weeks. No significant differences were seen for the components determined in this report.

Determination of Chemical Components

A 250 mL sample of each solution from the polyethylene bottle was filtered through a Millipore filter (0.45 um pore size). The concentrations of chloride, nitrate and sulfate ions in the filtrate were determined by ion chromatography using a YEW IC 100 of Yokogawa Hokushin Electric Co. Ltd. The concentrations of sodium and potassium were determined by flame emission spectrometry and concentrations of calcium and magnesium by atomic absorption spectrometry using a Hitachi 170-50 Atomic Absorption Spectrophotometer. An aliquot of each filtrate was used for the determination of Sr by ICP emission spectrometry after adding nitric acid (0.1 N), detailed analytical conditions of which are reported elsewhere (3).

Results and Discussion

1. Monthly deposition of soluble chemical components and the precipitation at eleven stations in Japan in 1984

Table 2 shows the amount of precipitation and the soluble chemical components for the eleven stations in 1984 and 1985. The results of sulfate for each month are summarized in Fig. 1. In the figure, the stations are listed in the following order; the first three stations in Hokkaido Is., together with Ishigaki at the right side, the station in Ryukyu Is., next four stations on the Pacific side of Honshu Is. and last four stations on the Japan Sea side of Honshu Is. and Kyushu Is.

As seen from Fig. 2a, the amount of precipitation was higher on the Japan Sea side of Honshu Is. especially during the winter when heavy snow is usually recorded at these sampling stations, compared with the stations in the Hokkaido Is. and on the Pacific side of Honshu Is. Ishigaki showed very high amounts of precipitation especially during spring and summer, presumably owing to typhoons.

Table 1   The location of sampling stations

sampling station	location		Description
	N	E	
1 Wakkanai	45 25	141 41	near the ses shore, weak trafic.
2 Sapporo	43 03	141 20	in a big city, moderate trafic.
3 Akita	39 43	140 54	area of government offices, moderate trafic.
4 Sendai	38 16	140 54	near a main road, heavy trafic.
5 Wajima	37 23	136 54	near the sea shore, weak trafic.
6 Tsukuba	36 03	139 30	area of research institutes, moderate trafic.
7 Tokyo	35 41	139 36	in a big city, near a highway, heavy trafic.
8 Yonago	35 26	133 21	near the sea shore, moderate trafic.
9 Osaka	34 41	135 31	in a big city, near a highway, heavy trafic.
10 Fukuoka	33 35	130 23	near a park, moderate trafic.
11 Ishigaki	24 20	124 10	on the coral leaf, weak trafic.

Table 2   Annual deposition of chemical components at 11 stations in Japan

station	amount of ppt. mm	Na	K	Ca	Mg	Sr	Cl	NO_3	SO_4
						mg/m^2			
1984									
Wakkanai	890.5	8700	640	2800	1300	12	18200	480	6400
Sapporo	725.0	2200	240	4100	300	9	4300	550	7900
Akita	1448.5	7600	700	1800	850	8	14200	1000	7000
Sendai	832.5	1050	220	2700	150	4	2200	930	4300
Wajima	2035.5	10600	560	1700	1100	11	20500	1500	8000
Tsukuba	825.5	720	150	660	140	4	2200	1600	3100
Tokyo	868.0	4600	730	9000	1120	30	8400	4800	20000
Yonago	1464.5	4900	370	2300	610	8	10300	1500	6700
Osaka	1059.5	860	320	2500	190	8	2600	1900	7100
Fukuoka	1169.0	2000	190	1600	230	5	3000	1300	4900
Ishigaki	2232.5	26500	1000	3100	670	21	30000	420	7500
1985									
Wakkanai	1113.5	7200	330	6900	1300	16	12800	770	6700
Sapporo	1045.5	1700	120	4300	420	8	4400	680	5400
Akita	1818.5	6900	450	3200	1200	11	15600	1000	9300
Sendai	1180.0	900	170	3800	280	5	3600	1800	5300
Wajima	2643.5	7800	340	4200	1650	13	23600	1580	8500
Tsukuba	1374.2	700	110	790	180	3	2400	1900	3000
Tokyo	1516.5	1960	270	6000	1000	18	5800	4080	15000
Yonago	1882.5	3360	170	2400	900	10	12500	1300	6700
Osaka	1255.0	500	200	3300	250	8	3100	1800	7400
Fukuoka	2024.5	1600	180	1700	430	6	4900	1050	5600
Ishigaki	2953.5	25500	1500	7200	4330	46	57600	720	13900

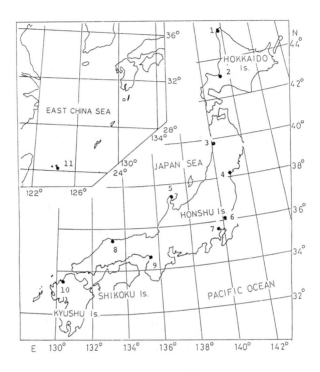

Fig. 1   Location of the sampling stations

a) 1984

b) 1985

Fig. 2   Monthly deposition amount of precipitation at 11
stations in Japan
a) 1984,   b) 1985

It should be noted that in 1984, the amount of precipitation was extraordinarily low (40-60% of the ordinary years) at the northeast Pacific side of Honshu Is. and at the south of Hokkaido Is., partly owing to the fact that no typhoon arrived at Honshu Is. in this year.

The amount of sodium deposition observed was high at Ishigaki. The station Ishigaki is on a small island in the sea. This is probably caused by sea salt.

At the stations on the Pacific side of Honshu Is., Sapporo and Fukuoka, the amount of sodium deposition was low throughout the year. On the other hand, it was high during winter time at the stations on the Japan Sea side of Honshu Is. and at Wakkanai, where heavy snows occur in the winter. It is known that the cold continental Westerly in winter time picks up high amounts of moisture, passing over the Japan Sea and this causes the heavy snow at these stations. From these data, the sodium in the deposition could be considered to be mainly from sea salt throughout Japan.

The deposition amounts for magnesium and chloride were similar to those of sodium with some small deviations, which suggest that these elements also come from sea salt.

The deposition amount of potassium was high at Tokyo and Ishigaki. The seasonal difference was not as clear for other metallic elements.

Calcium depositions and strontium (shown in Fig. 3a) were similar at Sapporo, Tokyo and Fukuoka. At the stations on the Japan Sea side, the contribution of sea salt strontium was also found in winter (4).

The deposition amount of nitrate ion is shown in Fig. 4a. The amount was high at Tokyo and Osaka, which are the highly populated and industrialized areas with heavy traffic. The values of nitrate in the summer season, however, should be treated with much care, because some microbiological change of nitrate to ammonium ions may have occurred during the sampling period of one month (5). It is of interest to mention, however, that the annual deposition amounts of nitrate at the stations on the Japan Sea side were fairly constant around the value of 1.3 g/m^2y which is comparable to the amount reported by EML for the polluted area of the east coast of the United States (6).

The deposition of sulfate, shown in Fig. 5a, was high in Tokyo. The amount which is thought to come from sea salt is calculated as follows:

$$SO_4^{2-} \text{ (sea salt)} = Mg^{2+} \times SO_4^{2-} \text{ (sea salt)}/Mg^{2+} \text{ (sea salt)}$$

$$SO_4^{2-} \text{ (excess)} = SO_4^{2-} \text{ (total)} - SO_4^{2-} \text{ (sea salt)}$$

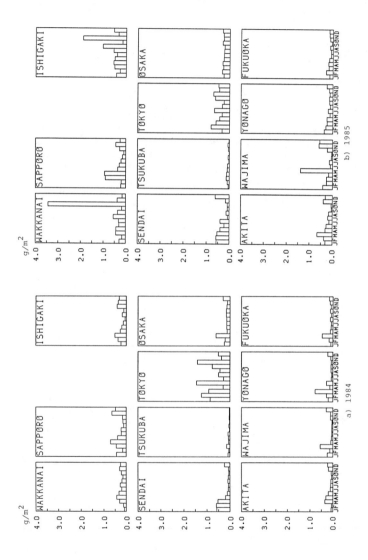

Fig. 3   Monthly deposition of Ca at 11 stations in Japan
a) 1984, b) 1985

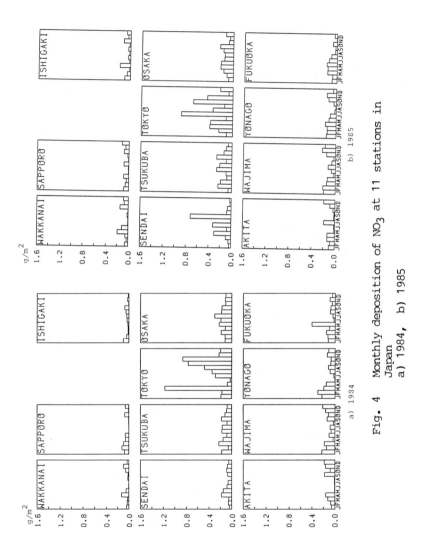

Fig. 4 Monthly deposition of NO$_3$ at 11 stations in Japan a) 1984, b) 1985

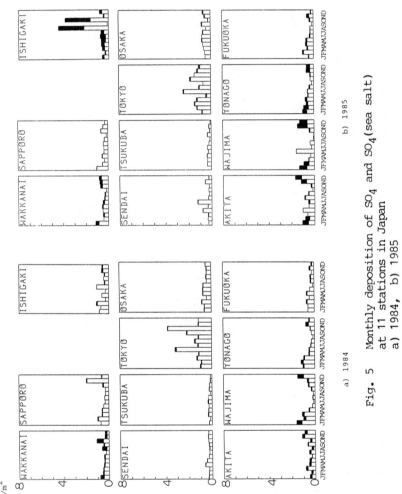

Fig. 5   Monthly deposition of SO_4 and SO_4(sea salt) at 11 stations in Japan a) 1984, b) 1985

The shadowed area in Fig. 5 shows the amount of sulfate which come from sea salt. As seen from the figure, the contribution of sea salt was high at the stations on the Japan Sea side and at Wakkanai in winter time. On the other hand, more than 90% of sulfate did not originate from sea salt at the stations on the Pacific side of Honshu Is. and at Sapporo. This indicates that anthropogenic sulfate might be one of the larger sources of sulfate in these stations. Unexpectedly low contribution of sea salt sulfate at Ishigaki needs some correction because the bed rocks of the Ryukyu Islands are rich in calcium carbonate or coral origin which might cause the different distribution of alkali and alkaline earth metals in the soil material.

2. Monthly deposition of soluble chemical components and the precipitation at eleven stations in Japan in 1985

Table 2 and Figs. 2b, 3b, 4b and 5b show the results for 1985. The amount of precipitation in 1985 was normal all over Japan except for somewhat higher values at Ishigaki and Fukuoka. Though the amount of precipitation was different from that of 1984, the depositions of chemical components were similar to those in 1984 as seen in the figure.

As seen in Fig. 5 at the site on the Pacific side was mainly that of sulfate (excess), while at the sites on the Japan Sea side, the amount of sea salt originated sulfate cannot be neglected in winter months when snow is heavy. The general trends were similar to those of 1984, except for some months at Ishigaki.

At Ishigaki, more typhoons occurred in 1985 than in 1984, and these might be the cause of the higher contribution of sea salt sulfate in August and in September.

3. Statistical analyses data

A principal component analysis was applied to the data of the chemical components and the amount of precipitation at eleven sampling stations to know the characteristics of stations. The eigen vectors for the first and second components are summarized in Tables 3 and 4. The first components were characterized by sodium, magnesium, strontium, chloride, and sulfate ions which means that the major chemical depositions are similar throughout Japan, even though the seasonal variation differed for the stations on the Japan Sea side and the Pacific side.

The second components were characterized by calcium and/or nitrate ions. At the big cities such as Tokyo, Osaka and Fukuoka, nitrate showed the major contribution in the second components. At Wakkanai, Sapporo, Sendai, Wajima and Yonago, Ca showed the major contribution in the second components. Thus, the second components might show the local characteristics. Nitrate ion was supposed to originate from transportation sources. The origin of Ca, however, for these stations might not be identical, including the high dust caused by automobiles in the spring, dust caused by agricultural activities, etc.

Table 3   Results of principal component analysis (1984)

Station	Contribution		Eigen Vector
Wakkanai	I	0.671	$0.43Mg + 0.42Cl + 0.41K + 0.40Na + 0.39Sr + 0.36SO_4$
	II	0.213	$0.70NO_3 + 0.66Ca + 0.24Sr$
Sapporo	I	0.568	$0.46Na + 0.46Mg + 0.45Cl + 0.44K + 0.34NO_3 + 0.21SO_4$
	II	0.271	$0.67Ca + 0.58Sr + 0.40SO_4$
Akita	I	0.591	$0.42Na + 0.41Cl + 0.40Sr + 0.39Mg + 0.39SO_4 + 0.32NO_3$
	II	0.170	$0.80K + 0.22Na - 0.51NO_3$
Sendai	I	0.417	$0.53Na + 0.43SO_4 + 0.41Mg + 0.40NO_3 + 0.39Cl$
	II	0.283	$0.60Sr + 0.55Ca + 0.27SO_4 - 0.47K$
Wajima	I	0.831	$0.38Na + 0.38Mg + 0.38SO_4 + 0.37Sr + 0.36Cl + 0.34NO_3 + 0.33K + 0.26Ca$
	II	0.106	$0.77Ca + 0.21NO_3 - 0.51K$
Tsukuba	I	0.378	$0.47Mg + 0.42SO_4 + 0.41NO_3 + 0.40Cl + 0.39Na + 0.28Ca$
	II	0.221	$0.48Ca + 0.40SO_4 + 0.39NO_3 + 0.35Sr - 0.39Cl - 0.33Na$
Tokyo	I	0.792	$0.39Mg + 0.39Sr + 0.39Cl + 0.39SO_4 + 0.38K + 0.37Na + 0.30Ca$
	II	0.118	$0.97NO_3$
Yonago	I	0.758	$0.40SO_4 + 0.39Mg + 0.39Cl + 0.36Sr + 0.35Na + 0.34K + 0.34NO_3 + 0.24Ca$
	II	0.130	$0.78Ca + 0.44Sr$
Osaka	I	0.454	$0.49SO_4 + 0.45Mg + 0.43Sr + 0.40Cl + 0.40Ca + 0.22NO_3$
	II	0.217	$0.57NO_3 + 0.38Cl + 0.29Cl + 0.20SO_4 - 0.40Ca - 0.36Sr - 0.31a$
Fukuoka	I	0.496	$0.48Sr + 0.43Cl + 0.40Ca + 0.39Mg + 0.36SO_4 + 0.30Na$
	II	0.183	$0.70NO_3 + 0.48SO_4 - 0.40Na$
Ishigaki	I	0.353	$0.54Ca + 0.47Sr + 0.40Mg + 0.20Cl - 0.33K - 0.30NO_3$
	II	0.307	$0.62SO_4 + 0.47Cl + 0.45Na + 0.37K$

I:first component, II:second component

Table 4 Results of principal component analysis(1985)

Station	Contribution		Eigen Vector
Wakkanai	I	0.615	$0.44Mg + 0.42Na + 0.42SO_4 + 0.40K + 0.39Cl$ + 0.30Sr
	II	0.245	$0.64Ca + 0.50Sr + 0.42NO_3$
Sapporo	I	0.596	$0.44Na + 0.44Mg + 0.44Cl + 0.43K + 0.37SO_4$ + $0.27NO_3$
	II	0.252	0.70Ca + 0.67Sr
Akita	I	0.697	$0.41Mg + 0.41Sr + 0.41Cl + 0.40Na + 0.36SO_4$ + $0.33K + 0.23NO_3 + 0.22Ca$
	II	0.159	$0.63NO_3 + 0.53Ca + 0.25SO_4$
Sendai	I	0.593	$0.44Mg + 0.44SO_4 + 0.43Na + 0.43Cl + 0.35Sr$ + 0.29K
	II	0.216	$0.68Ca + 0.44Sr - 0.44K - 0.38NO_3$
Wajima	I	0.785	0.39Na + 0.39K + 0.39Mg + 0.39Sr +0.39Cl + $0.34SO_4 + 0.31NO_3$
	II	0.179	$0.74Ca + 0.43SO_4 - 0.40NO_3$
Tsukuba	I	0.486	$0.45Ca + 0.45Mg + 0.41SO_4 +0.40Cl + 0.32Na$ +0.32K + 0.20Sr
	II	0.260	$0.66NO_3 + 0.33Cl + 0.32SO_4 - 0.48Na$
Tokyo	I	0.837	$0.37Na + 0.37Sr + 0.37Cl + 0.36K + 0.36SO_4$ + $0.32Ca + 0.31NO_3$
	II	0.085	$0.68NO_3 +0.43NO_3 + 0.20Cl - 0.32Mg$
Yonago	I	0.635	$0.43Mg + 0.41Cl + 0.39SO_4 + 0.38Na + 0.38Ca$ + $0.34Sr + 0.28NO_3$
	II	0.196	$0.73K + 0.35Na - 0.37NO_3$
Osaka	I	0.540	$0.41Mg + 0.41Cl + 0.38Na + 0.36K + 0.34Ca$ + $0.33Sr + 0.33SO_4$
	II	0.189	$0.59NO_3 + 0.48SO_4 + 0.27Cl - 0.41Na$
Fukuoka	I	0.647	$0.43Mg + 0.42Sr + 0.41Cl + 0.39Na + 0.38SO_4$ + 0.37Ca + 0.22K
	II	0.191	$0.77NO_3 + 0.37SO_4 + 0.27Ca - 0.33Na$
Ishigaki	I	0.818	$0.39K + 0.39Mg + 0.39Sr + 0.39SO_4 + 0.38Cl$ + 0.35Na + 0.35Ca
	II	0.128	$0.95NO_3 + 0.23Ca$

I:first component, II:second component

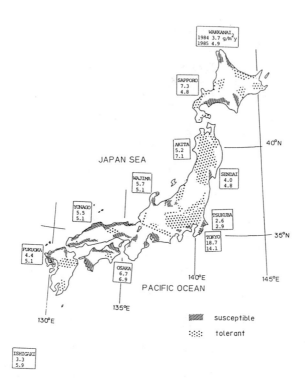

Fig. 6   Soil map for assessing the susceptibility to acid
          rain and the annual SO_4(excess) of 11 stations
          for 1984 and 1985

For the unusual behavior of potassium ion concentration at Akita in 1984 and Yonago in 1985, shown in the second components, more continuous investigation may be needed to check its reproducibility.

4. The effect of sulfate deposition on the chemistry of soil

The Japanese Society of Soil Science and Plant Nutrition provided the soil map for assessing the susceptibility of Japanese soils to acid precipitation (7). Fig. 6 shows a summary of the map together with the annual deposition of sulfate (excess) at eleven stations in Japan. The most susceptible and most tolerant areas are distinguished on the map. The soils in unmarked regions of the map have intermediate susceptability.

From the figure, it is seen that the northeastern part of Honshu Is. is relatively tolerant to acid deposition having relatively rich organic soils even though the chemistry of the soil itself is fairly acidic owing to its volcanic origin. This can be, therefore, one of the reasons why few typical symptoms of the effect of acid precipitations have been obvious in this area even though the deposition amount of sulfate was high near the industrialized area of metropolitan Tokyo.

Another point is that the western part of Honshu Is. is relatively susceptible to acid precipitation especially on the Japan sea side, thus this should be watched carefully because this area is at down wind of the Continental dust.

The source of sulfate can be roughly shown as follows:

$$SO_4^{2-} \text{ (dep)} = SO_4^{2-} \text{ (sea salt)} + SO_4^{2-} \text{ (local)}$$
$$+ SO_4^{2-} \text{ (transported)}$$

The third member of the equation should be studied further in relation to the meteorological conditions and other factors which are involved in the long-range transport of gaseous materials.

The effect of acid deposition on soil and eventually on land, water and the biosphere should also be studied further. The continuous observation of chemical deposition is needed with more suitable sampling sites and for more chemical components for these purposes.

References

1. K. Sekiguchi, Y. Hara and A. Ujiiye, Environ. Tech. Lett. Vol 7,263, 1986.

2. T. Okita and Y. Ota, Shissei-taikiosen (Wet Air Pollution), Sangyotosho (Tokyo), p203-231, 1983.

3. E. Yoshimura, A. Hamada and S. Toda, Proc. Annual Meeting, Japan Soc. Anal. Chem., 1984.

4. Y. Dokiya, E. Yoshimura and S. Toda, Proceedings of Pittsburg
    Conference and Exposition, p528, 1986

5. Y. Dokiya and S. Bessho, Anal. Sci., Vol 2,187, 1986.

6. EML-381, Dept. of Energy (environmental quality), 1980.

7. A. Wada et al, Map for assessing susceptibility of Japanese
    soils to acid precipitation, Japanese Society of Soil Sci. and
    Plant Nutrition, 1983.

RECEIVED May 15, 1987

EXPERIMENTAL METHODS

Chapter 24

Measurement of Atmospheric Gases by Laser Absorption Spectrometry

H. I. Schiff, G. W. Harris, and G. I. Mackay

Unisearch Associates, 222 Snidercroft, Concord, Ontario L4K 1B5 Canada

The advantages of Tunable Diode Laser Absorption
Spectrometry (TDLAS) for measuring trace atmospheric
gases are universality, positive identification, good
sensitivity and rapid response time. An instrument is
described which can measure two gases simultaneously
under automatic computer control with detection limits
better than 100 parts per trillion and with response
times better than 5 minutes. Procedures have been
established for the measurement of NO, NO_2, HNO_3, NH_3,
H_2O_2 and HCHO. These species have been measured under
a variety of conditions in smog chambers and in ambient
air from mobile laboratories and from aircraft.

Tunable diode laser absorption spectrometry offers an attractive
method for atmospheric measurements (1). Almost all gases of
atmospheric interest absorbs in the 2 to 15 micron region. The very
high spectral resolution of tunable diode lasers permit selection
of a single rotational-vibrational line which makes interferences
from other gases very unlikely. If an accidental interference
should happen to occur it can readily be identified by a change in
line shape and another line can be chosen. Unequivocal proof of
the absence of interference is obtained by measuring the
concentrations at 2 different lines. The probability of identical
interferences at 2 different lines is vanishingly small (2).

To get the desired sensitivity and detection limit a long
absorption path can be obtained by using a multi-pass White cell.
The absorption line can be scanned in a fraction of a second and
the response time of the measurement is normally limited by the
residence time of the sampled gas in the White cell which is
typically a few seconds.

Description of the Instrument

Figure 1 shows the schematic of a TDLAS system designed to operate
in field conditions from a mobile laboratory. Lead salt diodes
typically operate in the 20 to 80 K range and the wavelength region
over which they emit radiation depends on the temperature and the
current passing through them. Temperature control to $\pm$ .005 K is
provided by the combination of a closed cycle helium cryocooler, a
heater and a servo temperature system. Two cryostats are used,
each having a laser source assembly containing 4 laser diodes.
One laser diode from each assembly can be chosen to permit two
gases to be measured simultaneously. The emitted radiation from
each of the diodes is scanned over the selected absorption feature
by changing the current through the diode.

The laser beam from each head is collected and focussed by an
off-axis parabolic mirror, OAP_1 or OAP_2 and then directed to a
selection mirror, S which flips back and forth to permit the beam
from each of the diodes to enter the White cell in turn.

The 45° angle of the entrance window to the White cell splits
the laser beam. Most of the beam passes through the window into
the White cell but about 5% is reflected through a cell containing
high concentrations of the target gases onto a separate HgCdTe
detector. The output from this detector is used to lock the laser
radiation wavelength to the center of the absorption line.

The beam enters the 1.75 m Teflon-lined White cell containing
a corner cube reflector (3) and undergoes 102 passes before exiting
to the detector. Absorptions at least as low as 10^{-5} can be
measured which, for a total path length of 150 m corresponds to
detection limits in the range 25 to 100 parts per trillion by
volume for most atmospheric gases.

Sampled air enters through an inlet, flows continuously down the tube and is exhausted at the other end. A restriction at the inlet end and a servo valve at the exhaust end maintains a constant flow rate and pressure in the cell. Maintaining the cell at 25 Torr reduces pressure broadening of the absorption line which both increases the sensitivity of the measurement and minimizes the likelihood of interferences from other gases.

The absorption is measured in the frequency modulated, 2f, mode (4) which results in an increased signal-to-noise ratio compared to using direct absorption.

The unit operates under computer control. Laser temperature and current selections for each species are input to the computer. The system is then switched to automatic mode and can operate unattended for at least 24 hours.

The computer signals the selection mirror to position itself so that one of the beams enters the White cell. A ramp voltage is then produced with 128 steps over a range just wide enough to encompass the absorption feature used for the measurement of species A. The line is scanned under computer control at a rate of approximately 10 Hz for 3 seconds (the approximate residence time of the gas in the White cell) and an accumulated "2f" line shape is acquired.

At the end of the 3 sec averaging period the signal on the reference detector, D2 is checked. If the reference channel indicates that the line is not exactly at the center of the 128 step ramp the computer adjusts the laser temperature to bring the line back to the center.

The selection mirror is then commanded to bring the second beam into the White cell and the measurement procedure is repeated for species B. Each species is thus measured once every 6 sec. Data is accumulated in this way for a period of, for example, 3 min providing an average value for the "2f" line shapes over that time frame. The data set, which provides one mixing ratio for each species, is then stored on the computer disk.

The computer manipulates the solenoid valves and flow controllers to perform measurement and calibrations sequences automatically. In a typical sequence the valve system is commanded

to flow either zero (bottled) air or scrubbed, ambient air through
the White cell. Background spectra of the components are obtained
by scanning over the wavelength regions of the selected absorption
lines. A typical example is shown in Figure 2a.

Calibration gas is then added to the zero (or scrubbed) air
flow and allowed to stabilize for approximately 1 min. An averaged
calibration spectrum is then obtained for 3 min which also serves
as a reference spectrum and the raw data is archived (Figure 2b).

The background spectrum is subtracted (channel by channel)
from the reference spectrum. This procedure removes any frequency
dependent structure in the background from the reference spectra
provided it remains stable for the averaging period. The result
of this subtraction is shown in Figure 2c.

Valves are then reset to admit ambient air, and after another
stabilization period an ambient air spectrum is acquired for 3 min
(Figure 2d) and the background spectrum subtracted (Figure 2e).
The net ambient spectra is least square fitted to the net reference
spectrum. The same calibration sequence is followed for both gases
being measured.

The frequency of calibration and the time duration of the
various stages of the sequence can be altered by the operator. The
choice depends on the mixing ratios of the species being measured;
low ambient concentrations require more frequent determination of
background and reference spectra.

Measurement Requirements

The use of the system to measure an atmospheric component has 3
requirements: (1) selection of a laser and an absorption feature;
(2) establishment of a calibration procedure; (3) ensurance of
sampling integrity.

The selection of a laser and an absorption feature represents
a compromise between the absorption line strength, the
characteristics of the laser emission at the wavelength of the
line, and absence of interferences at this wavelength from other
atmospheric gases.

The calibration philosophy calls for the addition of a known
amount of the calibration gas to the sampled air stream at the

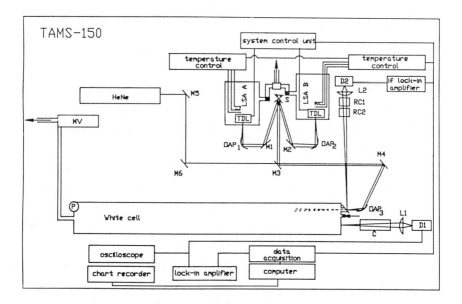

Figure 1.   Schematic of the optical system and control electronics

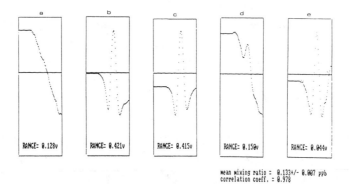

Figure 2.   Computer screen printouts for NO₂ aircraft measurements
            (a) raw background spectrum; (b) raw calibration
            spectrum: (c) calibration spectrum, background
            subtracted; (d) raw ambient spectrum; (e) ambient
            spectrum, background subtracted.

entrance to the sampling line. The concentration of the "spike" is
chosen to provide an increase in measured mixing ratio comparable
to the mixing ratio of the gas in the ambient air. In this way, any
surface effects that may occur will be the same for the sampled and
spiked air and should therefore be compensated.

Finally, tests are performed to ensure sampling integrity. The
air sample is continuously drawn through a short length of 6 mm
teflon tubing and the pressure reduced by an all Teflon needle
valve. The flow rate of the sampled air is typically 15 SLM giving
a residence time of a tenth of a sec in the sampling line and 4 sec
in the White cell. The response time of the system is defined as
the time required for the signal from an addition of the species to
drop to 90% of its value when the source is removed or the time for
the signal to reach 90% of its final value when the source is
introduced. Response times greater than the residence times are
indicative of interaction of the gases with the surfaces of the
sampling system and has been observed for HNO_3 and NH_3. In those
cases careful studies were performed to assess the nature of the
surface processes and sufficient sampling time is allowed for the
system to reach steady state with the ambient air.

These procedures have been established for NO, NO_2, HNO_3,
NH_3, SO_2, $HCHO$, and H_2O_2 and measurements of these gases have been
made under field conditions and in smog chamber experiments. A
modified version of the system in which a liquid N_2 Dewar was
substituted for the helium cryostat was flown successfully in and
above the boundary layer over the eastern Pacific to measure NO_2
and HNO_3.

Examples of Atmospheric Measurements

Nitric Oxide   The ro-vibrational line selected for NO
measurements is in the 1900 cm^{-1} region. Bottled gas of NO in N_2
at a concentration of a few ppmv, traceable to a National Bureau of
Standards determination, has been used as the calibration source
for NO. The response time of the system for this gas is the
residence time in the cell of 3 sec. The minimum detection limit,
MDC, defined as a signal to noise of unity, is better than 40 pptv
(parts per 10^{12} by volume) for an integration time of 5 min· The

accuracy of the measurements is estimated to be $\pm$ 15% based on a
composite of uncertainties of 2% in the concentration of the
bottled NO concentration, $\pm$ 5% from the measurement of total gas
flow into which the calibration gas streams are introduced and $\pm$ 5%
for the flow rate of the calibration gas.

Nitrogen Dioxide The line selected for NO_2 measurement lies in the
1600 cm^{-1} region. A commercial permeation tube is used for the
calibration source for NO_2. The permeation rate is determined by
weight loss and also checked by NO/O_3 titration with NO then
serving as the calibration standard. The response time is 3 sec
and the MDC is 25 pptv.

The accuracy of the NO_2 measurements is estimated to be $\pm$
15%. Calibration is the largest source of error in the
measurements. NO_2 permeation rates were determined by the rate of
weight loss. Weighing errors amount to $\pm$ 2%. The uncertainty in
the NO/O_3 titration method used to check the weight loss method is
about 5%. Additional calibration errors of $\pm$ 2% are caused by
temperature variations of the permeation devices.

Figure 3 shows typical diurnal variations of NO_2
concentrations measured at a relatively clean rural site. Peak
concentrations of about 3 ppbv decrease during the day as
photochemistry proceeds and increases again after sunset. Oxidation
by O_3 decreases the NO_2 concentration during the night.

Figure 4 shows an example of the higher concentrations
observed in a relatively polluted urban environment. Diurnal
variations are similar with mixing ratios as high as 150 ppbv
observed. This figure also shows an interesting example of how the
TDLAS technique can be used to serve as a reference method against
which other, less definitive methods can be compared. Simultaneous
measurements were also made with a Luminox instrument based on
chemiluminescence from a luminol solution. The two methods agree
except for two nights when the pollution levels were quite high.
On these occasions the luminol method gave values some 35% higher
than the TDLAS method, indicating that the luminol method was also
responding to some other species present under these conditions at
night.

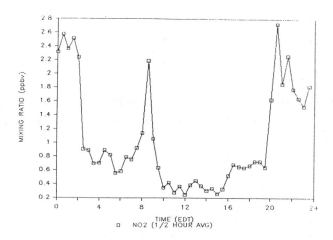

Figure 3. 30 min average NO₂ measurements at Cold Creek, Ontario,
          June,1985

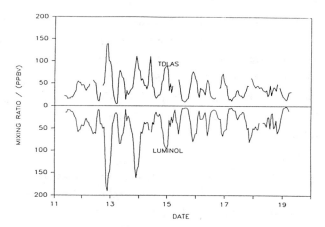

Figure 4. Comparison between 1 hr average NO₂ measurements made
          simultaneously with the TDLAS and Luminox instruments
          at Claremonet CA during Sept. 1985

Nitric Acid The line selected for HNO$_3$ lies in the 1720 cm^{-1}
region. The line strengths for HNO$_3$ are about 4 times lower than
for NO$_2$ resulting in an MDC of about 100 pptv. The calibration
source for HNO$_3$ is a specially designed permeation device in which
the carrier gas is passed through a Teflon tube immersed in a
solution of HNO$_3$ and H$_2$SO$_4$ acids. The permeation rate is
determined by potentiometric titration with standard NaOH solution.

The accuracy of the HNO$_3$ measurements is estimated to be $\pm$
20%. An uncertainty of $\pm$ 5% is attributable to the concentration of
the standard NaOH solution and $\pm$ 2% to the determination of the end
point.

Sampling integrity is the major problem with measuring HNO$_3$
since this gas is highly polar and absorbs readily on most
surfaces. The response time of the system decreases with
increasing flow rate of the sampled air through the system and is
about 5 min for flow rates greater than 15 standard liters per
minute (SLM).

Figure 5 shows typical diurnal behavior of measurements of
HNO$_3$ taken at a rural site. The concentration peaks in the early
afternoon and decreases rapidly in the late afternoon and evening,
indicative of the rapid dry deposition rate of this species. The
rapid dry deposition is also demonstrated in Figure 6 which shows
difference between measurements made at heights of 1 m and 8 m
above a snow surface.

Ammonia   The line selected for detection of NH$_3$ is in the 1050
cm^{-1} region. The line strengths for NH$_3$ are high permitting
detection limits of 25 pptv. But, like HNO$_3$, NH$_3$ is a "sticky"
molecule requiring air flows through the system of at least 15 SLM
to provide response times of 5 min. The calibration source is a
gas cylinder containing NH$_3$ in N$_2$ having a concentration of a few
ppmv which is checked periodically by potentiometric titration with
standard acid. The accuracy of the NH$_3$ measurements is estimated
to be $\pm$ 20% based on uncertainties of the flow calibrations and an
uncertainty of 6% for the NH$_3$ concentration of the calibration
standard.

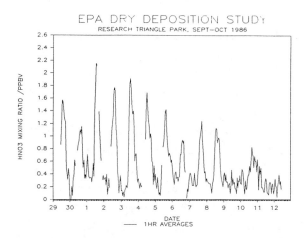

Figure 5. hourly average HNO₃ measurements at Rayleigh NC during
            Sept29-Oct 12, 1986

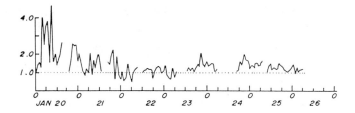

Figure 6. Average ratios of HNO₃ mixing ratios measured at 8 m and
            1 m above a snow surface at State College, PA, January,
            1984

Figure 7 shows simultaneous measurements of NH$_3$ and HNO$_3$ made at a rural site. The measurements show indication of anticorrelation which suggests mutual neutralization. However the product of the concentrations is much less than the equilibrium values with solid NH$_4$NO$_3$ and it is more likely that the anticorrelation results from mixing of different air masses.

Hydrogen Peroxide The line selected for measurement of H$_2$O$_2$ lies in the 1260 cm^{-1} region. The calibration source is a speciallly designed permeation device in which carrier gas is flowed through a 4 m coil of polyethylene immersed in a 50% solution of stabilized H$_2$O$_2$. The permeation rate of this device was determined by a modification of the colorimetric TiCl$_4$ method (5). The response time for H$_2$O$_2$ is about 40 sec; apparently some conditioning time with the apparatus is required for this species but much less than is required for HNO$_3$ or NH$_3$. The accuracy of the H$_2$O$_2$ measurements is estimated to be $\pm$ 20% based on the uncertainties of the flow rates and $\pm$ 10% for the H$_2$O$_2$ calibration.

The relatively weak line strengths for hydrogen peroxide limits the detection of hydrogen peroxide to 100 pptv for 5 min integration times. Measurements made with this system showed that the H$_2$O$_2$ mixing ratios in rural and ambient air is generally above this detection limit.

Figure 8 shows an example of H$_2$O$_2$ measurements made under relatively polluted conditions and Figure 9 shows measurements made under relatively clean conditions. Both studies showed similar diurnal variations with concentrations reaching maxima in the afternoon and minima during the night. The mixing ratios reach higher values in the clean air conditions.

Formaldehyde   The line selected for HCHO measurements lies in the 1740 cm^{-1} region. The calibration source for formaldehyde is a Teflon permeation device containing paraformaldehyde. The permeation rate is determined by a modification of the chromotropic acid colorimetric method (6). No sampling problems are encountered with this gas and the response time of the system is the 3 sec residence time. The detection limit for HCHO is better than 50 pptv. The accuracy of the HCHO measurements is estimated to be

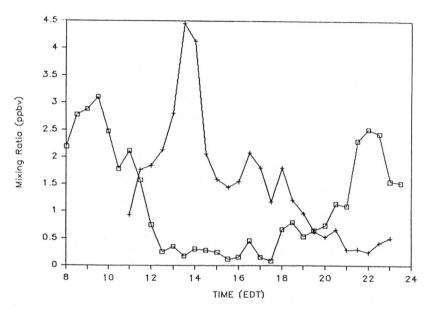

Figure 7. 30 min average mixing ratios measured at Cold Creek, Ont.
July 5, 1985   + NH₃   □ HNO₃

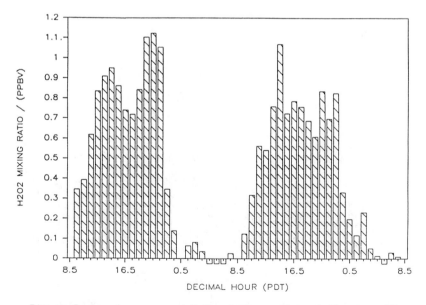

Figure 8. hourly averaged H₂O₂ mixing ratios at Glendora CA,
Aug.19-21, 1986

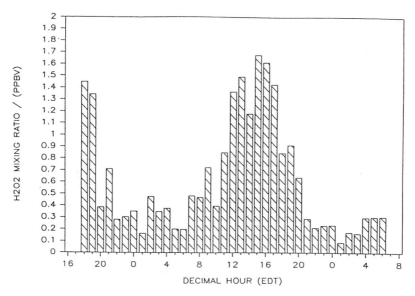

Figure 9. hourly averaged H₂O₂ mixing ratios at Rayleigh NC, June
          24-36, 1986

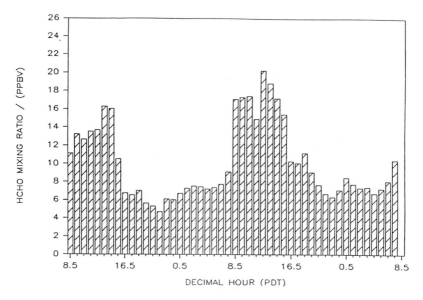

Figure 10. hourly averaged HCHO mixing ratios at Glendora CA, Aug
           19-21, 1986

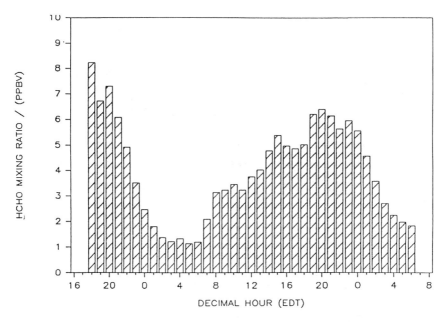

Figure 11. hourly averaged HCHO mixing ratios at Rayleigh NC, June
24-26, 1986

± 20% based on the combined uncertainties of the flow rates and the
± 10% uncertainty of the HCHO calibration.

Figures 10 and 11 show examples of HCHO measurements under
the same conditions as shown for H_2O_2 in the preceding figures. For
the polluted site the peak concentrations were observed near local
noon. For the relatively clean site the peak occurred somewhat
later in the afternoon and was considerably lower than for the
polluted site.

Conclusions

The tunable diode laser absorption spectrometer has been
shown to be a very versatile system for measuring trace atmospheric
gases from mobile laboratories and from aircraft under a number of
ambient and smog chamber air conditions. Its high specificity,
good sensitivity and rapid response time makes it a very suitable
standard against which other less definitive methods can be
compared.

Literature Cited

1.   Schiff, H.I.; Hastie D.R.; Mackay G.I.; Iguchi T; Ridley B.A.
       Envir. Sci. Technol. 1983, 17, 352A – 364A.
2.   Slemr F.; Harris G.W.; Hastie D.R.; Mackay G.I; and Schiff
       H.I.; J.Geophys. Res. 1986, 91, 5371–5378.
3.   Reid, J.; Garside, K.; Shewchun, J.; El-Sherbiny, M.; and
       Balik, E.A. Appl. Optics 1978 17, 1806.
4.   Horn, D.; Pimentel, G.C. Appl, Opt. 1971, 10, 1892.
5.   Pilz, W.; Johann, I. Int. J. Environ. Anal. Chem. 1974, 3, 257–
       270.
6.   Altshuller, A.P.; Miller, D.L.; Slera, S.F. Anal. Chem. 1961,
       33, 621.

RECEIVED May 21, 1987

Chapter 25

Chemical Instrumentation of Atmospheric Wet Deposition Processes

Roger L. Tanner

Environmental Chemistry Division, Department of Applied Science,
Brookhaven National Laboratory, Upton, NY 11973

Field studies of wet deposition processes require the
differentiation and determination of many reactive
species at trace levels in clear-air gaseous and aerosol phases and in air containing clouds and precipitation. These studies have placed extremely rigorous
requirements on existing analytical techniques and, in
several instances, required development of new
approaches to sampling and determination of critical
species. Measurement techniques for nitrogen oxides
and oxyacids, SO_2 and aerosol sulfate species, oxidant
species including hydrogen peroxide and PAN, and various organic species in the gas, aerosol and, where
appropriate, aqueous phases from airborne platforms
are reviewed. Emphasis is on recent developments in
real-time and short-term integrated measurements which
permit the differentiation of below-cloud, within-
cloud (interstitial), and aqueous phase species concentrations of oxidants, and of sulfuric and nitric
acids and their precursors. Recent developments in
measurement techniques for nitrogen oxides and gaseous
H_2O_2 applicable to airborne sampling are highlighted.

Field studies of wet deposition processes require the differentiation and determination of many trace reactive species in the several
phases (gaseous, aerosol, cloud water and precipitation) present in
the atmosphere. The requirements imposed on existing analytical
techniques by these studies have been extremely rigorous and, in
several cases, have necessitated the development of new approaches
to the sampling and determination of critical chemical species.
This paper reviews these technique developments in the context of
their use in airborne sampling during atmospheric field studies.
The focus of the review includes techniques for clear air gases and
aerosols, species in cloud liquid water, ice matrices and precipitation, as well as sampling techniques for gases and aerosols in
cloud interstitial air.

The range of chemical species to be determined include:
- sub-ppb levels of NO_x (NO_x = nitrogen oxides and oxyacids excluding N_2O) determined in real-time using ozone chemiluminescence or by other airborne integrative techniques;
- sub-ppb levels of sulfur dioxide (SO_2) and aerosol sulfate determined in real-time using the flame photometric detector, or in airborne integrated samples by other techniques;
- oxidants (ozone, peroxyacetylnitrate [PAN], hydrogen peroxide) in gaseous and aqueous phases.

Other considerations relevant to airborne collection and determination of atmospheric samples speciated by phase include:
- cloud- and raindrop-free air sampling;
- collection of aqueous liquid and solid samples;

In these discussions we will thus use the following explicit definition of a chemical measurement in the atmosphere: the collection of a definable atmospheric phase as well as the determination of a specific chemical moiety with definable precision and accuracy. This definition is required since most atmospheric pollutants are not inert gaseous and aerosol species with atmospheric concentrations determined by source strength and physical dispersion processes alone. Instead they may undergo gas-phase, liquid-phase, or surface-mediated conversions (some reversible) and, in certain cases, mass transfer between phases may be kinetically limited. Analytical methods for chemical species in the atmosphere must transcend these complications from chemical transformations and microphysical processes in order to be useful adjuncts to atmospheric chemistry studies.

The discussion that follows first describes techniques for the airborne collection of a definable atmospheric phase for subsequent determinations, then continues with discussion of the analysis techniques themselves including those for nitrogen oxides and oxyacids, sulfur oxides, oxidants and selected organic species. Emphasis is on the modified instrumentation devised and used by Brookhaven National Laboratory staff to improve the selectivity and lower the limits of detection of these techniques ($\underline{1}$).

Interstitial Air Sampling

Studies of in-cloud oxidation and wet scavenging processes require the sampling of gaseous species and/or fine aerosol particles in air which contains cloud droplets and/or precipitation. In order to accomplish this sampling of "interstitial" air, it is necessary to selectively remove cloud and rain droplet distributions; these distributions have geometric mean diameters of 10-20 µm and > 100 µm, respectively. Removal is usually achieved by the use of a cyclone device or a centrifugal rotor apparatus ($\underline{2}$) (see Figure 1) for liquid water clouds and precipitation. In addition, these larger particles are removed inadvertently by any curves in the sampling inlet on the aircraft.

Both cyclones and centrifugal rotor devices remove particles of larger aerodynamic diameter by impaction induced by abrupt changes in aerodynamic flow lines, followed by collection of the liquid water out of the flow stream. Coarse aerosol particle (> 2.5 µm diameter) distributions usually overlap the lower end of cloud droplet distributions, hence are removed to a substantial extent in the

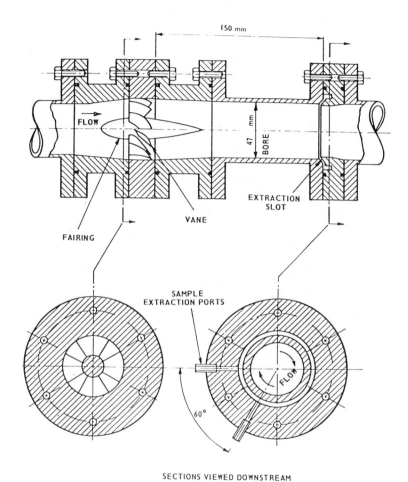

Figure 1. Cloud water sampler for aircraft experiments.
(Reprinted with permission from ref. 31. Copyright 1979 Central
Electric Research Laboratories.)

production of "cloud-free" air. However, fine aerosols and unscav-
enged gases (e.g., NO_2, O_3) may be sampled conveniently in cloud-
free air for subsequent sampling of aerosols (and SO_2, HNO_3, if
present) using the BNL high volume filter pack even at sampling
rates > 0.5 m^3/min (3). Analysis of cloudwater or precipitation
pre-removed by the rotor device is problematical, however, due to
liquid contamination from the inlet surfaces (3); it is preferable
to use the specifically designed atmospheric water collectors
described below.

Collection of Cloudwater and Precipitation

The collection of atmospheric water samples by airborne sampling is,
in the context of this paper, principally concerned with the definition of phase collected, collection efficiency (as influenced by the
droplet size spectra), prevention of contamination during sampling
and simply acquiring enough sample for analysis during the sampling
time available (i.e., spatial/temporal resolution). A device for
sampling liquid phases, designed by personnel at the Atmospheric
Sciences Research Center, SUNY at Albany (4) operates by impacting
droplets onto slotted rod(s) in an apparatus (see Figure 2) situated
external to the aircraft skin. The size and number of the slotted
rod(s) and their orientation are determined by the phase to be collected - cloudwater or rain - and its size spectra. Samples drain
from the rods to a collection vessel inside the aircraft. Because
the collector is made of plastic, it is somewhat flexible and, as a
result, the collection efficiency even for a single cloud droplet
size distribution is a function of aircraft speed and angle of
attack (5). Transient species (e.g. H_2O_2, S(IV)) must be stabilized
within a few hours of collection, whereas more stable species need
only be stored in a clean, cool place until analysis can be
performed.
         Collection of supercooled liquid water in clouds is simple,
using only a plate or screen exposed to RAM air; the water is later
melted and stored prior to analysis (6). Collection of frozen cloud
particles is a little more problematical since the liquid water
content can be low, and individual particles are more subject to
bounce-off during impactive collection. Collection of snow particles aboard the aircraft is most difficult of all due to the low
aerodynamic diameter exhibited by these particles in RAM air
streams. Successful methods for the collection of snow and ice
clouds are still in an active stage of development.

Determination of Nitrogen Oxides

The technique used for most real-time measurements of nitric oxide
(NO) and other nitrogen oxides and oxyacids in the ambient atmosphere is based on the detection of light from the chemiluminescent
reaction of ozone with NO (7,8). This light originates when a portion of excited state NO_2 molecules formed in the reaction luminesce
in a continuum from ~600 nm into the near infrared region. Ozone-
chemiluminescent (CL) instruments for NO_x consist of a chamber for
mixing ambient air with excess ozone and a window for viewing the
filtered luminescence with a photomultiplier tube. Nitrogen species
other than NO are converted thereto by passage over a heated

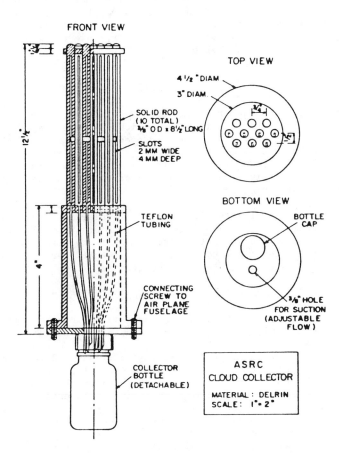

Figure 2.   ASRC cloud collector.   (Reprinted with permission from ref. 4.   Copyright 1979 Atmospheric Sciences Research Center.)

catalyst (typically molybdenum at ∼375°C). Two-channel instruments
for simultaneous determination of NO and NO_x are commercially available but generally have limits of detection (LODs) of ∼2 ppbv. Consideration has thus been given to improving the sensitivity and
lowering the LOD for measurements of NO and NO_x in non-urban and
background locations at which levels < 1 ppb are common. This is
done by reference to the response equation for the detector
(1,9,10), Equation 1:

$$S = GAI \qquad (1)$$

This relates the detector signal to the intensity (I) of light produced, the efficiency of light collection (G), and the PMT sensitivity (A). The intensity of light produced is expressed as the product of the NO concentration, the flow rate, and a series of fractions (fraction of NO_2 formed in the excited state, fraction of NO_2^*
decaying radiatively, and the fraction of $NO-O_3$ reaction occurring
within view of the detector).

Optimization of the response of the CL detector consists of
maximizing each of the factors in the governing response equation.
Collection efficiency (G) of the diffuse CL source is improved by
polishing and gold-coating the reaction chambers. Factor A is maximized by selecting a low-noise, infrared sensitive PMT. The intensity of CL light, I, is given in Equation 2:

$$I = f_1 f_2 (1 - exp[\tau_r/\tau_{NO}])(F/P)[NO] \qquad (2)$$

I is maximized by operating at high flow rates under reduced chamber
pressure in an enlarged chamber volume using increased concentrations of ozone.

A summary of the improvements in performance of the modified
Monitor Labs Model 8840 oxides of nitrogen monitor is given in Table
I (from Ref. 10) based on the instrument design shown in Figure 3.
The pre-reactor is designed to facilitate the accurate measurement
of the "zero air" signal - the response of the instrument in the
absence of NO. At the lowered LODs obtainable from the modified
NO_x instrument the possible presence of quenching gases and interfering compounds in ambient air negates the use of tank air in
determining the zero air signal. Reaction of ozone with sampled air
prior to admission to the reaction chamber allows for "zero air"
signal determination under ambient air conditions, hence determination of low ambient NO levels can be made with requisite precision
and accuracy.

Determination of nitric acid concentrations may be made using
the modified NO_x analyzer by diverting a portion of the air stream
through a nylon filter and molybdenum converter in series to obtain
a measure of NO_x-HNO_3; nylon removes acidic gases including HNO_3 and
HCl, but generally transmits other nitrogen oxide and organonitrogen
compounds with the possible exception of nitrous acid. Nitric acid
is thus determined in real-time from the difference between the 2
channels when the NO_x/NO_x-HNO_3 mode is selected. Difficulties in
obtaining accurate HNO_3 levels have been observed using filter pack
collection techniques. In Figure 4 we show a comparison of HNO_3
concentrations observed airborne in samples collected using the BNL

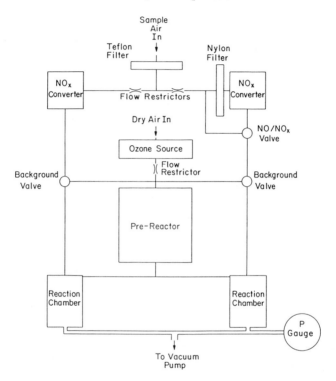

Figure 3. Improved chemiluminescent NO_x detector. (Reprinted with permission from ref. 10. Copyright 1986 Brookhaven National Laboratory.)

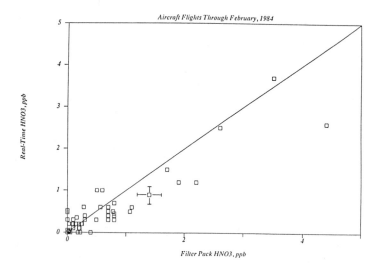

Figure 4. Comparison of airborne filter pack and real-time HNO₃ data. (Reprinted with permission from ref. 10. Copyright 1986 Brookhaven National Laboratory.)

Table I. Comparison of Characteristics of Modified and Unmodified
Monitor Labs 8840 NO_x Detector

Instrument Characteristic	Original 8840	Modified 8840
Compounds	NO and NO_x	NO and NO_x or NO_x and NO_x-HNO_3
Detection Limit (ppb)	2, NO and NO_x	*0.2, NO and NO_x 0.3, HNO_3
Lowest Range, ppb full scale	50	8.7
90% Response Time, seconds	120	10
Sample Flow Rate, sccm	1500	1500
Reaction Chamber Pressure, torr	250	10
Reaction Chamber Volume, cc	15	225
Reactor Internal Surface	Unpolished Stainless	Polished and Gold Coated Stainless
Pre-reactor (Y/N)	No	Yes

* Values are based on signal/peak-to-peak-noise ratio of 2 at an
instrument time constant of 5 seconds.

filter pack and determined by the continuous NO analyzer (10). The
median value is near the LOD of the real-time technique, in consideration of which the agreement between methods is quite good (least
squares slope 0.72, r^2 = 0.83, intercept not significantly different
than zero).

Further improvements in detector performance are desirable,
especially for determining low airborne concentrations of nitrogen
oxides and HNO_3 in remote areas or in the presence of clouds. As
outlined by Kelly (10), possible improvements include a still larger
ozone source, improved chamber design, PMT cooling and photon count-
ing signal processing.

Difficulties are encountered in determining NO_2 using the
ozone-chemiluminescence technique due to the non-specific conversion
of several nitrogen oxides/oxyacids on the Mo catalyst. Use of
$FeSO_4$ for NO_2-to-NO conversion has been described, but humidity-
dependent sorption/desorption effects have been reported, e.g., PAN
(11). Alternatively, a commercial NO_2 analyzer based on surface
chemiluminescence of NO_2 in the presence of a luminol solution, has
been introduced which exhibits the requisite sensitively and
selectivity.

Nitric acid and certain other gases can be sampled by diffusion
denuder tubes, eliminating artifacts associated with filter collection. The annular denuder variation of this technique permits sampling at higher flow rates (5 to 10 L/min), hence may be useful for
airborne sampling, although no airborne data have been reported to
date.

Determination of Sulfur Dioxide and Aerosol Sulfate

The most commonly used technique for the airborne determination of
ambient levels of sulfur dioxide (SO_2) and aerosol sulfur in real-
time involves the use of a modified commercial flame photometric
detector (FPD) (12), although recent versions of pulsed fluorescence
instrumentation (for SO_2) are becoming more promising. A procedure
for enhancing the sensitivity of the commercial FPD by addition of a
known background level of a sulfur compound, usually SF_6 (~100 ppb)
in the hydrogen supply (12), is now widely used, resulting in LODs
approaching 0.2 ppbv (10-sec time constant). Sulfur gases (mostly
SO_2 in ambient air) are determined after removal of aerosol S particles onto Teflon filters. Aerosol sulfur concentrations are determined after removal of gaseous sulfur compounds by passage through a
diffusion denuder tube. Mass flow controllers are inserted in the
hydrogen and exhaust gas lines (the latter after removal of conden-
sible water) to stabilize gas flows and hence, H_2/O_2 ratio in the
burner. This modification is required for airborne operation at
sub-ppb sulfur concentrations (13). Calibrations show linear
response with < 10 ppb full scale sensitivity. Successful airborne
use of a dual SO_2/aerosol S instrument for measurements in clear and
cloud-interstitial air has been extensively documented (1,13).

Determination of Atmospheric Oxidants

Determination of several atmospheric oxidant species is critical to
understanding gaseous and aqueous processes leading to acidic deposition. Hydrogen peroxide has a high Henry's Law solubility and
must be measured in gaseous and aqueous atmospheric samples to
better understand wet deposition processes. In contrast, measurements of ozone and peroxyacyl nitrates (PANs) (and probably alkyl
hydroperoxides and peracids) usually need to be made only in the gas
phase due to their low aqueous solubility (14).
   Measurement of ozone in the gas phase in real-time from airborne platforms at atmospheric concentrations using the ethylene-
chemiluminescence technique no longer presents significant technical
difficulties. Measurement of ambient concentrations of PANs and
other organic nitrates can now be done with automated apparatus from
ground-based or airborne platforms (15,16), using gas chromatography
of periodic, discrete air samples with electron capture detection.
Calibrations to establish absolute accuracy of determinations at low
ppb levels are difficult, and usually only peroxyacetyl nitrate data
are reported. Advances in this area using a new PAN preparative
technique (17) can be anticipated.
   Analysis of aqueous-phase hydrogen peroxide can now be performed at the μM-levels observed in cloudwater and rain samples
using several recently developed and/or modified techniques. The
author's preference is the fluorescence technique using the
peroxidase-catalyzed dimerization reaction of H_2O_2 with
p-hydroxyphenylacetic acid (POHPAA technique) of Lazrus et al. (18),
as modified by Kelly et al. (19) Data on atmospheric levels of
aqueous H_2O_2 have increased dramatically in the past two years with
these technique developments. indicating seasonal dependencies of
H_2O_2 sources and non-coexistence of SO_2 and H_2O_2 in non-
precipitating clouds (3).

Measurement of gas-phase H_2O_2 has lagged due to difficulties experienced in collecting $H_2O_2(g)$ into aqueous solution without generating "artifact" peroxide by radical scrubbing or surface-mediated ozone decomposition (20). Recently, in addition to the reported direct observation of $H_2O_2(g)$ by diode laser-based absorbance measurements (21), three methods for artifact-free collection of $H_2O_2(g)$ have been reported based on prompt derivatization and analysis (22) or ozone pre-removal techniques (see Figure 5), with determination of collected $H_2O_2(aq)$ by the POHPAA technique (23) or hemin-catalyzed luminol methodologies (24). Airborne measurements for gaseous H_2O_2 have been reported for only one of these techniques (25). Aqueous samples must be analyzed promptly or else fixed by addition of reagent in the case of the POHPAA technique (26).

Determination of Organics in Atmospheric Samples

Several classes of atmospheric organic compounds are of interest in deposition studies. Instrumentation for these species will be briefly reviewed.

Concentrations of total hydrocarbons (expressed as ppbv C) or non-methane hydrocarbons can be determined from airborne platforms using flame ionization detection, but their relevance to photochemical oxidant production, and hence to acidic deposition, is indirect. Reactive hydrocarbons have been determined in surface measurements using ozone chemiluminescence with optical filters (27), but the instrumentation has not been developed for airborne measurements. Aldehydes have been widely measured in aqueous and gas phase samples, usually using DNPH derivatizations and HPLC-UV determination (28,29); however, few airborne measurements have been reported. Organic acids have been reported to be important sinks from the atmosphere for oxidized atmospheric carbon (30), based on surface measurements using ion-exclusion chromatography with UV or conductivity detections. Lastly, organic peroxides and peracids have relatively low aqueous solubility, but have been hypothesized to be important oxidants in the gas phase. Methodologies for their unambiguous determination in atmospheric samples are still being developed.

Summary

Several areas in which chemical measurement technologies have become available and/or refined for airborne applications have been reviewed in this paper. It is a selective review and many important meteorological and cloud physics measurement capabilities of relevance to atmospheric chemistry and acid deposition (e.g., measurement of cloud liquid water content) have been ignored. In particular, we have not discussed particle size spectra measurements for various atmospheric condensed phases (aerosols, cloud droplets and precipitation). Further improvements in chemical measurement technologies can be anticipated especially in the areas of free radicals, oxidants. organics, and SO_2 and NO_2 at very low levels. Nevertheless, major incremental improvements in the understanding of acid deposition processes can be anticipated from the continuing airborne application of the techniques described in this review.

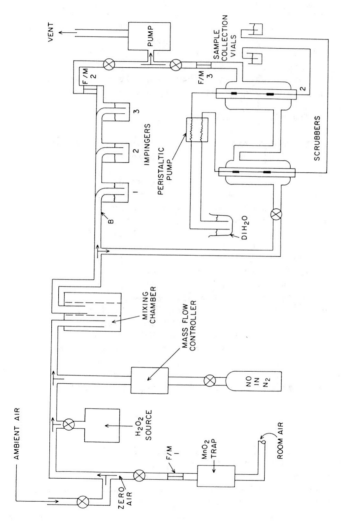

Figure 5. Schematic of ambient air sampling apparatus for gaseous hydrogen peroxide. (Reprinted from ref. 23. Copyright 1986 American Chemical Society.)

Acknowledgments

The author acknowledges many informative discussions with T.J. Kelly and P.H. Daum. This work was conducted under the auspices of the U.S. Department of energy under contract No. DE-AC02-76CH00016.

References

1. Tanner, R.L.; Daum, P.H.; Kelly, T.J. *Intern. J. Environ. Anal. Chem.*, 1983, 13, 323-335.
2. Walters, P.T.; Moore, M.J.; Webb, A.H. *Atmos. Environ.*, 1983, 17, 1083-1091.
3. Daum, P.H.; Kelly, T.J.; Schwartz, S.E.; Newman, L. *Atmos. Environ.*, 1984, 18, 2671-2684.
4. Winters, W.; Hogan, A.; Mohnen, V.; Barnard, S. "ASRC airborne cloud water collection system", Atmospheric Sciences Research Center, State University of New York at Albany, ASRC-SUNYA Publication No. 728, 1979.
5. Huebert, B.J.; Baumgardner, D. *Atmos. Environ.*, 1985, 19, 843-846.
6. Scott, B.C.; Laulainen, N.S. *J. Appl. Meteor.*, 1979, 18, 138-147.
7. Fontijn, A.; Sabadell, A.J.; Ronco, R.J. *Anal. Chem.*, 1970, 42, 575-579.
8. Stedman, D.H.; Daby, E.E.; Stuhl, F.; Niki, H. *J. Air Poll. Contr. Assoc.*, 1972, 22, 260-263 (1972).
9. Delany, A.C.; Dickerson, R.R.; Melchoir, F.L., Jr.; Wartburg, A.F. *Rev. Sci. Instrum.*, 1983, 53, 1899-1903.
10. Kelly, T.J. "Modifications of Commercial Oxides of Nitrogen Detectors for Improved Response", Brookhaven National Laboratory, Upton, NY, Report No. BNL-38000, 1986.
11. Tanner, R.L.; Lee, Y.-N.; Kelly, T.J.; Gaffney, J.S. "Ambient HNO_3 Measurements-Interference from PAN and Organo-Nitrogen Compounds", presented at the 25th Rocky Mountain Conference, Denver, CO, 1983.
12. D'Ottavio, T.; Garber, R.; Tanner, R.; Newman, L. *Atmos. Environ.*, 1981, 15, 197-203.
13. Garber, R.W.; Daum, P.H.; Doering, R.F.; D'Ottavio, T.; Tanner, R.L. *Atmos. Environ.*, 1983, 17, 1381-1385.
14. Lind, J.; Kok, G.L. *J. Geophys. Res.*, 1986, 91, 7889-7895.
15. Spicer, C.W.; Holdren, M.W.; Keigley, G.W. *Atmos. Environ.*, 1983, 17, 1055-1058.
16. Singh, H.B.; Salas, L.J. *Nature*, 1983, 302, 326.
17. Gaffney, J.S.; Fajer, R.; Senum, G.I. *Atmos. Environ.*, 1984, 18, 18215-18218.
18. Lazrus, A.L.; Kok, G.L.; Gitlin, S.N.; Lind, J.A.; McLaren, S.E. *Anal. Chem.*, 1985, 57, 917-920.
19. Kelly, T.J.; Daum, P.H.; Schwartz, S.E. *J. Geophys. Res.*, 1985, 90, 7861-7871.
20. Heikes, B.G. *Atmos. Environ.*, 1984, 18, 1433-1445.
21. Schiff, H.I.; Mackay, G.I. "The Development of a Method for Measuring H_2O_2 in Real Air Using a Tunable diode Laser Absorption Spectrometer", Final Report of Research Project RP 2023-5, prepared by Unisearch Associates, Inc., for the Electric Power Research Institute, 1984.

22. Lazrus, A.L.; Kok, G.L.; Lind, J.A.; Gitlin, S.N.; Heikes,
     B.G.; Shetter, R.E. Anal. Chem., 1986, 58, 594-597.
23. Tanner, R.L.; Markovits, G.Y.; Ferreri, E.M.; Kelly, T.J.
     Anal. Chem., 1986, 58, 1857-1866.
24. Groblicki, P.J.; Ang, C.C. "Measurement of H_2O_2 without Ozone
     Interference", Proceedings of the Symposium on Heterogeneous
     Processes in Source-Dominated Atmospheres, New York, 1985,
     86-88.
25. Heikes, B.G.; Lazrus, A.L.; Kok, G.L. "Measurements of H_2O_2 in
     the Lower Troposphere", presented at the 17th International
     Symposium on Free Radicals, Granby, CO, 1985.
26. Kok, G.L.; Thompson, K.; Lazrus, A.L.; McLaren, S.E. Anal.
     Chem., 1986, 58, 1192-1194.
27. Kelly, T.J.; Gaffney, J.S.; Phillips, M.F.; Tanner, R.L.
     Anal. Chem., 1983, 55, 135-138.
28. Grosjean, D.; Fung, K. Anal. Chem., 1982, 54, 1221-1224.
29. Tanner, R.L.; Meng, Z. Environ. Sci. Technol., 1984, 18,
     723-726.
30. Keene, W.C.; Galloway, J.N.; Holden, J.D. J. Geophys. Res.,
     1983, 88, 5122-5130.
31. Kallend, A.S. "The Fate of Atmospheric Emissions along Plume
     Trajectories over the North Sea: First Annual Report to EPRI,
     March, 1979", Central Electric Research Laboratories,
     Leatherhead, Surrey, England, Report No. RO/L/R 1998, 1979.

RECEIVED March 10, 1987

FUNDAMENTAL PROCESSES

Chapter 26

Factors Affecting NO$_x$ Production During Char Oxidation

Gregory J. Orehowsky, Alan W. Scaroni, and Francis J. Derbyshire

Fuel Science Program, Department of Materials Science and Engineering, Pennsylvania State University, University Park, PA 16802

The oxidation of chars prepared from nitrogen-containing precursors has been investigated. Chars produced from the nitrogen-containing compounds acridine and phenanthridine were oxidized at atmospheric pressure at temperatures of 773-873 K. The relative rates of nitrogen and carbon release and the formation of NO$_x$ have been determined in relation to char nitrogen content and precursor type.

At 773 K carbon was found to be preferentially oxidized at low burnoff; at higher temperatures the rates of carbon and nitrogen oxidation were indistinguishable. The conversion of char nitrogen to NO$_x$ was dependent upon the char structure and composition, much less NO$_x$ being produced from the phenanthridine char. It is assumed that the remainder of the nitrogen is released as N$_2$, presumably formed by the reduction of NO$_x$ with C and/or CO. The conversion of nitrogen to NO$_x$ was also found to decrease with increasing oxidation temperature, char nitrogen content and with sample bed height.

Although SO$_x$ emissions are most often identified as the principal precursors to acid rain, NO$_x$ emissions also play an important role in acid rain formation ([1]). Before methods for limiting NO$_x$ emissions from solid fuel combustors can be fully developed, a more detailed understanding of the reaction chemistry of fuel bound ntirogen oxidation must be obtained.

During combustion, NO$_x$ is formed either by the reaction of oxygen and atmospheric nitrogen (thermal NO$_x$) or the oxidation of chemically bound nitrogen in the fuel (fuel NO$_x$). The production of thermal NO$_x$ can be minimized by various techniques which lower the flame temperature. The reduction of thermal NO$_x$ alone may not lower NO$_x$ emissions to within acceptable regulatory limits. Thus, it will be necessary to limit fuel NO$_x$ emissions.

There have been a limited number of studies which indicate that the conversion of char nitrogen to NO$_x$ can make a significant contribution to the total NO$_x$ emissions. The oxidation of char nitrogen

has been found to account for between 20 and 40 percent of the total
fuel NO$_x$ emissions during pulverized coal combustion ($\underline{2}$).   Since
fluidized bed combustors operate at lower temperatures than pulverized coal combustors, more nitrogen is retained in the char.   The char
has been shown to be the major contributor to NO$_x$ formation until approximately 1200 K during fluidized bed combustion ($\underline{3}$).

Fuel nitrogen is converted to NO$_x$ through two pathways; homogeneous oxidation of nitrogen-containing volatiles and heterogeneous oxidation of the nitrogen contained in the char.   It is the latter
mechanism of NO$_x$ production that is the subject of this paper.

In the present work the oxidation of nitrogen-containing chars
prepared from model compound precursors was studied.   The relative
rates of nitrogen and carbon depletion and the mode of nitrogen release were investigated.   The influence of the char nitrogen content,
the precursor composition, and the oxidation temperature on NO$_x$ production were studied.

Sample Preparation

The nitrogen-containing heterocyclic compounds, acridine and phenanthridine, and the polycyclic aromatics, anthracene and phenanthrene,
were used as char precursors.   Acridine has the three-ringed structure of anthracene with a nitrogen atom substituted for a carbon atom
in the 9 position.   Similarly, phenanthridine is the nitrogen containing analog of phenanthrene.   The nitrogen contents of both acridine and phenanthridine are 7.8 wt%.   The nitrogen contents of chars
prepared from these compounds were varied by blending various amounts
of acridine with anthracene and phenanthridine with phenanthrene.
All of the compounds, ~ 98% purity, were obtained commercially.

Although it is recognized that a study of coal char oxidation is
very useful, the fundamental understanding of the oxidation pro-
cess(es) is complicated by the indeterminate structure of the char,
by the presence of other heteroatoms, and by the presence of inorganic components, some of which may possess catalytic activity.   To cir-
cumvent these difficulties, model compound char precursors were used
in this research.   The high purity of the starting materials ensured
that the chars were comprised principally of carbon and nitrogen,
with low concentrations of hydrogen and ash.

The char precursors were carbonized at 823 K for 90 minutes
under a nitrogen pressure of 0.68 MPa in tubing bomb reactors.   The
carbonaceous residues were subsequently heat treated at 1273 K for
1 hour under argon in a tube furnace to drive off residual volatile
matter.   The carbonization was conducted to increase char yield; direct heat treatment of the precursors would result in very low char
yeilds.   The high heat treatment temperature was chosen to ensure
that at the lower temperature used in the oxidation experiments,
there would be no volatile material, thus ensuring that the reaction
was heterogeneous.

Air oxidations of the 1273 K chars were performed over the temperature range of 773 K to 873 K at atmospheric pressure.   In these
experiments, two grams of char were placed in a quartz tube reactor
held vertically in a fluidized bed sandbath.   Preheated air, at a
flow rate of 1.7 l/m, was passed upward through the sample.   The char
was oxidized to the desired burnoff and the residual char was examined to determine changes in the concentration of C, H, and N as a

function of burnoff. The effluent gases were analyzed by a nondispersive infrared CO/CO_2 analyzer and a chemiluminescent NO_x analyzer. The CO/CO_2 analyzer was calibrated using N_2 as a zero gas and a certified mixture of 1.7% CO_2, 0.7% CO, and balance N_2 as a span gas. The NO_x analyzer was calibrated using air as a zero gas and a certified mixture of 920 ppm NO and balance N_2 as a span gas.

Results and Discussion

Elemental Analyses of Chars. Elemental analyses of the chars produced after heat treatment are presented in Table I. The char precursors had nitrogen contents ranging from 1.0 to 7.8 percent by weight. The nitrogen contents of the corresponding chars were lower

Table I. Elemental Analyses of 1273 K Chars

Precursor (mol.)	C (wt%)	H (wt%)	N (wt%)	H/N
13% acridine- 87% anthracene	98.2	0.35	1.16	4.22
38% acridine- 62% anthracene	96.9	0.37	2.93	1.77
64% acridine- 36% anthracene	95.9	0.24	4.56	0.74
100% acridine	92.1	0.42	6.66	0.88
13% phenanthridine- 87% phenanthrene	94.0	0.32	0.98	4.57
38% phenanthridine- 62% phenanthrene	93.7	0.55	2.25	3.42
64% phenanthridine- 36% phenanthrene	96.4	0.28	3.71	1.06
100% phenanthridine	94.6	0.56	5.25	1.17

because of nitrogen loss to the vapor phase during carbonization and heat treatment. In addition, the phenanthridine-phenanthrene chars had lower nitrogen contents than the corresponding acridine-anthracene chars.

Carbon and Nitrogen Reactivities in Pure Acridine and Phenanthridine Chars. Chars formed from pure acridine and phenanthridine were oxidized to various levels of burnoff and the residual chars were analyzed to determine the changes in carbon, hydrogen, and nitrogen concentration (wt%). The acridine char was oxidized at 773, 798, and 823 K and the phenanthridine char at 773 K. Above this temperature, due to its high reactivity, the phenanthridine char ignited producing uncontrolled burnoff. Since the oxidations were performed at temperatures below the char heat treatment temperature, carbon and nitrogen removal should be through oxidation only (i.e., not through devolatilization). Plots of the carbon and nitrogen retained in the char are shown as a function of weight loss in Figures 1-4).

At 773 K, carbon and nitrogen oxidation rates were different for both the acridine and phenanthridine chars, Figures 1 and 2. For

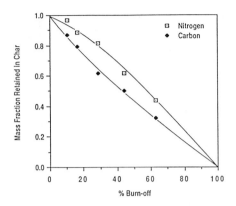

Figure 1.   Retention of Acridine Char Nitrogen as a Function of Burnoff in Air at 773 K

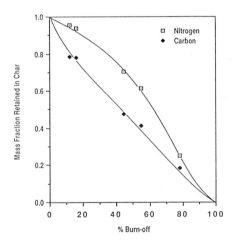

Figure 2.   Retention of Phenanthridine Char Nitrogen as a Function of Burnoff in Air at 773 K

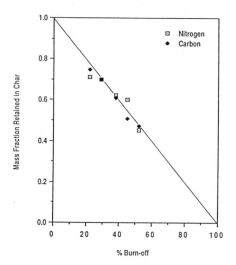

Figure 3.   Retention of Acridine Char Nitrogen as a Function of

Burnoff in Air at 798 K

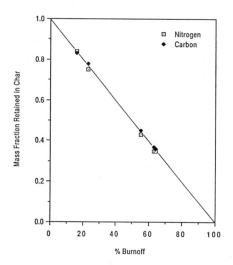

Figure 4.   Retention of Acridine Char Nitrogen as a Function of

Burnoff in Air at 823 K

both chars at 773 K, carbon was preferentially oxidized until between 30-40% weight loss. From this point, the rate of nitrogen release exceeded that of carbon and the two curves in Figures 1 and 2 converged. At 798 and 823 K (unlike at 773 K), the rates of carbon and nitrogen oxidation appear to be equal for the acridine char, Figures 3 and 4.

Char nitrogen enrichment which occurs at low burnoff at 773 K, has been observed during the partial combustion of shale particles (4). The results at 798 and 823 K are in agreement with the results of Song (5) for the oxidation of a 1750 K lignite char at 1250 K. It appears that the rates of oxidation of char carbon and nitrogen are equal at the temperatures of interest in practical combustors.

NO$_x$ Formation. The mass fraction of char nitrogen evolved and the proportion converted to NO$_x$ are shown as a function of carbon loss for pure acridine and phenanthridine chars in Figures 5 and 6, respectively. Carbon loss was determined from on-line monitoring of CO and CO$_2$ concentrations. The carbon loss calculated in this way was 5% and 7% higher than that determined by elemental analysis of the residual chars. The phenanthridine char had a much lower conversion of char nitrogen to NO$_x$ than did the acridine char. At 60% carbon loss, there was a 32% conversion of char nitrogen to NO$_x$ for the acridine char, while for the phenanthridine char it was only 14%. Although not directly measured, it is assumed that the remaining nitrogen was evolved as N$_2$. These results illustrate that the conversion of char nitrogen to NO$_x$ is dependent upon the char precursor, and presumably the way in which this influences the chemical and physical structure of the char.

Figure 7 shows the extent of conversion to NO$_x$ and the total nitrogen released from the char as a function of weight loss for the acridine char oxidized at 823 K. At complete burnoff, 50% of the char nitrogen was converted to NO$_x$ and 50% of the nitrogen was released as N$_2$. The ratio of nitrogen released as NO$_x$ to the total nitrogen released from the char, as shown in Figure 8, was between 0.45 and 0.50 over the range of acridine char burnoff from 20 to 100%.

Effect of Temperature on Conversion of Char Nitrogen to NO$_x$. The effect of oxidation temperature upon the proportional release of NO$_x$ is tabulated in Table II for pure acridine and phenanthridine chars at

Table II. Effect of Temperature on Conversion of Char Nitrogen to NO$_x$

	Acridine (6.66% N)	
Temperature, K	823	873
NO$_x$ Conversion, %	50	9.2
	Phenanthridine (5.25% N)	
Temperature, K	823	873
NO$_x$ Conversion, %	13	6.1

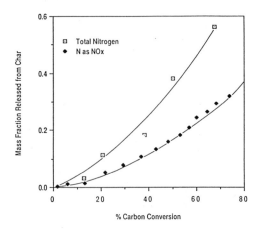

Figure 5.   Mass Fraction of N Released from Acridine Char as a

Function of Carbon Conversion in Air at 773 K

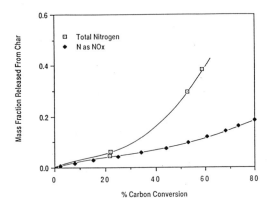

Figure 6.   Mass Fraction of N Released from Phenanthridine

Char as a Function of Carbon Conversion in Air at 773 K

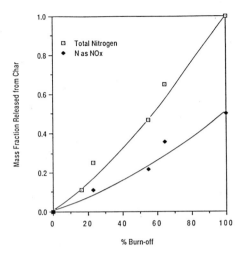

Figure 7.   Mass Fraction of N Released from Acridine Char as a
Function of Burnoff in Air at 823 K

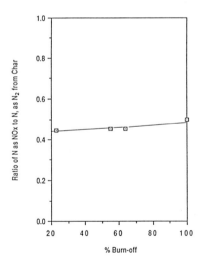

Figure 8.   Ratio of N Released as NO_x to Total N Released as a
Function of Burnoff in Air at 823 K for Acridine Char

complete burnoff. The char nitrogen to NO_x conversion for the acridine char decreased from 50% to 9.2% when the furnace temperature was raised from 823 K to 873 K. The same conversion decreased ca. 50% for phenanthridine char over the same temperature range. Similar results have been reported by Song (6) for the oxidation of a coal char at higher temperatures (1250-1750 K).

The nitrogen conversions reported in Table II were measured with the chemiluminescent NO_x analyzer. During the oxidation of the phenanthridine char at 873 K, no differences were seen in the instrumentally measured concentration of NO and NO_x. This indicates that NO and N_2 are the principal nitrogen species present. Both NH_3 and HCN and can be converted to NO by the stainless steel catalyst in the analyzer (7). If either of these two species were present, the measured NO_x value would be higher than the NO value.

The dramatic decrease in char nitrogen to NO_x conversion for the acridine char cannot be attributed only to a 50 K increase in temperature. The char ignited at 873 K but not at 823 K. The bed temperature during oxidation at 873 K was probably considerably higher than 873 K. The bed temperature during oxidation of the phenanthridine char at the furnace temperature of 873 K is shown in Figure 9. A maximum temperature of 1006 K was reached within 3 minutes and the bed temperature remained 50 K higher than the furnace temperature even after 30 minutes.

Effect of Char Nitrogen Content on Conversion to NO_x. The effect of the char nitrogen content on conversion to NO_x is shown in Figure 10. The conversion decreased slightly with increasing nitrogen content for the acridine-based chars. Conversion decreased sharply at first, and then more gradually, with increasing nitrogen content for the phenanthridine-based chars. The conversion of fuel nitrogen to NO_x has been reported to decrease with increasing nitrogen content in coal (8) and petroleum (9) combustion and in nitrogen-doped flames (10). The phenanthridine-based chars, with one exception (the char with 0.98 wt% nitrogen) had lower conversions than the acridine-based chars. This suggests further that the char precursor can influence char nitrogen conversion to NO_x.

The Effect of Char Sample Size on Conversion to NO_x. The effect of char sample weight on conversion of char nitrogen to NO_x is shown in Figure 11. The conversion decreases with increasing sample size or more importantly with increasing height of the char bed. The lower conversion to NO_x with increasing sample size may be a consequence of increased reduction of NO_x to N_2 by the char bed. The NO_x formed at the bottom of the bed is reduced to N_2 as it passes upward through the bed, as previously observed by Baskakov (11).

One or more of the following reactions may be responsible for limiting NO_x formation during char oxidation:

$$CO + NO \rightarrow 0.5 \ N_2 + CO_2 \tag{1}$$

$$NO + C \rightarrow 0.5 \ N_2 + CO \tag{2}$$

$$2NO + C \rightarrow N_2 + CO_2 \tag{3}$$

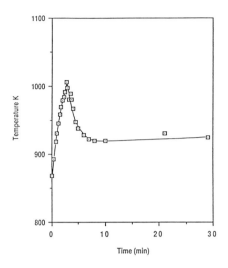

Figure 9. Bed Temperature as a Function of Time for Phenanthridine
Char Oxidation in Air for a Furnace Temperature
of 873 K

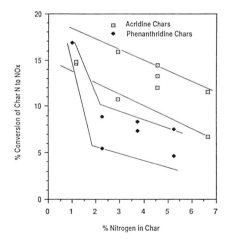

Figure 10. Conversion of Char N to NO$_x$ as a Function of Char N
Content for a Range of Acridine and Phenanthridine-
Based Chars

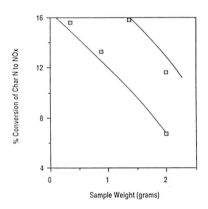

Figure 11. Effect of Acridine Char Sample Weight on Conversion

of Char N to NO_x during Oxidation in Air at 873 K

The first reaction is reportedly slow in the gas phase (12).
Metal catalysts are often used to promote the reaction.

Reactions (2) and (3) have been the subject of other studies in
which synthetic mixtures of combustion products were passed over a
heated bed of carbon particles. The results have indicated that the
reduction of NO_x is enhanced by: (a) increasing the temperature
(13-15), (b) increasing surface area (13), and (c) increasing the
carbon bed height (11). As indicated earlier in this work, the conversion of char nitrogen to NO_x was found to decrease with increasing
reaction temperature, increasing sample size, and was dependent on
the type of char precursor. The results of this study are in agreement with the conclusion that NO_x formation is limited by reactions
(2) and (3).

As shown in Figure 10, the acridine-based chars, with one exception, gave higher conversions of char nitrogen to NO_x than did the
phenanthridine-based chars. The phenanthridine chars, with one exception, had a higher reactivity in air at 873 K than the acridine-
based chars, Table III. This would suggest that the phenanthridine-
based chars have a structure more ammenable to gasification by oxygen
and/or NO_x.

Table 3.   Time Required for 50% Burnoff for 1273 K Chars

Precursor	Time to 50% (minutes)
13% acridine-87% anthracene	64.5
38% acridine-62% anthracene	42.0
64% acridine-36% anthracene	49.0
100% acridine	56.6
13% phenanthridine-87% phenanthrene	103.8
38% phenanthridine-62% phenanthrene	22.3
64% phenanthridine-36% phenanthrene	39.1
100% phenanthridine	34.9

Conclusions

This paper has reported on the relative rates of carbon and nitrogen
release and the factors affecting NO_x formation during char oxidation. At 773 K and at low burnoff, carbon was selectively oxidized;
above this temperature, the rates of carbon and nitrogen oxidation
were found to be equal. The conversion of char nitrogen to NO_x was
found to be strongly dependent on the char precursor; the proportion
of nitrogen converted to NO_x was much lower for the phenanthridine
char than the acridine char. The nature of the char precursor influences the chemical and physical structure of the carbonized product. The high reactivity of the phenanthridine char in air suggests
that its structure may be more accessible to diffusing gases and that
it may contain a higher proportion of carbon active sites than the
acridine char.

The proportion of the liberated nitrogen which was converted to
NO_x was also lower for the phenanthridine than the acridine char. It
is believed that the balance of nitrogen is released as N_2 due to
the reduction of NO_x by C and/or CO. A high concentration of carbon

active sites capable of effecting NO_x reduction would be consistent with the observed behavior of the phenanthridine chars.

It was also found that the conversion of released nitrogen to NO_x decreased with increasing reaction temperature, increasing char nitrogen content (for both acridine and phenanthridine-based chars) and with increasing sample weight (bed height).

It appears that NO_x reduction could provide an effective means to further limit the production of NO_x from char oxidation.

Acknowledgments

This research was supported by the Coal Cooperative Program of The Pennsylvania State University and by the Alcoa Foundation.

Literature Cited

1. Smith, I., Nitrogen Oxides from Coal Combustion - Environmental Effects, IEA Coal Research Report Number IC TIS/TR10, October 1980.
2. Pershing, D. W., and Wendt, J. O. L., Ind. Eng. Chem., 18(1), 60, (1979).
3. Pereira, F. J., Beer, J. M., Gibbs, B., and Hedley, A. B., Fifteenth Symposium (International) on Combustion, P. 1149, The Combustion Institute, Pittsburgh, PA, (1974).
4. Manor, Y., Suuberg, E. M., Ho, M., and Toor, H. L., Nineteenth Symposium (International) on Combustion, P. 1103, The Combustion Institute, Pittsburgh, PA, (1982).
5. Song, Y. H., Beer, J. M., and Sarofim, A. F., Comb. Sci. Tech., 28, 177, (1982).
6. Song, Y. H., Pohl, J. H., Beer, J. M., and Sarofim, A. F., Comb. Sci. Tech., 28, 31, (1982).
7. Mathews, R. D., Sawyer, R. F., and Schefer, R. W., Env. Sci. Tech., 11, 1092, (1977).
8. Pershing, D. W., and Wendt, J. O. L., Sixteenth Symposium (International) on Combustion, P. 389, The Combustion Institute, Pittsburgh, PA, (1977).
9. Turner, D. W., Andrews, R. L., and Siegmund, C. W., Combustion, 44, 21, (1972).
10. Sarofim, A. F., AIChE Symposium Series, No. 148, 71, 51, (1972).
11. Basakov, A. P., Berg, B. V., Shikov, V. N., Volkova, A. A., Tsymbalist, M. M., Turkoman, A., Ashikhmin, A. A., Shul'Man, V. L., Berzrukov, M. V., and Unterbef, O. G., Thermal Engineering, 29, 496, (1982).
12. Fenimore, C. P., J. Am. Chem. Soc., 69, 3143, (1947).
13. Bedjai, G., Orbach, H. K., and Riesenfeld, F. C., Ind. Eng. Chem., 50, 1165, (1958).
14. Fursawa, T., Kunii, D., Oguma, A., and Yamada, N., Kagaku Kogaku, 562, (1977).
15. Shelef, M., and Otto, K., J. Coll. Interfac. Sci., 31, 73, (1969).

RECEIVED May 13, 1987

Chapter 27

Acid Clusters

R. G. Keesee and A. W. Castleman, Jr.

Department of Chemistry, Pennsylvania State University, University Park, PA 16802

Gas phase molecular aggregates that contain acid molecules
have been produced with free jet expansion techniques and
detected by using electron impact ionization mass spectrometry. The clusters of aqueous nitric acid paralleled many
properties of the condensed phase. Multiple nitric acid
molecules were found in the clusters that were sufficiently
dilute. The acid molecule was absent in the ionized clusters
involving HCl and only water was evident. Experiments also
demonstrated the reactivity of ammonia with aqueous nitric
acid and sulfur dioxide clusters and of sulfur trioxide with
water clusters. The natural occurrence of acid cluster
negative ions offers a means to probe the gas phase acid
loading of the atmosphere through laboratory and field studies
of the ion chemistry.

The laboratory investigation of a phenomenon such as acid rain may
proceed along several avenues. One extreme involves simulation of
conditions as in smog or cloud chambers in which many processes may
occur during the course of an experiment. In this manner, some
idea of the overall picture may be gained. The other approach is
devoted to understanding basic properties, such as a specific
reaction rate, upon which the larger picture may be built. The
latter tack is that which is undertaken in our laboratory. Specifically, we are examining the chemical and physical properties of
molecular clusters.

Molecular clusters can be considered to be the smallest size
range of an aerosol particle size distribution. Nucleation from
the gas phase to particles or droplets involves, in the initial
stages, the formation of clusters. Research on clusters provides
a valuable approach to understanding, on a molecular level, the
details of the transfer of molecules from the gaseous to the
condensed state by either new particle formation or heterogeneous
processes including adsorption onto or dissolution into particles.

The oxidation of species such as SO_2, NO_x, and organic
compounds via gas-phase reactions, aqueous phase reactions in the
solutions of droplets and aerosol particles, or surface reactions
on particles (either surface-gas or solid-liquid interfaces)
produce acids in the atmosphere. The relative importance of the
various mechanisms depends on factors such as the aerosol loading,
relative humidity, and solar intensity. The study of clusters is
most relevant to conditions in which gas-phase reactions dominate
acid production and gas-to-particle conversion proceeds through
nucleation. For instance, the propensity of sulfuric acid
molecules to form small hydrated clusters is important to the
nucleating ability of sulfuric acid (1). A major impetus, which
is applicable to the heterogeneous chemistry of the atmosphere as
well as other areas of reearch, for the study of clusters is the
prospect that such work will lead to a better understanding of
surface interactions (2). Consequently, knowledge of the
properties and formation of clusters containing acids contributes
to an understanding of some of the processes involved in the
development of acid rain. This paper presents an overview of
results on the formation and stability of both neutral and ionic
acid clusters.

Neutral Acid Clusters

With free jet expansion techniques, we have produced clusters of
aqueous nitric acid (3), hydrochloric acid, sulfuric acid (4), pure
acetic acid (5), and sulfur dioxide (6). For analogy to buffering,
the formation of clusters containing ammonia have also been
examined. These have included ammonia with aqueous nitric acid
(7), hydrogen sulfide (7), and sulfur dioxide (8). The basic
experiment involves expansion of vapor through a nozzle, collima-
tion of the jet with a skimmer to form a well-directed molecular
beam, and detection of clusters via electron impact ionization and
quadrupole mass spectrometry. Some variations include the introduction of a reactive gas into vacuum near the expansion as
described elsewhere (4,8) and the implementation of an electrostatic quadrupolar field to examine the polarity of the neutral
clusters. The electric deflection technique is described by
Klemperer and coworkers (9).

Background on the properties of free jet expansions is
described by Anderson (10) and Hagena (11). A few important points
to note follow. The cluster distributions themselves are
kinetically quenched due to a transition to a free molecular flow
(essentially collisionalless) regime after a short distance (a few
nozzle diameters) from the nozzle tip. The directed motion of the
gas created by the expansion leads to a cooling of the transla-
tional temperature due to a narrowing of the velocity distribution
of the molecules in the jet. Relaxation of internal degrees of
freedom also occurs but generally the quenched temperatures are in
the order $T(vib) > T(rot) > T(trans)$. With clustering, the latent
heat of condensation contributes to an excitation of the internal

modes of the cluster which the cold collisions may not fully relax.

A further note is that for purposes of mass identification and detection, the neutral clusters are ionized. The ionized distribution of cluster sizes may not faithfully represent the neutral size distribution in a one-to-one correspondence due to fragmentation upon ionization, ion stability, ionization cross-sections, and mass discrimination in the spectrometer. For most of the clusters described here which involve hydrogen bonding, ionization of the neutral cluster usually leads to a protonated cluster via a reaction typified by

$$(NH_3)^+(NH_3)_n \rightarrow NH_4^+(NH_3)_{n-1} + NH_2 \qquad (1)$$

where the ionized molecular unit of the cluster spontaneously reacts with a neighboring molecule (12). The product ion may be vibrationally hot and undergo further dissociation. Attempts to understand these dissociation processes in our laboratory (12) as well as others (13,14) are being made in order to better interpret results such as those described below. With these fundamental processes in mind, we can proceed to discuss results concerning acid clusters.

In the study of aqueous nitric acid (3), deuterated species were used to avoid ambiguity in stoichiometry. Clusters were produced by the expansion of the vapor from heated concentrated aqueous nitric acid. Electron impact ionization of the clusters produced ions of the form $D^+(DNO_3)_x(D_2O)_y$. In the case of the clusters containing one nitric acid molecule, a distinct local minimum of the signal intensity in the size distribution occurs at the cluster size $D^+(DNO_3)(D_2O)_4$. Since no explanation based on ion stability seems feasible, an attractive explanation of the position of the minimum is that it is indicative of some rather abrupt transformation of the precursor neutrals in this size range. Such a situation might occur if a complex became sufficiently hydrated to enable the formation of solvated ion pairs. A large change in the charge distribution within the cluster should occur upon solvation to form an ion pair $NO_3^-(H_2O)_nH_3O^+$. A more polar species should have a larger collision rate and hence a faster growth rate. This effect should manifest itself in the observed intensity distribution as an increase in intensity of the larger sized clusters just beyond the cluster that underwent the ion-pair formation.

Recently ion-pair formation in clusters has been suggested to explain the abrupt linewidth broadening and spectral changes in the fluorescence of α-naphthol$(NH_3)_n$ when n reaches four apparently to yield α-naphtholate$^-\cdot(NH_3)_3NH_4^+$ (15). Ab initio calculations on the hydration of NH_4F (16) and NaH_2PO_4 (17) have shown that as few as six water molecules are sufficient to create a solvated ion pair in which the ions become separated by solvent.

For clusters with more than one nitric acid molecule, the species $(DNO_3)_x(D_2O)_y$ ($1 < x \leqslant 6$) each have a minimum degree of hydra-

tion below which clusters are not observed. Both this minimum y
and the most probable degree of hydration for a cluster of x DNO_3
molecules increase with x. Furthermore, the homomolecular species
$D^+(DNO_3)_x$ (x>1) are not detected even though the HNO_3 dimer has
been observed (18) in an expansion involving anhydrous HNO_3. The
interesting analogy in this case is that concentrated aqueous
nitric acid solutions are photochemically and thermally unstable
and decompose via the stoichiometry

$$2HNO_3 \rightarrow 2NO_2 + H_2O + 1/2 \; O_2 \tag{2}$$

Apparently the exothermicity of the clustering or electron impact
ionization supplies the energy which initiates this decomposition
in the clusters that contain too much nitric acid compared to the
number of solvent water molecules.

When introduced as a reactant, ammonia appears to be
preferentially incorporated (via H_2O replacement) into clusters
containing HNO_3 leaving the pure H_2O clusters relatively unaffected
(7). Product ions of the form $H^+(HNO_3)_x(NH_3)_y(H_2O)_z$ with x=0,1,
y=0,1,2, and z up to 7 are easily resolvable. Higher clusters are
also observed, but with low intensity; the NH_3/H_2O stoichiometry
was unresolved for these because of poorer mass resolution.

When the vapor from a boiling solution of 6M HCl is expanded,
the detected cluster ions lack HCl as evidenced by the absence of
the characteristic m+2 isotope due to ^{37}Cl. On the other hand, the
observed $H^+(H_2O)_n$ distribution is noticeably different than that
obtained in the expansion of pure water. For instance, the usual
prominent discontinuities at $H^+(H_2O)_4$ and $H^+(H_2O)_{21}$ are not evident
and a slight local minimum in intensity occurs at $H^+(H_2O)_{13}$. The
indication is that HCl is initially present in the neutral cluster
but that ionization leads to "boiling off" of HCl. The molecular
ions $H^{35}Cl^+$ and $H^{37}Cl^+$ are observed. Expansion of the vapor over
NH_4S also results in an ionized cluster distribution in which one
of the expected components, namely H_2S, is absent (7). Quite
unlike the distribution obtained from the expansion of pure
ammonia, a strong local minimum similar to the $H^+(HNO_3)(H_2O)_n$
distribution is present.

In order to explore adsorption and heterogeneous processes on
a molecular scale, it is of interest to study the reactions of
gases with clusters. We have performed one series of experiments
in which ammonia was expanded from the nozzle and SO_2 was
introduced as a reactant through the annular opening around the
nozzle, and another series in which the roles of the gases were
reversed (8). With ammonia introduced via the nozzle (500 torr
stagnation pressure) and when the SO_2 pressure behind the outer
annular opening is 40 torr, ionized clusters of the form $(NH_3)_nSO_2^+$
and $H^+(NH_3)_nSO_2$ are detected. When the SO_2 pressure is reduced to
20 torr, no evidence of SO_2 incorporation into the ammonia clusters
is found. A peculiar feature is that the unprotonated species
exhibit a normal size distribution, whereas the protonated clusters
are strongly peaked at $NH_4^+NH_3SO_2$. On the other hand, ionization

of pure ammonia clusters results almost exclusively in protonated
clusters due to the internal cluster reaction (3).

When sulfur dioxide is introduced through the nozzle and the
amount of ammonia behind the annular opening varies from 6 to 50
torr, the extent of ammonia incorporation into the clusters
dramatically increases with increasing ammonia pressure. Up to two
ammonia molecules were observed to be incorporated into the
clusters with 20 torr of ammonia behind the annular opening. With
40 torr, up to four NH_3 molecules were observed in the clusters.
In addition, clusters containing one NH_3 molecule become more
prevalent than the pure $(SO_2)_n^+$ clusters. The probability that a
cluster of n SO_2 molecules contained one or more NH_3 molecules
approximately doubled from n=2 to 8 in a gradual manner. Based on
only the cluster hard-sphere collision cross-section, a dependence
of $n^{2/3}$ (or a factor of 4 increase) might be expected. However,
several other effects must also be considered including the extent
of dissociation upon ionization, the relative internal temperatures
of the clusters, and the limited number of internal degrees of
freedom in the clusters.

In general, the observed cluster distributions are smooth and
in neither series of experiments is any preference for a particular
stoichiometric ratio apparent, except for $NH_4^+NH_3SO_2$ in the
protonated distribution. These experiments also demonstrate that
the nozzle design results in the reaction of the species exiting
from the annular opening with clusters of the species introduced
through the inner nozzle. The addition of ammonia to SO_2 clusters
was found to be more effective than the addition of SO_2 to NH_3
clusters. Some explanations include a higher probability of SO_2
evaporation upon ionization, less severe beam scattering with NH_3
collisions on SO_2 clusters, or a different reactivity (accommodation
coefficients) in the two cases.

A study of the reaction of sulfur trioxide with water clusters
has also been made (4). The ion clusters observed in these
experiments were a series of protonated water clusters $H^+(H_2O)n$
with n up to 14 and another less abundant series of the form
$SO_3(H_2O)_nH^+$ with n up to 9. The $H^+(H_2O)_n$ series could result from
the ionization of unreacted water clusters and also from the
ionization of $SO_3(H_2O)_m$ clusters. The relative distribution of the
$H^+(H_2O)_n$ series, however, was not appreciably affected by the
introduction of SO_3. The $SO_3(H_2O)_nH^+$ distribution was very similar
in form to the $H^+(HNO_3)(H_2O)_n$ distribution observed from the
expansion of aqueous nitric acid vapor in that a local intensity
minimum (at n=4 for the $SO_3(H_2O)_nH^+$ distribution) was observed.
The SO_3 flux was such that no masses corresponding to more than one
SO_3 molecule in a cluster were detected. Electrostatic focusing
demonstrated that the $SO_3 \cdot H_2O$ adduct, expected to be the initial
product, rapidly isomerized to H_2SO_4.

Electrostatic deflection experiments have shown the acid-water
adducts to be polar. However, larger clusters exhibit defocusing
behavior indicative of a polarizable, but essentially nonpolar,
species. Only for the pure acetic acid clusters, specifically the

trimer and indications also for the pentamer or larger clusters, was polarity of larger clusters evident (5).

Ionic Acid Clusters

Examination of the clustering of neutral molecules onto ions is another approach to the study of acid clusters. Cluster ions observed in the atmosphere reflect the role of acids. Strong acids are preferentially clustered to negative ions which act as bases. Under normal atmospheric conditions, ambient ions of the type $HSO_4^-(H_2SO_4)_x(HNO_3)_y$ or $NO_3^-(HNO_3)_n$ (the latter also probably hydrated in the lower troposphere) have been observed throughout the lower atmosphere (19,20).

Laboratory studies have been made of the thermodynamic stability of $NO_3^-(HNO_3)_n$ clusters (21,22) and the reactivity of nitric acid (23) and sulfuric acid (24) with negative ions. Through these studies, an understanding of the pathways to the productions of the acid clusters and their relationship to the gas-phase acid loading of the atmosphere has been developed. Consequently, in conjunction with these laboratory results, in situ detection of the relative ambient abundance of these ionic clusters allows estimates to be made of the gas-phase concentration of these acids. Heitman and Arnold (19) estimate from their measurements that the gaseous acidic sulfur concentration in the 12 to 8 km altitude range is 10^6 to 10^7 molecules cm^{-3}. Once again, the largest uncertainty in these results is fragmentation; in this case the fragmentation that occurs upon extracting ambient ions into the mass spectrometer. Recent studies indicate that observations of SO_3 or HSO_3 associated with ambient cluster ions of the stratosphere probably are not due to clustering with the ambient gases, but result from fragmentation of sulfuric acid in the cluster ions (25).

The observed positive ions are protonated clusters containing water and high proton affinity species such as acetonitrile in the lower stratosphere (26) or ammonia in the lower troposphere (20). Other high proton affinity species such as pyridine and picolines may enter into the positive ion chemistry of the lower troposphere (27,28). Further discussion of these studies and the experimental techniques can be found elsewhere (28,29).

Acknowledgments

Support by the Department of Energy, Grant No. DE-ACO2-82-ER60055, and the National Science Foundation, Grant No. ATM-82-04010, is gratefully acknowledged.

Literature Cited

1. Heist, R. H.; Reiss, H. J. Chem. Phys. 1974, 61, 573.
2. Whetten, R. L.; Cox, D. M.; Trevor, D. J.; Kaldor, A. Surf. Sci. 1985, 156, 8. See also other papers in that volume.

3. Kay, B. D.; Herman, V.; Castleman, A. W., Jr. Chem. Phys
    Lett. 1981, 80, 469.
4. Sievert, R.; Castleman, A. W. Jr. J. Phys. Chem. 1984, 88,
    3329.
5. Sievert, R.; Cadez, I.; Van Doren, J.; Castleman, A. W., Jr.
    J. Phys. Chem. 1984, 88, 4502.
6. Castleman, A. W., Jr.; Kay, B. D.
    Int. J. Mass Spectrom. Ion Proc. 1985, 66, 217.
7. Kay, B. D.; Hofmann-Sievert, R.; Castleman, A. W., Jr.
    Chem. Phys. 1986, 102, 407.
8. Keesee, R. G.; Kilgore, K.; Breen, J. J.; Castleman, A. W.,
    Jr. J. Aerosol Sci. Tech., in press.
9. Falconer, W. E.; Buchler, A.; Stauffer, J. L.; Klemperer, W.
    J. Chem. Phys. 1968, 48, 312.
10. Anderson, J. B. In "Molecular Beams and Low Density Gas
    Dynamics"; Wegener, D. P., Ed.; Marcel Dekker:New York, 1974,
    pp. 1-91.
11. Hagena, O. F. In "Molecular Beams and Low Density Gas
    Dynamics"; Wegener, D. P., Ed.; Marcel Dekker:New York, 1974,
    pp. 93-181.
12. Echt, O.; Dao, P. D.; Morgan, S.; Castleman, A. W., Jr.
    J. Chem. Phys. 1985, 82, 4076.
13. Buck, U.; Meyer, H. Phys. Rev. Lett. 1984, 52, 109.
14. Kamke, W.; Kamke, B.; Kiefl, H. U.; Hertel, I. V.
    J. Chem. Phys. 1986, 84, 1325.
15. Cheshnovsky, O.; Leutwyler, S. Chem. Phys. Lett. 1985, 121, 1.
16. Odutola, J. A.; Dyke, T. R. J. Chem. Phys. 1978, 68, 5663.
17. Kollman, P.; Kuntz, I. J. Am. Chem. Soc. 1976, 98, 6820.
18. Lee, W. K.; Prohofsky, E. W. Chem. Phys. Lett. 1982, 85, 98.
19. Heitmann, H.; Arnold, F. Nature. 1983, 306, 747.
20. Perkins, M. D.; Eisele, F. L. J. Geophys. Res. 1984, 89,
    9649.
21. Davidson, J. A.; Fehsenfeld, F. C.; Howard, C. J.
    Int. J. Chem. Kinet. 1977, 9, 17.
22. Lee, N.; Keesee, R. G.; Castleman, A. W., Jr. J. Chem. Phys.
    1980, 72, 1089.
23. Fehsenfeld, F. C.; Howard, C. J.; Schmeltekopf, A. L.
    J. Chem. Phys. 1975, 63, 2835.
24. Viggiano, A. A.; Perry, R. A.; Albritton, D. L.; Ferguson, E.
    E.; Fehsenfeld, F. C. J. Geophys. Res. 1982, 87, 7340.
25. Schlager, H.; Arnold, F. Planet. Space Sci. 1986, 34, 245.
26. Arijs, E.; Brasseur, G. J. Geophys. Res. 1986, 91, 4003.
27. Eisele, F. L.; McDaniel, E. W. J. Geophys. Res. 1986, 91,
    5183.
28. Keesee, R. G.; Castleman, A. W., Jr. J. Geophys. Res. 1985,
    90, 5885.
29. Keesee, R. G.; Castleman, A. W., Jr. Ann. Geophys. 1983, 1,
    75.

RECEIVED May 5, 1987

INDEXES

Author Index

Affiliation Index

Subject Index

Production by Barbara J. Libengood
Indexing by Keith B. Belton
Jacket design by Carla L. Clemens

Elements typeset by Hot Type Ltd., Washington, DC
Photo on jacket courtesy of National Oceanic and
Atmospheric Administration, Rockville, MD
Printed and bound by Maple Press Co., York, PA
Dust jackets printed by Atlantic Research Corporation, Alexandria, VA